1984
AND ALL THAT

Modern Science, Social Change, and Human Values

1984
AND ALL THAT

Modern Science, Social Change, and Human Values

1984
AND ALL THAT

Modern Science, Social Change, and Human Values

Edited by

Fred H. Knelman
Sir George Williams University

Wadsworth Publishing Company, Inc.
Belmont, California

ISBN: 0-534-0089-4

L. C. Catalog Card Number: 70-169-593

Printed in the United States of America

1 2 3 4 5 6 7 8 9 10—75 74 73 72 71

To Miss Julie Parker, Miss Beverley Granich, and Miss Karen Cherry

without whose valuable assistance

this book would never have been completed.

Preface

This reader is a general text in the sociology of science—the social interactions of science representing the editor's concept of a sociological model of science and technology. This model, called the "technological order," imposes an overall discipline on the structure and content of the reader.

Essential to the sociological view of science is recognition of the social character and sociohistorical evolution of science. Equally essential is the view that technology is perhaps the major determinant of social change. Culture, the totality of spiritual and physical goods produced by society in its social evolution, is also treated as a social product. Given this approach, there is an intimate connection between technology and social and cultural changes and stresses.

These conditions have produced new levels of despair and unrest over the entire face of our planet. A key to understanding this age of unrest lies in analyzing the relationships of science and social change.

The second half ot the twentieth century is witnessing an unprecedented technological revolution. The scientific explosion has created a new technological environment that has transformed our physical environment, shattered traditional values, destroyed old institutions, and modified our cultural perceptions. Science and technology are the new social dynamics of our age dominating economics, politics, and culture. The world explosion of technology has infected our environment with pollutants, creating new and largely unassessed health hazards and intensifying known toxic substances in air and water. The incidence of chronic and degenerative diseases has increased, perhaps, in large part, because of the combination of population increase, urbanization, and pollution. Our respiratory systems are now measuring pollution by a vast and steady increase in the incidence of respiratory ailments, chronic bronchitis, and irreversible pulmonary diseases. Equally serious crises of the uncontrolled expansion of technology are military and civil nuclear problems and an acceleration in the maldistribution of consumer goods, which has created a widening imbalance of health, wealth, and justice between the developed and underdeveloped countries.

This reader is a response to genuine educational and social needs. Interdisciplinary courses, departments, and institutes in the history and philosophy of science, as well as "science for art's sake" natural science courses, are among the most rapidly growing curricular areas in higher education. The former group has often suffered from a narrow eclectic view that rigidly confines science to the area of the history of ideas, and the latter group has adopted a variety of forms, the major problem being the balance between breadth and depth. Nevertheless these courses have emerged in response to the need to understand the social interactions of science and technology, recognizing the dominant role that they play in the modern world. A liberal education in the second half of the twentieth century is no longer relevant without such courses.

This movement for relevance in our schools has been taken up by science itself. Relevance in science means identification of social problems arising from science and technology; determination of priorities for the direction of research, development, and problem solving; and technology assessment, social control, and future creation. With the recognition of the enormous social impact of science and with the new concern for the world's most urgent problems—population, pollution, war, and maldistribution of wealth and resources—the need to examine, understand, and cope with this new social dynamic has become even greater. This reader makes some attempt to be conceptually controlled along lines previously discussed but is also selective and open. It is predicated on the social need for the urgency, relevance, and perspective required for survival.

The incredible growth of science and technology has transformed them into Big Science, the complex socialized process of innovation and invention. Science and technology are woven into the web of culture, politics, and economics, welding the world commitment to growth and development to the power of technology. This growth has created a world crisis in human values, a value confrontation between uncontrolled growth and survival. All uncontrolled growth carries with it an inherent Malthusian dilemma and, left to proliferate, will lead to disasters. Population, pollution, nuclear proliferation, and maldistribution are all examples.

The key concepts of the editor's model of the technological order form the major themes of the reader. These are: (1) the relationship of technology and social change; (2) the emergence of Big Science—with its exponential growth rates; (3) the tendency for technology to be an autonomous, self-perpetuating system operating outside the natural milieu; (4) the consequent cultural lag of the institutions necessary to control and direct technology for human welfare; (5) the integration of technology with dominant political and economic structures largely independent of ideology in developed states; (6) the technological backlash—the unanticipated hazards arising from the uncontrolled growth of technology; (7) the crisis in human values arising from the technological order. All these themes are covered by articles in the first section of the reader and in later sections are applied to particular cases.

Each of these technologies has the problems of cultural lag, value crisis, and technological backlash. These problems are identified and discussed in each section. However, because the environmental issue has caused global concern and because pollution in all its forms is a major example of technological backlash, the second section of the reader deals in some detail with the environmental crisis as a sociological phenomenon. In the third section the models of the technological order are tested in the area of biology by predicting the emerging nature of Big Biology and a biological order. The next three sections deal with full-fledged existing technologies—chemical, nuclear, and electronic—whose level of development has reached the full expression of the technological order. The final section of the book deals explicitly with values and techniques for technological assessment and control.

The choice of material reflects the editor's bias toward issue orientation and thematic unity. As mentioned, the potential impact of the new biology seems to warrant a fairly extensive treatment in this reader. In each section the major themes of social implication, model analysis, and value crisis are repreated. The anatomy of the technological order, technological backlash, and problems of social control and human values are discussed in terms of each technological area.

Finally it should be emphasized that the purpose of the book is to raise the issues of disaster in the spirit of seeking solutions. The disease must be understood if the cure is to be effective.

Contents

Section 1

The Technological Order

The technological order is a sociological model of technology in western urbanized industrialized societies. Its basic characteristics are the dominance of science and technology over the economics, politics, and culture of these societies, the relative autonomy of technological growth, acting outside both the natural world and rational human choice. An equally significant aspect of the technological order is the exponential growth rate of all areas of science and technology. Given this phenomenal growth and the irresistible rewards, in terms of political and economic power, for technological eminence, technology tends to be anti-ecological in operation and in values.

The consequences of the technological order and the inevitable cultural lags between the growth of technology and the growth of social and belief systems to control and use it for human welfare has created a world crisis in values. An inevitable backlash also occurs in the form of the largely unprecedented and unassessed hazards of technology. Pollution in all its forms is the prime example of this backlash having brought us to a global environmental crisis.

One of the most complete and compelling technological models is the essay by Ellul in this section. According to Ellul's theory, technology results in complete human subversion through the accumulation and supremacy of techniques, that is, of means over ends. Man becomes the victim of technique. This is the price we pay for both progress and survival. His model does not allow for the intervention of human will or choice, the renunciation of technology, or the possibility of social control. It is a totally determinist theory. This is one of the major distinctions from the editor's model, which views technology as being

1

amenable to human will, given the necessary changes in political and economic structures and belief systems.

Ellul's concepts represent an enormous challenge to those who equate technology with progress, those who believe technology is an ultimate cure-all, those who believe technology is ethically neutral, and those who think technology can serve mankind if only directed by the proper ideology. Ellul's ideas have come to dominate the dialogue and debate on modern technology. (Limitations of space made it impossible to include the various other models discussed here, beyond their general identification.)

Ellul speaks of a new technical milieu that operates outside of and indifferent to the natural environment. By implication, technology is anti-ecological, predicated on its supreme confidence to cure even the ills it cannot imagine. On the other hand, Ellul talks about the ambivalence of technological power and the hidden unanticipated hazards but suggests that these too are amenable to further applications of technology by the technological fix, a modification or change in a specific technology designed to cure or remove hazards—for example, the various devices used to decrease toxic emissions from automobiles. The problem with the technological fix is that it often creates new hazards, a technological backlash of the second order. Every aspect of human life—including religion, myth, irrational forms of behavior, art, and culture—is directly affected by "la technique." And nobody, including society, controls it. Everybody is controlled by it.

In some ways, although not directly, Ellul suggests a theology of technology that incorporates a belief in its own absolute power, or, as Hardin suggests in his article "The Tragedy of the Commons," the twin concepts that we can invent anything we dream and that we must use everything we invent. This theology is also the theology of growth, progress, and development. Ellul's model is a modified doom theory, for he suggests man's immortal soul with its manifest need for freedom and mobility is imperiled by such "progress." The price we pay for survival is their loss. We gain a world but lose our souls. His concepts also incorporate a "death of ideology" view, seeing little distinction between nations having different ideologies in the role of technology.

Other thinkers have developed forms of technological determinism, sometimes incorporating doom theories—ecological or nuclear cataclysm, population explosions and biological time bombs, new worlds of Huxley bravery or Orwellian doom—all of which involve human subversion by machines and techniques.

Ellul does not use conventional sociological concepts, although they are often implicit in his analysis. The editor has attempted to develop the Ellulian model by filling in critical elements in the sociology of science that make the model more explicit. Basic among these elements are: (1) the nature of social change and its relation to technology—the question of whether human will or technology is the source of social change; (2) the emergence of Big Science with its exponential growth; (3) and the hypothesis of cultural lag.

Ogburn's useful but largely qualitative concept of "cultural lag" is conceived of as a lag between technological growth and the development of social systems designed to control and confine it for purposes of human welfare. While the usefulness of the concept is somewhat limited due to the difficulty of quantifying it, it gives us a valuable insight into the anatomy of technological backlash. The lack of social controls, including prior assessment of technology, leads to unanticipated hazards (pollution) and to the misuse and abuse of technology (invasion of privacy, automobile accidents). Because of the present ambivalence of technology and its uncontrolled, anti-ecological development, these hazards tend to become inevitable.

To sum up, the growth of science and technology are largely uncontrolled, because of the amount of power they produce. Serving the economic and political imperatives of all major states independently of ideology, science out of control is becoming an unparalleled threat to human survival, a series of Malthusian dilemmas of growth and control any of which could lead to major disasters or cataclysms. Dennis Gabor, in his book *Inventing the Future,* refers to these as the "trilemma" but this author prefers quadrilemma—the environmental crisis, the nuclear threat, the population explosion, and the maldistribution of health, wealth, and justice. Thus, a world crisis of survival has arisen, which ultimately is a crisis in human values.

This approach largely determines the choices of readings in this section, commencing with two selections by Ogburn on technology and social change, followed by Ellul's essay describing the technological order. Then comes de Solla Price's essay on the exponential growth of science, which has also been confirmed for technology. Because the generalized exponential growth rates of all viable areas of science and technology far exceed the social and belief systems necessary for their control and because technology has a laissez-faire nature, we have cultural lags. This concept is treated by Hart. Then a more detailed analysis of Big Science is presented by Weinberg. Finally, it was thought appropriate to include something on C. P. Snow's concept of the "two cultures," the schism of communication and culture that tends to divide scientists and humanists. Boulding's essay deals with this. Taken altogether and subtracting Ellul's tendency toward technological determinism, the selections in this section approximate the editor's sociological model of contemporary technology and provide a general theoretical background from which to view the specific issues associated with biological, nuclear, electronic, and chemical technologies.

The Meaning of Technology

William F. Ogburn

Technology is like a great mountain peak. It looks different according to the side from which one views it. From one vantage point only a small part may be seen, from another the outlook is clouded; yet we may get a clear view from still another side. Few of us see it from all its sides; so each of us is likely to have a very limited conception of its nature. It is desirable, then, to look at technology from various points of view; for in this way we get a less narrow picture.

Different Viewpoints Toward Technology

Technological Schools. To many young students who have not thought very much about it, technology is understood as something that is taught at an institute of technology or something they learn about in a technological high school. It has to do with engineering, mechanics, electricity, chemistry, laboratories, shop work, and various studies that one does not find in the curriculum of a liberal arts college or an ordinary secondary school. Graduates of these technological schools get jobs with engineering companies in construction work, or go out to develop new countries, or are associated with architectural firms. To them, technology is very definitely not a social science such as history, economics, or politics.

Gadgets and Push Buttons. An even more narrow view is found among those who think of technology only as the source of the many gadgets that are finding their way into our homes, offices, restaurants, automobiles, and other places frequented by the mass of the people. These gadgets may be radio sets, pipes for radiant heat, deep-freeze lockers, automatic gear shifts, microfilm readers, tape recorders, copying machines, electric blankets, automatic door

From: *Technology and Social Change* edited by F. R. Allen et al. Copyright © 1957. Reprinted by permission of Appleton-Century-Crofts, Educational Division, Meredith Corporation. Trained in sociology, history and economics, Ogburn took his Ph.D. at the Columbia Graduate School. In the course of his teaching career at the University of Chicago and several other major institutions he taught political science and statistics as well as sociology. Among Ogburn's most famous books are *Social Change* (1922), *Recent Social Changes* (1933), and *The Social Effects of Aviation* (1946). Ogburn died in 1959.

openers, or ultra-violet-ray lamps. Hundreds of such gadgets are being placed at our disposal for our convenience and comfort. These are the products of technology with which we come in daily contact, their newness forced upon our attention by advertisements. Thus it is natural that we should think of technology as something that furnishes the mechanical devices which appeal to us as aids; although sometimes they may appear to some of us as nuisances.

Destroyer of Artistic Skills. The great flowering of technology as we know it today, based on metals and mechanical power, succeeded an era of handicrafts based upon wood and muscle. The age of handicrafts was one of great individual skill, and it resulted in productions of charm and artistic merit. A single craftsman would fabricate a whole product—a chair, a clock, a costume, or a curtain. We may suppose that he derived a certain joy in his creation, much as an artist does in painting a picture. But as the machine age replaced handicrafts, the individual worker created only part of a product. His skill and the joy that went with it were destroyed. In their place came routine, monotony, and toil, with a workman assigned only a fragment of a complete job, for example, sawing a piece of wood, winding a wire, sewing a buttonhole, or unfolding a bolt of cloth. This repetition daily, monthly, and yearly meant utilizing only a minute part of man's great capabilities. Thus the workman and the artist tend to view technology as the destruction of an artistic and humanly wholesome way of life and a replacement of these by long hours and monotonous toil in a factory.[1]

Technological Unemployment. To some observers, technology suggests unemployment and little else. To them the social implications of technology, particularly in the 1920's and the 1930's in the United States, were the loss of a job and the replacement of men by machines.[2] There was a good deal of unemployment in these decades, and the idea that it was caused by technological innovations was widely spread in writings and discussions in newspapers, magazines, and books. Other influences of technology were only dimly seen at the time, and technology came to signify this social problem of unemployment. Since the prosperous years of the 1940's and 1950's, marked by a scarcity of labor, little has been heard of technological unemployment.

Aid to Non-industrial Peoples. Another aspect of technology has been introduced to the popular mind in the 1940's and the 1950's. It is that technology will raise the standard of living of peoples who are as yet without much industrialization.[3] This idea was presented to the general public as the fourth point in a program submitted by President Truman to the Congress.

---

[1] John Ruskin, *The Crown of Wild Olive* (Philadelphia, H. Altemus, 1895).

[2] Corrington Gill, *Unemployment and Technological Change*, Report to the Temporary National Economic Committee (Philadelphia, Work Projects Administration, 1940).

[3] "Factors of Economic Progress," *International Social Science Bulletin*, Vol. VI, No. 2 (1954), Part I, pp. 159-294.

"Point Four" came to symbolize technological aid to less-developed countries. World War II made Americans more familiar with many distant peoples. Soldiers and travelers were impressed with the rudimentary nature of the tools used, for example, in parts of the Far East, as compared with those in the United States and in Western industrial countries. If an iron plow could replace a wooden one, the productivity of a farm worker could be increased, and his labor lessened. To do something to help the so-called "backward" peoples appealed to the imagination of Americans who had been forced by war to kill and destroy. The exportation of machinery and tools no doubt appealed to our businessmen, for raising the incomes of these peoples would create a better market. But experience had taught that it was not enough to export equipment to peoples who would not know how to make the best use of it or repair it. So there arose the necessity of exporting "know-how" as well as the implements. Thus was technology to be exported. The idea was also in line with the ameliorative aims of other organizations such as UNESCO. Teams of technicians were, therefore, sent to the different peoples to teach them the best ways to use these new tools and machines. In this manner, then, Americans began to learn another influence of technology: its capability of raising the standard of living of slightly-industrialized peoples.

Maker of Wealth. Technology can not only improve the material well-being of peoples with low per capita incomes, but it can also raise the standard of living of highly industrialized peoples. The standard of living of the people of the United States in 1950 is twice as high as it was in 1900. This doubling of per capita income in dollars of the same purchasing power is due largely to developments in technology and applied science.[4] There are valid reasons to think that, short of destructive war, the already high incomes in the United States will be increased even more during the second half of the twentieth century as a result of continued inventions and discoveries in science. A mechanical cotton picker now exists which can do the work of twenty-three laborers picking by hand. Today we are discussing the coming of automatism in industry when only a few will be needed in a factory to push buttons, to run the machinery that will manufacture products without further assistance from human beings. Nearly automatic factories will greatly increase productivity per worker and our standard of living will be raised, for national income is a function of the rate of production. Technological development, thus, may be seen as the force which raises the standard of living of peoples of any level.

Materialization versus Spiritualization. The peoples who were to benefit from "Point Four" programs in material wages and standards of living generally had a set of values which emphasized religion, the life of the spirit, or such human values as happiness. New and better tools brought material advantages,

---

[4] W. F. Ogburn, "Technology and the Standard of Living in the United States," *American Journal of Sociology*, Vol. LX, No. 4 (January, 1955), pp. 380-386.

but they did little or nothing to help the human spirit in its search for sustaining philosophies.

In the highly industrialized countries of the West, technology brought about an increased emphasis on material things that seemed relatively to deemphasize spiritual values. Many religious and moral groups see this aspect of technology, namely, that it is a force seemingly antagonistic to the life of the spirit. To them, technology stands for the secularization of life. One goes to a school of technology now instead of to a school of theology as in former times. To these followers of the spirit, technology is a false god. They resent the sight of our young people with no higher aim than material success.

Machine the Master.   The view of technology as a tempter which leads us away from the true values of the good life changes rather readily into the view that technology is a dictator that controls our lives. When the factory whistle blows, we must be up and at work. The railroad runs on a time table that we must follow and obey. The automobile maims and kills. We listen to the radio and watch television, but we seem to be unable to do anything to improve their programs.[5] Factories close down in a business depression, and we lose our jobs. The assembly line moves by, and the workers must keep up with its speed. The typist works for a typewriter which makes her sit before it for eight hours a day. To those groups of people whose temperament is tinged with rebelliousness, or who love the open road or the ways of nature, technology dictates a schedule that takes away freedom and makes daily life a routine.

Technology as a Worker of Miracles.   By contrast, technology appears as a mechanical slave to do our bidding. It helps us do the things we want to do. It makes for us the things we want.[6] An automobile is ours to command, to take us anywhere at any time we wish. The airplane enables us to fly over mountains and over seas, and with it we can travel around the world in two or three days. By means of radio we can speak instantly to millions of people on the other side of the world. We can measure the distance of the sun and tell the composition of distant stars. A block of wood can be made into silken stockings, and one element can be changed into another. A lump of coal will yield dyes of more colors than are found in nature. We can record a symphonic concert on coiled wire no bigger than a spool of thread. From this viewpoint technology is a servant, but it is more. With its aid we can work miracles undreamed of by the ancients. It will continue in the future to give us power to do things that we now cannot even imagine. To these observers, technology is a great boon because it extends the capabilities and powers of men.

---

[5] Siegfried Giedion, *Mechanization Takes Command* (New York, Oxford University Press, 1948).

[6] Waldemar Kaempffert, *Modern Wonder Workers: A Popular History of American Invention* (New York, Blue Ribbon Books, 1931).

A Precipitator of Change.   A banker once defined an invention as that which made his securities insecure. The securities of the railroads fell with the invention of the motor truck and the airplane, and the nitrate industry of Chile lost its market in the United States when nitrate was made from the nitrogen of the air. Inventions in technology bring profits and prosperity to some, woe and destruction to others. Technology is seen, at any rate, as a cause of changes for better or worse.[7]

The range of inventions is wide, and changes are occurring in many different phases of life.[8] To agriculture, oil and electricity have brought the power revolution. Warfare is mechanized and the great powers among nations are reranked. Science is changing the forms and nature of religious beliefs. These changes may or may not be progress, but the new replaces or is added to the old. So to many, technology is viewed as a disturber of the status quo, a destroyer of peace and quiet by precipitating unanticipated changes. These changes may offer prospects for new business or opportunities to make the world a better place in which to live, or they may bring threats that we feel we should oppose.

A Changing Environment to Which We Adjust.   Like other animals, man adjusts to his environment; otherwise he does not live. Man's material environment, however, unlike that of the lower animals, does not consist only of land, water, air, fauna, flora, temperature, and pressure. It also consists of buildings, tools, clothing, fire, vehicles, books, schools, clocks, churches, munitions, writing materials, medicines, contraceptives, machines, prime movers, and the various objects that we call material culture. These are the products of technology and applied science.[9] The natural environment in any one place is quite stable except for diurnal and seasonal changes, but the technological environment in recent years is a whirling mass of change. This change in modern material culture is partly owing to inventions and scientific discoveries. Technology may thus be viewed as a changing environment of mankind.

The natural environment changes from winter to summer, to which a man must adjust as he also does when he goes from, say, the arctic to the tropics. Likewise, man has had to adjust as his technological environment changes. The life of a farmer differed from that of a hunter. The way of life in a city is different from the life in the open country. In recent years we have changed our habits as we use television. We read less; we stay at home more; we go to motion pictures less frequently; our children play at athletic sports less. We make similar adjustments to the automobile and the airplane. And just now we are concerned with what adjustments we must make to the atom bomb and the thermonuclear bomb. The harnessing of atomic energy for peaceful purposes will occasion still

---

[7]Lewis Mumford, *Technics and Civilization* (New York, Harcourt, Brace, 1934).

[8]M. D. C. Crawford, *The Influence of Invention on Civilization* (New York, World Publishing Company, 1942).

[9]Stuart Chase, *Men and Machines* (New York, Macmillan, 1929).

other adjustments. We have, then, a technological environment which is changing rapidly and to which we must make continuous adjustments.

Creator of Cultural Lags. Adjustment to a changing environment is difficult for many reasons. One is that the change in the technological environment is seldom foreseen, and preparation for it is rarely ever made. The automobile was first thought not to be practical; and the railroads, much of whose business was taken away by automotive vehicles, made no prior adjustment to it. City streets were not widened in anticipation; nor were through highways constructed in time. That airplanes carrying bombs would bring war to the civilian population and would find great cities ideal targets was not foreseen, nor have adjustments to this yet been made. That the hydrogen bomb would change international relations, make alliances more difficult, and increase the tendency toward neutrality was not anticipated.

There are delays and lags in adjusting to new technological developments, and during this period of lag man's adjustment is generally worse than it was before the technological change.[10] Thus cities in a farming area draw families to higher-paying jobs, and mothers leave crowded quarters to work away from home. Their unsupervised children join city gangs of youngsters with thieving and juvenile crime as a result, a worse adjustment for children than on the farms and in the villages. There are some groups who make a quick adjustment and profit thereby. Such are the business groups who make money out of new inventions, for instance, motion pictures, metals, and mowing machines. However, in some situations, adjusting is more difficult than inventing. Thus making atomic bombs was quicker and less difficult than is the abolition of war, the dispersal of cities, the formation of a one-world government, or the effective prohibition of the manufacture and use of atomic bombs. From this standpoint, technology is seen as the generator of social problems because of lags in adjustments to new mechanical inventions. . . .

---

[10]W. F. Ogburn, *Social Change* (New York, The Viking Press, 1950).

How Technology Causes Social Change

William F. Ogburn

In describing how technological developments cause social changes, we have noted that change takes place over a period of time. Hence any account of why a change takes place must explain why it took place in one period of time and not at some other.

If we attribute the cause of the change to leaders, then we imply that there were no such leaders at a prior time. We cannot define such a leader as one who produced the change, for that is defining the cause in terms of the result—which is what we wish to explain.

If we define leaders in terms of heredity and maintain that such hereditary capability exists year after year, then leaders cannot be regarded as a cause; for a variable cannot be explained by a constant.

To the extent that leadership acquired through learning and experience varies from period to period, then leaders may be a cause. But if the learned leadership is a result not of a changing heredity but of the changing social environment, then the leaders whose numbers vary over time become media through which the forces of a changing social environment operate. Some of the forces of this changing social environment are technological.

Technological forces in the changing social environment are obscured by descriptions in terms of human behavior. These descriptions are common in newspapers, in histories, in conversation. We thus tend to see change in terms of the actors: Lincoln freed the slaves. Similarly the role of technology is not appreciated when, in making choices, we do not think in terms of the factors that affect our choices.

How technological changes cause social changes depends on an understanding of the nature of causation, and is seen to be a process. Basic to the process is the fact that a technological influence does not always stop at its first direct effect upon users and producers, but often has a succession of derivative effects which follow one another like the links of a chain. These are often not recognized, because an effect is generally not the result of one cause alone but of several converging causes. Also, since the impact of an invention may have several effects dispersed in different directions, the process is more like a network than a chain.

The chainlike nature of technological effects and the easy recognition of the first, the direct effect, has meant that we often do not credit technology with being a cause of the derivative effects. This lack of recognition of technological change as a cause of derivative effects is made more frequent because there are also other causes of derivative effects than that of particular inventions, some of which are not caused by technology.

This chapter does not, of course, claim that all social changes are caused by technological changes, nor does it claim that any definite proportion of such changes is caused by mechanical invention and scientific discovery. Its purpose has been to outline the process of how technology causes social change.

Ideas of Technology

Jacques Ellul

I. I refer the reader to my book *La Technique* for an account of my general theses on this subject. I shall confine myself here to recapitulating the points which seem to me to be essential to a sociological study of the problem:

1. Technique[1] has become the new and specific *milieu* in which man is required to exist, one which has supplanted the old *milieu*, viz., that of nature.

Reprinted from *The Technological Order* by Carl F. Stover by permission of the Wayne State University Press. Copyright ©1963 by Wayne State University Press, Detroit 2, Michigan. Jacques Ellul is a Professor in the Faculty of Law at the University of Bordeaux. His books include *La Technique* (Paris, 1954), *Le Fondement théologique du droit* (Geneva, 1946), and *Présence au monde moderne* (Geneva, 1948). John Wilkinson, translator of this article, is Professor of Philosophy at the University of California at Santa Barbara. Wilkinson has also translated Ellul's *La Technique*, which will be published early next year.

[1] In his book *La Technique*, Jacques Ellul states he is "in substantial agreement" with H. D. Lasswell's definition of technique: "the ensemble of practices by which one uses

2. This new technical *milieu* has the following characteristics:

a. It is artificial;

b. It is autonomous with respect to values, ideas, and the state;

c. It is self-determining in a closed circle. Like nature, it is a closed organization which permits it to be self-determinative independently of all human intervention;

d. It grows according to a process which is causal but not directed to ends;

e. It is formed by an accumulation of means which have established primacy over ends;

f. All its parts are mutually implicated to such a degree that it is impossible to separate them or to settle any technical problem in isolation.

3. The development of the individual techniques is an "ambivalent" phenomenon.

4. Since Technique has become the new *milieu*, all social phenomena are situated in it. It is incorrect to say that economics, politics, and the sphere of the cultural are influenced or modified *by* Technique; they are rather situated *in* it, a novel situation modifying all traditional social concepts. Politics, for example, is not modified by Technique as one factor among others which operate upon it; the political world is today *defined* through its relation to the technological society. Traditionally, politics formed a part of a larger social whole; at the present the converse is the case.

5. Technique comprises organizational and psycho-sociological techniques. It is useless to hope that the use of techniques of organization will succeed in compensating for the effects of techniques in general; or that the use of psycho-sociological techniques will assure mankind ascendancy over the technical phenomenon. In the former case, we will doubtless succeed in averting certain technically induced crises, disorders, and serious social disequilibrations; but this will but confirm the fact that Technique constitutes a closed circle. In the latter case, we will secure human psychic equilibrium in the technological *milieu* by avoiding the psycho-biologic pathology resulting from the individual techniques taken singly and thereby attain a certain happiness. But these results

---

available resources in order to achieve certain valued ends." Commenting on Lasswell's definition, Ellul says: "In the examples which Lasswell gives, one discovers that he conceives the terms of his definition in an extremely wide manner. He gives a list of values and the corresponding techniques. For example, he indicates as values riches, power, well-being, affection, and so on, with the techniques of government, production, medicine, the family. This notion of value may seem somewhat novel. The expression is manifestly improper. But this indicates that Lasswell gives to techniques their full scope. Besides, he makes it quite clear that it is necessary to bring into the account not only the ways in which one influences things, but also the ways one influences persons." "Technique" as it is used by Ellul is most nearly equivalent to what we commonly think of as "the technological order" or "the technological society." (Trans.)

will come about through the *adaptation of human beings to the technical milieu.* Psycho-sociological techniques result in the *modification* of men in order to render them happily subordinate to their new environment, and by no means imply any kind of human domination over Technique.

6. The ideas, judgments, beliefs, and myths of the man of today have already been essentially modified by this technical *milieu*. It is no longer possible to reflect that, on the one hand, there are techniques which may or may not have an effect on the human being; and, on the other, there is the human being himself who is to attempt to invent means to master his techniques and subordinate them to his own ends by *making a choice* among them. Choices and ends are both based on beliefs, sociological presuppositions, and myths which are a function of the technological society. Modern man's state of mind is completely dominated by technical values, and his goals are represented only by such progress and happiness as is to be achieved through techniques. Modern man in choosing is already incorporated within the technical process and modified in his nature by it. He is no longer in his traditional state of freedom with respect to judgment and choice.

II. To understand the problem posed to us, it is first of all requisite to disembarrass ourselves of certain fake problems.

1. We make too much of the disagreeable features of technical development, for example, urban over-crowding, nervous tension, air pollution, and so forth. I am convinced that all such inconveniences will be done away with by the ongoing evolution of Technique itself, and indeed, that it is only by means of such evolution that this can happen. The inconveniences we emphasize are always dependent on technical solutions, and it is only by means of techniques that they can be solved. This fact leads to the following two considerations:

a. Every solution to some technical inconvenience is able only to reinforce the system of techniques *in their ensemble;*

b. Enmeshed in a process of technical development like our own, the possibilities of human survival are better served by more technique than less, a fact which contributes nothing, however, to the resolution of this basic problem.

2. We hear too often that morals are being threatened by the growth of our techniques. For example, we hear of greater moral decadence in those environments most directly affected technically, say, in working class or urbanized *milieux.* We hear, too, of familial disintegration as a function of techniques. The falseness of this problem consists in contrasting the technological environment with the moral values inculcated by society itself.[2] The presumed opposition between ethical problematics and technological systematics probably at the present is, and certainly in the long run will be, false. The

---

[2] Cf. K. Horney.

traditional ethical *milieu* and the traditional moral values are admittedly in process of disappearing, and we are witnessing the creation of a *new* technological ethics with its own values. We are witnessing the evolution of a morally consistent system of imperatives and virtues, which tends to replace the traditional system. But man is not necessarily left thereby on a morally inferior level, although a moral relativism is indeed implied—an attitude according to which everything is well, *provided* that the individual obeys some ethic or other. We *could* contest the value of this development *if* we had a clear and adequate concept of what good-in-itself is. But such judgments are impossible on the basis of our general morality. On *that* level, what we are getting is merely a substitution of a new technological morality for a traditional one which Technique has rendered obsolete.

3. We dread the "sterilization" of art through technique. We hear of the artist's lack of freedom, calm, and the impossibility of meditation in the technological society. This problem is no more real than the two preceding. On the contrary, the best artistic production of the present is a result of a close connection between art and Technique. Naturally, new artistic form, expression, and ethic are implied, but this fact does not make art less art than what we traditionally called such. What assuredly is *not* art is a fixation in congealed forms, and a rejection of technical evolution as exemplified, say, in the neoclassicism of the nineteenth century or in present day "socialist realism." The modern cinema furnishes an artistic response comparable to the Greek theater at its best; and modern music, painting, and poetry express, not a canker, but an authentic esthetic expression of mankind plunged into a new technical *milieu*.

4. One last example of a false problem is our fear that the technological society is completely *eliminating* instinctive human values and powers. It is held that systematization, organization, "rationalized" conditions of labor, overly hygienic living conditions, and the like have a tendency to repress the forces of instinct. For some people the phenomenon of "beatniks," "*blousons noirs*,"[3] and "hooligans" is explained by youth's violent reaction and the protestation of youth's vital force to a society which is overorganized, overordered, over-regulated, in short, technicized.[4] But here too, even if the facts are established beyond question, it is very likely that a superior conception of the technological society will result in the integration of these instinctive, creative, and vital forces. Compensatory mechanisms are already coming into play; the increasing appreciation of the esthetic eroticism of authors like Henry Miller and the rehabilitation of the Marquis de Sade are good examples. The same holds for music like the new jazz forms which are "escapist" and exaltative of instinct;

---

[3] A kind of French beatnik. (Trans.)

[4] The psychoanalyst Jung has much to say along this line.

item, the latest dances. All these things represent a process of *"défoulement"*[5] which is finding its place in the technological society. In the same way, we are beginning to understand that it is impossible indefinitely to repress or expel religious tendencies and to bring the human race to a perfect rationality. Our fears for our instincts *are* justified to the degree that Technique, instead of provoking conflict, tends rather to *absorb* it, and to *integrate* instinctive and religious forces by giving them a place within its structure, whether it be by an adaptation of Christianity[6] or by the creation of new religious expressions like myths and mystiques which are in full compatibility with the technological society.[7] The Russians have gone farthest in creating a "religion" compatible with Technique by means of their transformation of Communism into a religion.

III. What, then, is the real problem posed to men by the development of the technological society? It comprises two parts: 1. Is man able to remain master[8] in a world of means? 2. Can a new civilization appear inclusive of Technique?

1. The answer to the first question, and the one most often encountered, seems obvious: Man, who exploits the ensemble of means, *is* the master of them. Unfortunately, this manner of viewing matters is purely theoretical and superficial. We must remember the autonomous character of Technique. We must likewise not lose sight of the fact that the human individual himself is to an ever greater degree the *object* of certain techniques and their procedures. He is the object of pedagogical techniques, psychotechniques, vocational guidance testing, personality and intelligence testing, industrial and group aptitude testing, and so on. In these cases (and in countless others) most men are treated as a collection of objects. But, it might be objected, these techniques are exploited by other men, and the exploiters at least remain masters. In a certain sense this is true; the exploiters *are* masters of the particular techniques they exploit. But, they, too, are subjected to the action of yet other techniques, as, for example, propaganda. Above all, they are spiritually taken over by the technological society; they believe in what they do; they are the most fervent adepts of that society. They themselves have been profoundly technicized. They never in any way affect to despise Technique, which to them is a thing good in itself. They never pretend to assign values to Technique, which to them is in itself an entity working out its own ends. They never claim to subordinate it to any value because for them Technique *is* value.

---

[5] An untranslatable French play on words. *Défoulement* is an invented word which presumably expresses the opposite of *refoulement,* i.e., repression.

[6] Teilhard de Chardin represents, in his works, the best example of this.

[7] Examples of such myths are: "Happiness," "Progress," "The Golden Age," etc.

[8] French *sujet.* The usual rendering, "subject," would indicate exactly the contrary of what is meant here, viz., the opposite of "object." The present sense of "subject" is that in virtue of which it governs a grammatical object, for example. (Trans.)

It may be objected that these individual techniques have as their end the best adaptation of the individual, the best utilization of his abilities, and, in the long run, his happiness. This, in effect, is the objective and the justification of all techniques. (One ought not, of course, to confound man's "happiness" with capacity for mastery with, say, freedom.) If the first of all values is happiness, it is likely that man, thanks to his techniques, will be in a position to attain to a certain state of this good. But happiness does not contain everything it is thought to contain, and *the absolute disparity between happiness and freedom* remains an ever real theme for our reflections. To say that man should remain *subject* rather than *object* in the technological society means two things, viz., that he be capable of giving direction and orientation to Technique, and that, to this end, he be able to master it.

Up to the present he has been able to do neither. As to the first, he is content passively to participate in technical progress, to accept whatever direction it takes automatically, and to admit its autonomous meaning. In the circumstances he can either proclaim that life is an absurdity without meaning or value; *or,* he can predicate a number of indefinitely sophisticated values. But neither attitude accords with the fact of the technical phenomenon any more than it does with the other. Modern declarations of the absurdity of life are not based on modern technological efflorescence, which none (least of all the existentialists) think an absurdity. And the predication of values is a purely theoretical matter, since these values are not equipped with any means for putting them into practice. It is easy to reach agreement on what they are, but it is quite another matter to make them have any effect whatever on the technological society, or to cause them to be accepted in such a way that techniques must evolve in order to realize them. The values spoken of in the technological society are simply there to justify what is; *or,* they are generalities without consequence; *or* technical progress realizes them automatically as a matter of course. Put otherwise, neither of the above alternatives is to be taken seriously.

The second condition *that man be subject rather than object,* i.e., the imperative that he exercise mastery over technical development, is facilely accepted by everyone. But factually it simply does not hold. Even more embarrassing than the question "How?" is the question "Who?" We must ask ourselves realistically and concretely just who is in a position to choose the values which give Technique its justification and to exert mastery over it. If such a person or persons are to be found, it must be in the Western world (inclusive of Russia). They certainly are not to be discovered in the bulk of the world's population which inhabits Africa and Asia, who are, as yet, scarcely confronted by technical problems, and who, in any case, are even less aware of the questions involved than we are.

Is the arbiter we seek to be found among the *philosophers,* those thinking specialists? We well know the small influence these gentry exert upon our society, and how the technicians of every order distrust them and rightly refuse to take their reveries seriously. Even if the philosopher could make his voice heard, he would still have to contrive means of mass education so as to communicate an effective message to the masses.

Can the *technician* himself assume mastery over Technique? The trouble here is that the technician is *always* a specialist and cannot make the slightest claim to have mastered any technique but his own. Those for whom Technique bears its meaning in itself will scarcely discover the values which lend meaning to what they are doing. They will not even look for them. The only thing they can do is to apply their technical specialty and assist in its refinement. They cannot *in principle* dominate the totality of the technical problem or envisage it in its global dimensions. *Ergo,* they are completely incapable of mastering it.

Can the *scientist* do it? There, if anywhere, is the great hope. Does not the scientist dominate our techniques? Is he not an intellectual inclined and fit to put basic questions? Unfortunately, we are obliged to re-examine our hopes here when we look at things as they are. We see quickly enough that the scientist is as specialized as the technician, as incapable of general ideas, and as much out of commission as the philosopher. Think of the scientists who, on one tack or another, have addressed themselves to the technical phenomenon: Einstein, Oppenheimer, Carrel. It is only too clear that the ideas these gentlemen have advanced in the sphere of the philosophic or the spiritual are vague, superficial, and contradictory *in extremis.* They really ought to stick to warnings and proclamations, for as soon as they assay anything else, the other scientists and the technicians rightly refuse to take them seriously and they even run the risk of losing their reputations as scientists.

Can the *politician* bring it off? In the democracies the politicians are subject to the wishes of their constituents who are primarily concerned with the happiness and well-being which they think Technique assures them. Moreover, the further we get on, the more a conflict shapes up between the politicians and the technicians. We cannot here go into the matter which is just beginning to be the object of serious study. But it would appear that the power of the politician is being (and will continue to be) outclassed by the power of the technician in modern states. Only dictatorships can impose their will on technical evolution. But, on the one hand, human freedom would gain nothing thereby, and, on the other, a dictatorship thirsty for power has no recourse at all but to push toward an excessive development of various techniques at its disposal.

Any of us? An individual can doubtless seek the soundest attitude to dominate the techniques at his disposal. He can inquire after the values to impose on techniques in his use of them, and search out the way to follow in order to remain a man in the fullest sense of the word within a technological society. All this is extremely difficult, but it is far from being useless, since it is apparently the only solution presently possible. But the individual's efforts are powerless to resolve in any way the technical problem in its universality; to accomplish this would mean that *all* men adopt the same values and the same behavior.

2. The second real problem posed by the technological society is whether or not a new civilization can appear which is inclusive of Technique. The elements of this question are as difficult as those of the first. It would obviously be vain to deny all the things that can contribute something useful to a new civilization: security, ease of living, social solidarity, shortening of the work week, social security, and so forth. But a civilization in the strictest sense of the term is not brought into being by all these things.

A threefold contradiction resides between civilization and Technique of which we must be aware if we are to approach the problem correctly:

a. The technical world is the world of material things; it is put together out of material things and with respect to them. When Technique displays any interest in man, it does so by converting him into a material object. The supreme and final authority in the technological society is fact, at once ground and evidence. And when we think on man as he exists in this society it can only be as a being immersed in a universe of objects, machines, and innumerable material things. Technique indeed guarantees him such material happiness as material objects can. But, the technical society is not, and cannot be, a genuinely humanist society since it puts in first place not man but material things. It can only act on man by lessening him and putting him in the way of the quantitative. The radical contradiction referred to exists between technical perfection and human development because such perfection is only to be achieved through quantitative development and necessarily aims exclusively at what is measurable. Human excellence, on the contrary, is of the domain of the qualitative and aims at what is not measurable. Space is lacking here to argue the point that spiritual values cannot evolve as a function of material improvement. The transition from the technically quantitative to the humanly qualitative is an impossible one. In our times, technical growth monopolizes all human forces, passions, intelligences, and virtues in such a way that it is in practice nigh impossible to seek and find anywhere any distinctively human excellence. And if this search is impossible, there cannot be any civilization in the proper sense of the term.

b. Technical growth leads to a growth of power in the sense of technical means incomparably more effective than anything ever before invented, power which has as its object only power, in the widest sense of the word. The possibility of action becomes limitless and absolute. For example, we are confronted for the first time with the possibility of the annihilation of all life on earth, since we have the means to accomplish it. In *every* sphere of action we are faced with just such absolute possibilities. Again, by way of example, governmental techniques, which amalgamate organizational, psychological, and police techniques, tend to lend to government absolute powers. And here I must emphasize a great law which I believe to be essential to the comprehension of the world in which we live, viz., that when power becomes absolute, values disappear. When man is able to accomplish anything at all, there is no value which can be proposed to him; when the means of action are absolute, no goal of action is imaginable. Power eliminates, in proportion to its growth, the boundary between good and evil, between the just and the unjust. We are familiar enough with this phenomenon in totalitarian societies. The distinction between good and evil disappears beginning with the moment that the ground of action (for example the *raison d'état,* or the instinct of the proletariat) claims to have absolute power and thus to incorporate *ipso facto* all value. Thus it is that the growth of technical means tending to absolutism forbids the appearance of values, and condemns to sterility our search for the ethical and the spiritual. Again, where Technique has place, there is the implication of the impossibility of the evolution of civilization.

c. The third and final contradiction is that Technique can never engender freedom. Of course, Technique frees mankind from a whole collection of ancient constraints. It is evident, for example, that it liberates him from the limits imposed on him by time and space; that man, through its agency, is free (or at least tending to become free) from famine, excessive heat and cold, the rhythms of the seasons, and from the gloom of night; that the race is freed from certain social constraints through its commerce with the universe, and from its intellectual limitations through its accumulation of information. But is this what it means really to be free? Other constraints as oppressive and rigorous as the traditional ones are imposed on the human being in today's technological society through the agency of Technique. New limits and technical oppressions have taken the place of the older, natural constraints, and we certainly cannot aver that much has been gained. The problem is deeper—the operation of Technique is the contrary of freedom, an operation of determinism and necessity. Technique is an ensemble of rational and efficient practices; a collection of orders, schemas, and mechanisms. All of this expresses very well a necessary order and a determinate process, but one into which freedom, unorthodoxy, and the sphere of the gratuitous and spontaneous cannot penetrate. All that these last could possibly introduce is discord and disorder. The more technical actions increase in society, the more human autonomy and initiative diminish. The more the human being comes to exist in a world of ever increasing demands (fortified with technical apparatus possessing its own laws to meet these demands), the more he loses any possibility of free choice and individuality in action. This loss is greatly magnified by Technique's character of self-determination, which makes its appearance among us as a kind of fatality and as a species of perpetually exaggerated necessity. But where freedom is excluded in this way, an authentic civilization has little chance. Confronted in this way by the problem it is clear to us that no solution can exist, in spite of the writings of all the authors who have concerned themselves with it. They all make an unacceptable premise, viz., rejection of Technique and return to a pre-technical society. One may well regret that some value or other of the past, some social or moral form, has disappeared; but, when one attacks the problem of the technical society, one can scarcely make the serious claim to be able to revive the past, a procedure which, in any case, scarcely seems to have been, globally speaking, much of an improvement over the human situation of today. All we know with certainty is that it was different, that the human being confronted other dangers, errors, difficulties, and temptations. Our duty is to occupy ourselves with the dangers, errors, difficulties, and temptations of modern man in the modern world. All regret for the past is vain; every desire to revert to a former social stage is unreal. There is no possibility of turning back, of annulling, or even of arresting technical progress. What is done is done. It is our duty to find our place in our present situation and in no other. Nostalgia has no survival value in the modern world and can only be considered a flight into dreamland. . . .

Prologue to a Science of Science

Derek J. de Solla Price

During a meeting at which a number of great physicists were to give firsthand accounts of their epoch-making discoveries, the chairman opened the proceedings with the remark: "Today we are privileged to sit side-by-side with the giants

Derek J. de Solla Price, "Prologue to a Science of Science," in *Little Science, Big Science* (New York: Columbia University Press, 1963), pp. 1-13, 20-22, 30-32. De Solla Price is Avalon Professor of the History of Science and Chairman of the Department of History of Science and Medicine at Yale University, New Haven, Connecticut. A British subject, resident in the United States since 1956, he took a Ph.D. (London, external) in experimental physics. Returning to Cambridge in 1950 as a graduate student in the history of science, he took a second Ph.D. there, working on the history of scientific instruments and medieval astronomy. In 1946, he first wrote on the exponential growth of science. Among his books are *Science since Babylon* (Yale University Press, 1961) and *Little Science, Big Science* (Columbia University Press, 1963).

on whose shoulders we stand."[1] This, in a nutshell, exemplifies the peculiar immediacy of science, the recognition that so large a proportion of everything scientific that has ever occurred is happening now, within living memory. To put it another way, using any reasonable definition of a scientist, we can say that 80 to 90 percent of all the scientists that have ever lived are alive now. Alternatively, any young scientist, starting now and looking back at the end of his career upon a normal life span, will find that 80 to 90 percent of all scientific work achieved by the end of the period will have taken place before his very eyes, and that only 10 to 20 percent will antedate his experience.

So strong and dominant a characteristic of science is this immediacy, that one finds it at the root of many attitudes taken by scientist and layman toward modern science. It is what makes science seem essentially modern and contemporaneous. As a historian of science, I find myself doing annual battle to justify and uphold the practice of spending more than half our time on the period before Newton, whereas every contemporary scientist around knows that what really counts is science since Einstein.

Because the science we know now so vastly exceeds all that has gone before, we have obviously entered a new age that has been swept clear of all but the basic traditions of the old. Not only are the manifestations of modern scientific hardware so monumental that they have been usefully compared with the pyramids of Egypt and the great cathedrals of medieval Europe, but the national expenditures of manpower and money on it have suddenly made science a major segment of our national economy. The large-scale character of modern science, new and shining and all-powerful, is so apparent that the happy term "Big Science" has been coined to describe it.[2] Big Science is so new that many of us can remember its beginnings. Big Science is so large that many of us begin to worry about the sheer mass of the monster we have created. Big Science is so different from the former state of affairs that we can look back, perhaps nostalgically, at the Little Science that was once our way of life.

If we are to understand how to live and work in the age newly dawned, it is clearly necessary to appreciate the nature of the transition from Little Science to Big Science. It is only too easy to dramatize the change and see the differences

---

[1] Gerald Holton, "On the recent past of physics," *American Journal of Physics*, 29 (December, 1961), 805. I should like to draw attention to the fine study published while this work was in progress: Gerald Holton, "Models for Understanding the Growth and Excellence of Scientific Research," in S. R. Graubard and G. Holton, eds., *Excellence and Leadership in a Democracy* (New York, Columbia University Press, 1962), 94-131, first published as "Scientific research and scholarship: notes towards the design of proper scales," in *Proceedings of the American Academy of Arts and Sciences*, 91 (No. 2), 362-99 (*Daedalus*, March, 1962). My work derives much from this previous publication, though its author and I do not always agree in detail in the conclusions we derive from the statistical data.

[2] Alvin M. Weinberg, "Impact of large-scale science on the United States," *Science*, 134 (July 21, 1961), 164. I am indebted to this paper for many ideas. See also further comments by Weinberg in "The Federal Laboratories and science education," *Science*, 136 (April 6, 1962), 27.

with reckless naiveté. But how much truth is there in the picture of the Little Scientist as the lone, long-haired genius, moldering in an attic or basement workshop, despised by society as a nonconformist, existing in a state of near poverty, motivated by the flame burning within him? And what about the corresponding image of the Big Scientist? Is he honored in Washington, sought after by all the research corporations of the "Boston ring road," part of an elite intellectual brotherhood of co-workers, arbiters of political as well as technological destiny? And the basis of the change—was it an urgent public reaction to the first atomic explosion and the first national shocks of military missiles and satellites? Did it all happen very quickly, with historical roots no deeper in time than the Manhattan Project, Cape Canaveral rocketry, the discovery of penicillin, and the invention of radar and electronic computers?

I think one can give a flat "No" in answer to all these questions. The images are too naïvely conceived, and the transition from Little Science to Big Science was less dramatic and more gradual than appears at first. For one thing, it is clear that Little Science contained many elements of the grandiose. And, tucked away in some academic corners, modern Big Science probably contains shoestring operations by unknown pioneers who are starting lines of research that will be of decisive interest by 1975. It is the brave exception rather than the rule that key breakthroughs are heralded at birth as important work done by important people.

Historically, there have been numerous big national efforts: the great observatories of Ulugh Beg in Samarkand in the fifteenth century, of Tycho Brahe on his island of Hven in the sixteenth century, and of Jai Singh in India in the seventeenth century, each of which absorbed sensibly large fractions of the available resources of their nations. As international efforts, there were the gigantic expeditions of the eighteenth century to observe the transits of Venus. And, as large-scale hardware, there were the huge electrical machines, produced most notably in Holland in the eighteenth century, machines that in their time seemed to stretch man's scientific engineering to its ultimate capability and to give him the power to manufacture the most extreme physical forces of the universe, rivaling the very lightning and perhaps providing keys to the nature of matter and of life itself. In a way, our dreams for modern accelerators pale by comparison.

But let us not be distracted by history. What shall concern us is not so much the offering of counterexamples to show that Little Science was something big, and Big Science little, but rather a demonstration that such change as has occurred has been remarkably gradual. To get at this we must begin our analysis of science by taking measurements, and in this case it is even more difficult than usual to make such determinations and find out what they mean.

Our starting point will be the empirical statistical evidence drawn from many numerical indicators of the various fields and aspects of science. All of these show with impressive consistency and regularity that if any sufficiently large segment of science is measured in any reasonable way, the normal mode of growth is exponential. That is to say, science grows at compound interest, multiplying by some fixed amount in equal periods of time. Mathematically, the law of exponential growth follows from the simple condition that at any time the rate of growth is proportional to the size of the population or to the total magnitude already achieved—the bigger a thing is, the faster it grows. In this respect it agrees with the common natural law of growth governing the number of human beings in the population of the world or of a particular country, the number of fruit flies growing in a colony in a bottle, or the number of miles of railroad built in the early industrial revolution.

It might at first seem as if establishing such an empirical law of growth for science was neither unexpected nor significant. The law has, however, several remarkable features, and from it a number of powerful conclusions can be drawn. Indeed, it is so far-reaching that I have no hesitation in suggesting it as the fundamental law of any analysis of science.

Its most surprising and significant feature is that, unlike most pieces of curve-fitting, the empirical law holds true with high accuracy over long periods of time. Even with a somewhat careless and uncritical choice of the index taken as a measure, one has little trouble in showing that general exponential growth has been maintained for two or three centuries. The law therefore, though at this stage still merely empirical, has a status immediately more significant than the usual short-term economic time series. This leads one to a strong suspicion that the law is more than empirical—and that with suitable definitions of the indices that grow exponentially, one may show, as we later shall, that there is a reasonable theoretical basis for such a law.

A second important feature of the growth of science is that it is surprisingly rapid however it is measured. An exponential increase is best characterized by stating the time required for a doubling in size or for a tenfold increase.[3] Now, depending on what one measures and how, the crude size of science in manpower or in publications tends to double within a period of 10 to 15 years. The 10-year period emerges from those catchall measures that do not distinguish low-grade work from high but adopt a basic, minimal definition of science; the 15-year period results when one is more selective, counting only some more stringent definition of published scientific work and those who produce it. If this stringency is increased so that only scientific work of *very* high quality is counted, then the doubling period is drawn out so that it approaches about 20 years.

The following list shows the order of magnitudes of an assortment of measurable and estimatable doubling times and shows how rapidly the growth of science and technology has been outstripping that of the size of the population and of our nonscientific institutions.

100 years
Entries in dictionaries of national biography

---

[3] It is easy enough to convert from one to the other by noting, as a rough approximation, that 10 doubling periods correspond to a factor of 1024, or about 3 tenfolding periods.

50 years
  Labor force
  Population
  Number of universities
20 years
  Gross National Product
  Important discoveries
  Important physicists
  Number of chemical elements known
  Accuracy of instruments
  College entrants/1000 population
15 years
  B.A., B.S.
  Scientific journals
  Membership of scientific institutes
  Number of chemical compounds known
  Number of scientific abstracts, all fields
10 years
  Number of asteroids known
  Literature in theory of determinants
  Literature in non-Euclidean geometry
  Literature in x-rays
  Literature in experimental psychology
  Number of telephones in United States
  Number of engineers in United States
  Speed of transportation
  Kilowatt-hours of electricity
5 years
  Number of overseas telephone calls
  Magnetic permeability of iron
1½ years
  Million electron volts of accelerators

Bearing in mind the long period of validity of exponential growth, let us note that a 15-year doubling time extended over three centuries of growth corresponds to an increase of 20 powers of two, or a factor of about one million. Thus, in the interval from 1660 to the present day, such indices of the size of science should have increased by the order of a million. To offer the soundest explanation of the scientific and industrial revolutions is to posit that this is indeed what has been happening.

Just after 1660, the first national scientific societies in the modern tradition were founded; they established the first scientific periodicals, and scientists found themselves beginning to write scientific papers instead of the books that hitherto had been their only outlets. We have now a world list of some 50,000 scientific periodicals (Fig. 1) that have been founded, of which about 30,000 are still being published; these have produced a world total of about six million scientific papers (Fig. 2) and an increase at the approximate rate of at least half a

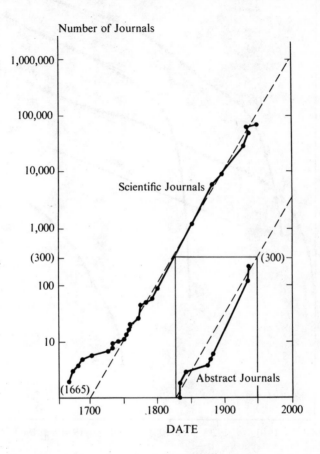

Fig. 1. Total number of scientific journals and abstract journals founded, as a function of date. Note that abstracts begin when the population of journals is approximately 300. Numbers recorded here are for journals founded, rather than those surviving; for all periodicals containing any "science" rather than for "strictly scientific" journals. Tighter definitions might reduce the absolute numbers by an order of magnitude, but the general trend remains constant for all definitions. From Derek J. de Solla Price, Science Since Babylon (New Haven, Yale University Press, 1961).

hitherto had been only abstracts. We have now a world list of some 70,000 scientific periodicals (Fig. 1) that have been founded, of which about 30,000 are still being published; these have maintained an increase at the approximate rate of at least half a million a year.[4]

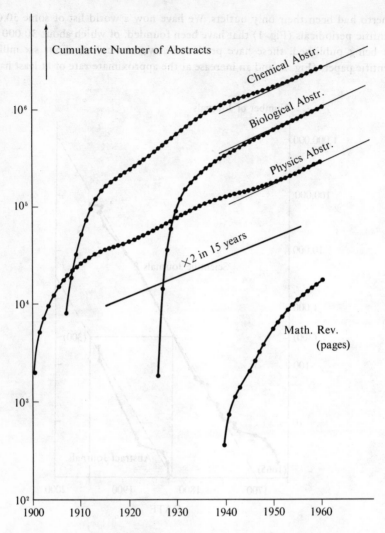

Fig. 2. Cumulative number of abstracts in various scientific fields, from the beginning of the abstract service to given date. It will be noted that after an initial period of rapid expansion to a stable growth rate, the number of abstracts increases exponentially, doubling in approximately 15 years.

million a year.[4] In general, the same applies to scientific manpower. Whereas in the mid-seventeenth century there were a few scientific men—a denumerable

[4] For a more detailed discussion of this see Derek J. de Solla Price, *Science Since Babylon* (New Haven, Yale University Press, 1961), Chapter 5.

who were countable and namable—there is now in the United States alone a population on the order of a million with scientific and technical degrees (Fig. 3). What is more, the same exponential law accounts quite well for all the time in between. The present million came through intermediate stages of 100,000 in 1900, 10,000 in 1850, and 1000 in 1800. In terms of magnitude alone, the transition from Little Science to Big Science has been steady—or at least has had only minor periodic fluctuations similar to those of the stock market—and it has followed a law of exponential growth with the time rates previously stated.

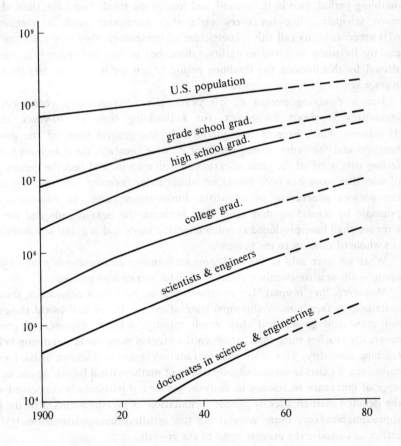

Fig. 3. Growth of scientific manpower and of general population in the United States. It may be seen that the more highly qualified the manpower, the greater has been its growth rate. It will also be noted that there appears a distinct tendency for the curves to turn toward a ceiling value running parallel with the population curve.

Thus, the steady doubling every 15 years or so that has brought us into the present scientific age has produced the peculiar immediacy that enables us to say that so much of science is current and that so many of its practitioners are alive. If we start with the law that the number of living scientists doubles in, let us say, 15 years, then in any interval of 15 years there will come into being as many scientists again as the whole of time preceding. But at any moment there coexists a body of scientists produced not over 15 years but over an interval nearer to the 45 years separating average date of arrival at the research front from average date of retirement from active scientific work. Thus, for every one person born before such a period of 45 years, we now have one born in the first doubling period, two in the second, and four in the third. There are, then, about seven scientists alive for every eight that have ever been, a fraction of 87½ percent; let us call this a coefficient of immediacy. One may calculate this exactly by using actuarial mortality tables, but in fact the result is not much altered by this because the doubling period of science is so much less than the average working life of a scientist.

For a doubling period of 10 years, the corresponding coefficient of immediacy is about 96 percent; for a doubling time of 20 years, about 81 percent. Thus, even if one admits only the general form of the growth function and the order of magnitude of its time constant, these account for the feeling that most of the great scientists are still with us, and that the greater part of scientific work has been produced within living memory, within the span of the present generation of scientists. Furthermore, one can emphasize the principle by remarking that some time between the next decade and the one after we shall have produced as much scientific work and as many scientists as in the whole of time up to the present.

What we have said so far is by now well known and reasonably well agreed upon by those who speculate about science for fun or high policy. . . .

Moreover, the "normal" law of growth that we have been considering thus far describes, in fact, a most abnormal state of events. In the real world things do not grow and grow until they reach infinity. Rather, exponential growth eventually reaches some limit, at which the process must slacken and stop before reaching absurdity. This more realistic function is also well known as the logistic curve, and it exists in several slightly different mathematical forms. Again, at this stage of ignorance of science in analysis, we are not particularly concerned with the detailed mathematics or precise formulation of measurements. For the first approximation (or, more accurately, the zeroth-order approximation) let it suffice to consider the general trend of the growth.

The logistic curve is limited by a floor—that is, by the base value of the index of growth, usually zero—and by a ceiling, which is the ultimate value of the growth beyond which it cannot go in its accustomed fashion (Fig. 4). In its typical pattern, growth starts exponentially and maintains this pace to a point almost halfway between floor and ceiling, where it has an inflection. After this, the pace of growth declines so that the curve continues toward the ceiling in a manner symmetrical with the way in which it climbed from the floor to the

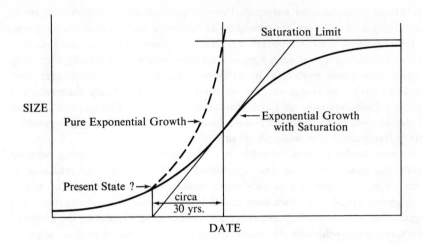

*Fig. 4. General form of the logistic curve. From
Derek J. de Solla Price,* Science Since Babylon *(New
Haven, Yale University Press, 1961).*

midpoint. This symmetry is an interesting property; rarely in nature does one find asymmetrical logistic curves that use up one more parameter to describe them. Nature appears to be parsimonious with her parameters of growth.

Because of the symmetry so often found in the logistic curves that describe the growth of organisms, natural and man-made, measuring science or measuring the number of fruit flies in a bottle, the width of the curve can be simply defined. Mathematically, of course, the curve extends to infinity in both directions along the time axis. For convenience we measure the width of the midregion cut off by the tangent at the point of inflection, a quantity corresponding to the distance between the quartiles on a standard curve of error or its integral. This midregion may be shown necessarily to extend to either side of the center for a distance equal to about three of the doubling periods of the exponential growth. . . .

From this we are led to suggest a second basic law of the analysis of science: all the apparently exponential laws of growth must ultimately be logistic, and this implies a period of crisis extending on either side of the date of midpoint for about a generation. The outcome of the battle at the point of no return is complete reorganization or violent fluctuation or death of the variable.

Now that we know something about the pathological afterlife of a logistic curve, and that such things occur in practice in several special branches of science and technology, let us reopen the question of the growth curve of science as a whole. We have seen that it has had an extraordinarily long life of purely exponential growth and that at some time this must begin to break down and be followed by a generation-long interval of increasing restraint which may tauten its sinews for a jump either toward escalation or toward violent fluctuation. The detailed nature of this change, and any interpretation of it, must depend on what we are measuring and on how such an index is compiled.

Even without such definition and analysis one can immediately deduce various characteristics of such a period. Clearly there will be rapidly increasing concern over those problems of manpower, literature, and expenditure, that demand solution by reorganization. Further, such changes as are successful will lead to a fresh escalation of rapid adaptation and growth. Changes not efficient or radical enough to cause such an offshoot will lead to a hunting, producing violent fluctuations that will perhaps smooth out at last.

Such an analysis seems to imply that the state called Big Science actually marks the onset of those new conditions that will break the tradition of centuries and give rise to new escalations, violent huntings, redefinitions of our basic terms, and all the other phenomena associated with the upper limit. I will suggest that at some time, undetermined as yet but probably during the 1940s or 1950s, we passed through the midperiod in general logistic growth of science's body politic.

Thus, although we recognize from our discussion so far that saturation is ultimately inevitable, it is far too approximate to indicate when and in what circumstances saturation will begin. We now maintain that it may already have arrived. It may seem odd to suggest this when we have used only a few percent of the manpower and money of the country, but [it appears] that this few percent actually represents an approach to saturation and an exhausting of our resources that nearly (within a factor of two) scrapes the bottom of the barrel.

At all events, the appearance of new phenomena in the involvement of science with society seems to indicate something radically different from the steady growth characteristic of the entire historic past. The new era shows all the familiar syndromes of saturation. This, I must add, is a counsel of hope rather than despair. Saturation seldom implies death, but rather that we have the beginning of new and exciting tactics for science, operating with quite new ground rules.

It is, however, a grave business, for Big Science interpreted thus becomes an uncomfortably brief interlude between the traditional centuries of Little Science and the impending period following transition. If we expect to discourse in scientific style about science, and to plan accordingly, we shall have to call this approaching period New Science, or Stable Saturation; if we have no such hopes, we must call it senility.

The Hypothesis of Cultural Lag:
A Present-Day View

Hornell Hart

... *cultural lag* may be defined as consisting in a time interval between two phases in the development of a culture complex, or of two different culture complexes, where the length of the interval requires shortening in order better to promote generally accepted social ends, and where such shortening is regarded as potentially possible through social planning. When specific examples are studied, it becomes evident that two extremes must be distinguished.

One of these is implied by Stuart Chase's theory and may be referred to as *tandem lag.* In this sense, cultural lag consists in the time interval between a specific invention and the achievement of a specific adjustment called for by that invention. An example would be the lag between the invention of the automobile and the development of radar speed-timing.

The second type may be referred to as *complex lag.* This consists in the time interval between emergence of a stated social need (as the result of the development of a stated culture complex) and the meeting of that need by the development of adequate adaptive complexes. An example is the gap between the accelerating development of mass-destructive military technology and the lagging development of the international-law-and-order complex. A more generalized example is the lag which has often been pointed out between technology and social science.

Once the contrast is stated, it becomes evident that tandem lag and complex lag merge into each other. To regard the automobile as a single, specific invention is an obvious oversimplification. Traffic accidents are the result of the developing highway-speed complex and of the lagging highway-safety complex. On the other hand, specific developments in the mass-destruction complex, such as the invention of the atomic bomb, have provided focal points of evident need for adaptive social inventions.

The Valuation Aspects of the Lag Concept

One of the most frequent objections raised against the cultural-lag concept is that it inherently involves valuation. The issue reduces really to this question: "Can the value judgment implied in the term *lag* be reduced to objective and verifiable facts?" In considering this issue it is essential to recognize that all cultural behavior is dynamic, that most if not all invention is goal-directed, and that valuational aspects therefore cannot be excluded. Social change results from the dynamics involved in valuational behavior. The process can be understood only when this valuational behavior is dispassionately and fully understood, and when the problems involved are worked out along appropriate dynamic lines.

Any legitimate objection to the valuational implications of the cultural-lag concept may be eliminated by stating, explicitly and objectively, the value frame within which the lag to be investigated is conceived. A comprehensive study of the attitudes of sociologists toward value judgments has led to the formulation of certain conclusions which seem to be practically universally accepted. Among these is the proposition that it is entirely proper, scientifically, for applied sociology, having discovered what human purposes are most fundamental, or what ones are most widely accepted as ideal, to seek and disseminate knowledge as to how these purposes may be more adequately fulfilled.[1]

For example, it is almost universally conceded that the killing and maiming of human beings through automobile accidents is undesirable. When technological progress increased the speed of automobiles, there was at first no concomitant increase in methods for preventing accidents. Granted that resulting rises in traffic death rates are contrary to the general welfare, it is a proper function of social science to work out methods for curing this particular form of lag.

The Measurement of Cultural Lag

One of the criticisms of loose uses of the cultural-lag concept has been that quite frequently a quantitative variable was implied but never actually defined or measured.[2]

The seriousness of this difficulty becomes increasingly evident when one attempts to reduce to actually quantitative terms some of the purportedly quantitative formulations of cultural lag. For example, how might one measure the "strain which exists between two correlated parts of culture which change at unequal rates," which strain constitutes cultural lag as defined by Professor Ogburn?

---

[1] Hornell Hart, "Value Judgments in Sociology," *American Sociological Review,* Vol. 3 (December, 1938), pp. 864-865.

[2] E.g., John Mueller, "Present Status of the Cultural Lag Hypothesis," *American Sociological Review,* Vol. 3 (June, 1938), p. 320.

One method of measuring lag is in terms of a gap between two indexes using the same units. For example, one phase of the recent biological phenomenon of a rising birth rate is the increase which is now going on in the number of children of school age. This biological aspect of the family complex calls for an expansion in the material level of the school complex. But there is a marked lag in such expansion. The leading development can be measured in terms of the number of children needing places in school buildings, and the lagging variable can be measured in terms of the number of places available in the appropriate schools. The resulting lag variable has two dimensions—time and number of places lacking in schools.

A second method of measuring cultural lag is to find a quantitative index of the unprevented or potential damage resulting from the innovation for which adaptive measures are lagging. . . .

Impact of Large-Scale Science
on the United States

Alvin M. Weinberg

Throughout history, societies have expressed their aspirations in large-scale, monumental enterprises which, though not necessary for the survival of the societies, have taxed them to their physical and intellectual limits. History often views these monuments as symbolizing the societies. The Pyramids, the Sphinx, and the great temple at Karnak symbolize Egypt; the magnificent cathedrals symbolize the church culture of the Middle Ages; Versailles symbolizes the France of Louis XIV; and so on. The societies were goaded into these extraordinary exertions by their rulers—the pharaoh, the church, the king—who

Alvin M. Weinberg, "Impact of Large-Scale Science on the United States," *Science*, Vol. 134, No. 3473, July 21, 1961, pp. 161-164. Copyright 1961 by the American Association for the Advancement of Science. Reprinted by permission of the author and publisher. The author is director of Oak Ridge National Laboratory, Oak Ridge, Tenn. This article is based on a talk given before the American Rocket Society—Oak Ridge National Laboratory Space-Nuclear Conference, Gatlinburg, Tenn., 4 May 1961.

invoked the cultural mystique when this was sufficient, but who also used force when necessary. Sometimes, as with the cathedrals, local pride and a sense of competition with other cities helped launch the project. In many cases the distortion of the economy caused by construction of the big monuments contributed to the civilization's decline.

When history looks at the 20th century, she will see science and technology as its theme; she will find in the monuments of Big Science—the huge rockets, the high-energy accelerators, the high-flux research reactors—symbols of our time just as surely as she finds in Notre Dame a symbol of the Middle Ages. She might even see analogies between our motivations for building these tools of giant science and the motivations of the church builders and the pyramid builders. We build our monuments in the name of scientific truth, they built theirs in the name of religious truth; we use our Big Science to add to our country's prestige, they used their churches for their cities' prestige; we build to placate what President Eisenhower suggested could become a dominant scientific caste, they built to please the priests of Isis and Osiris.

The emergence of Big Science and its tools as a supreme outward expression of our culture's aspirations has created many difficult problems, both philosophic and practical. Some of the problems concern science itself, some the relation between science and our society. I shall address myself to three specific questions, all of which arise from the growth of Big Science: first, Is Big Science ruining science?; second, Is Big Science ruining us financially?; and third, Should we divert a larger part of our effort toward scientific issues which bear more directly on human well-being than do such Big-Science spectaculars as manned space travel and high-energy physics? These questions are so broad, and so difficult, that I cannot do more than raise them here. Since they involve the issue of the scientist's responsibility to his science and to his society, I believe I shall have done some service merely by urging scientists to think seriously about them.

Is Big Science Ruining Science?

The English astronomer Fred Hoyle recently set off a lively controversy by arguing against the United Kingdom's going into large-scale space research. His argument, which applies to much of Big Science, is twofold: first, that the intrinsic scientific interest of space research is not worth the money and man-power that goes into it and certainly does not justify spending more on it than on any other branch of science; and second, that wherever science is fed by too *much* money, it becomes fat and lazy. He claims to see evidence that the tight intellectual discipline necessary for science is, especially in America, being loosened. I shall touch later upon Hoyle's first point: Is Big Science giving us our money's worth? For the moment I want to discuss his second point, which can be paraphrased as, "Is Big Science ruining science?"

I confess that I share Hoyle's misgivings. In the first place, since Big Science needs great public support it thrives on publicity. The inevitable result is the injection of a journalistic flavor into Big Science which is fundamentally in conflict with the scientific method. If the serious writings about Big Science were carefully separated from the journalistic writings, little harm would be done. But they are not so separated. Issues of scientific or technical merit tend to get argued in the popular, not the scientific, press, or in the congressional committee room rather than in the technical-society lecture hall; the spectacular rather than the perceptive becomes the scientific standard. When these trends are added to the enormous proliferation of scientific writing, which largely remains unread in its original form and therefore must be predigested, one cannot escape the conclusion that the line between journalism and science has become blurred.

In the second place, one sees evidence of scientists' spending money instead of thought. This is one of the most insidious effects of large-scale support of science. In the past the two commodities, thought and money, have both been hard to come by. Now that money is relatively plentiful but thought is still scarce, there is a natural rush to spend dollars rather than thought—to order a 10^7 nuclear reactor instead of devising a crucial experiment with the reactors at hand, or to make additional large-scale computations instead of reducing the problem to tractable dimensions by perceptive physical approximation. The line between spending money and spending thought is blurring.

Finally, the huge growth of Big Science has greatly increased the number of scientific administrators. Where large sums of public money are being spent there must be many administrators who see to it that the money is spent wisely. Just as it is easier to spend money than to spend thought, so it is easier to tell other scientists how and what to do than to do it oneself. The big scientific community tends to acquire more and more bosses. The Indians with bellies to the bench are hard to discern for all the chiefs with bellies to the mahogany desks. Unfortunately, science dominated by administrators is science understood by administrators, and such science quickly becomes attenuated if not meaningless.

But it is fruitless to wring one's hands over the bad effects of Big Science. Big Science is an inevitable stage in the development of science and, for better or for worse, it is here to stay. What we must do is learn to live with Big Science. We must make Big Science flourish without, at the same time, allowing it to trample Little Science—that is, we must nurture small-scale excellence as carefully as we lavish gifts on large-scale spectaculars.

In respect to Big Science, huge laboratories like Oak Ridge play a central role. They were established to encourage Big Science yet to segregate it and prevent it from taking over Little Science. Big-scale science's triple diseases—journalitis, moneyitis, administratitis—have always been with us in the big laboratories. Being aware of these pitfalls we have made conscious efforts to cope with them—by requiring internal review of each publication, by occasionally sending an administrator back to his laboratory, by subjecting large expenditures to enough scrutiny so that money is not as easy to get as it may outwardly seem to be. I do not believe that we at Oak Ridge, or I suspect at other such institutions, are completely successful in these efforts. We do the best we can, however; and at least, by confining Big Science to such institutions, we prevent the contagion from spreading.

What really bothers me is the evidence that Big Science is invading the universities. One need not look far to find Bev accelerators and megawatt research reactors on many campuses. The justification for putting these devices on university campuses is that such gadgets of Big Science are now needed to perform large parts of basic research, and that basic research is best done in conjunction with education. But I think there is a very grave danger to our universities in this incursion of Big Science. A professor of science is chosen because he is extremely well qualified as a scientist, as a thinker, or as a teacher. If he becomes too involved with Big Science he will have to become a publicist, if not a journalist, an administrator, and a spender of big money. I do not for a moment suggest that college professors are less able big-time administrators than are professional administrators. I merely point out that the proper function of a professor is to be a professor; that once Big Science has invaded his precincts and he becomes an operator (even though a very effective one), his students and his intellectual eminence and proficiency are bound to suffer. Thus, though my question "Is Big Science ruining science?" is irrelevant, since Big Science is here to stay, I do believe that Big Science can ruin our universities, by diverting the universities from their primary purpose and by converting university professors into administrators, housekeepers, and publicists.

Are there ways of bringing Big Science into the educational stream other than by converting our universities into National Laboratories? One way which is tentatively suggested in the report of the President's Science Advisory Committee, "Scientific Progress, The Universities, and The Federal Government," is to strengthen the already close relationships between the government laboratories and the universities. I would go a step further and propose the creation of technical universities close to or in conjunction with the large government laboratories. One advantage of such a scheme would be that the National Laboratories have already made their peace with Big Science—the onerous housekeeping function, the layer of inevitable administrators and publicists, is already in being. Professors in such collaborating universities, who might be drawn in part, but not wholly, from the existing scientific staffs of the big laboratories, would not have to get involved so strongly in activities not related to their science as they would if they had to start Big Science from the beginning. In addition, the big government laboratories have facilities and technically trained personnel that are not now pulling their full weight in the educational job which must be done.

Exactly what pattern should be established would vary from institution to institution. The Rockefeller Institute for Medical Research has recently been rechartered as the Rockefeller University—this is the most extreme possibility. I think that a more generally appropriate pattern would involve, first, a great expansion in the use of short-tenure, postdoctoral fellows at the big laboratories, and second, the establishment of independent graduate schools of technology in close proximity to the big laboratories, and with some inter-locking staff. Such schools would have as much claim to federal support as do the universities which receive money for direct educational purposes as part of their payment for conducting research.

Is Big Science Ruining Us Financially?

My second question is, Is Big Science ruining us financially? The present federal expenditure on research and development is $\$8.4 \times 10^9$ which is about 10 percent of the federal budget, about 1.6 percent of the gross national product. The money spent on research and development is the largest single *controllable* item in the federal budget in the sense that, unlike wheat subsidies or interest on the national debt, it can be changed at the President's discretion. It is not surprising, therefore, that the Bureau of the Budget has taken such an interest in our research and development budget.

The rate of change of our research and development budget, averaged over the past ten years, has been 10 percent per year; this corresponds to a doubling time of seven years. Since the doubling time of the gross national product is about 20 years, at the present rate we shall be spending *all* of our money on science and technology in about 65 years. Evidently something will have to be done or Big Science will ruin us financially.

The amount that we spend on research and development is only one-fifth of our military budget—and of course over 80 percent of the $\$8.4 \times 10^9$ is for military purposes. There are many analogies between research expenditures and military expenditures. In neither case can one guarantee that anything useful will come of a specific expenditure; yet, on the average, we know that we must spend money for science and for defense. In both cases there is a high rate of obsolescence. Both our military and our scientific might are instruments of national policy. It therefore seems to me that the general principles which have guided our military-fiscal policy should be useful in guiding our science-fiscal policy.

We have decided, though implicitly, that our military budget shall represent about 10 percent of our gross national product. In the same way we ought soon to decide to devote a certain fraction of our gross national product to non-defense science rather than pay for each scientific expenditure on an *ad hoc,* item-by-item basis. At the moment science grows much more rapidly than does the gross national product. I suggest that we settle on some figure—say something less than 1 percent of the gross national product—as the long-term bill for federally supported, nondefense science, and that we stick to it for a period of, say, 15 years. Our science budget will then increase only as fast as our gross national product does, but we scientists shall have to get used to that idea.

If we settle on an over-all science budget which is geared to the gross national product, we shall have to make choices. At present each scientific expenditure is considered separately. The merits of desirable projects are argued by interested and clever proponents, but the relative merit of a project in high-energy physics as compared to a project in space or in atomic energy is not weighed in the balance. The system works because the science budget is expanding so fast. Fortunately, the President's Science Advisory Committee and the Federal Council for Science and Technology give us a mechanism for establishing an over-all science budget and for making the hard choices when we shall have to make them. These choices, which will require weighing space against biology, atomic energy against oceanography, will be the very hardest of all to make—if for no other reason than that no man knows enough to make such comparative judgments on scientific grounds. The incentive for creating a favorable public opinion for a pet scientific project will become much greater than it now is; the dangers of creating a political "in" group of scientists who keep worthy outsiders from the till will be severe. Nevertheless, it is obvious that we shall have to devote much more attention than we now do to making choices between science projects in very different fields.

Can We Divert the Course of Big Science?

As an example of the kind of choice which we shall have to make, let us consider whether there are alternative scientific fields which ought to have prior claim on our resources, ahead of manned space flight or high-energy physics.

It would be naive, if not hopeless, to argue that we should not use scientific achievement as a means of competing with the U.S.S.R. Major Gagarin's feat has caught the world's fancy, and we may as well face up to it. The question is, are we wise in choosing manned flight into space as the primary event in these scientific Olympic Games? I shall argue against doing so, on three grounds—hazard, expense, and relevance.

It is my impression that the hazard of space flight, particularly the radiation hazard, is not fully assessed as yet. An admirable analysis of the radiation hazard of manned space travel is given by T. Foelsche of Langley Field. Foelsche's estimates are given in Table 1.

It is obvious from these figures that the radiation shielding for a space craft could be formidable. To shield an entire capsule against high-energy solar flares with shielding of 25 grams per square centimeter might require about 10 tons of material; to shield a man individually would require about a ton. These figures are not catastrophic. Yet I find them disturbing for several reasons. First, the measurements of the solar-flare radiation, if not of the Van Allen belt radiation, are still very uncertain. Second, the values used in all of the calculations on space shielding for relative biological effectiveness of fast heavy particles have been much lower than those used in estimates of the shielding required for the manned nuclear aircraft. This difference is usually justified by the difference in energy of the radiations in the two cases; the space radiation, being harder, has a low linear energy transfer and therefore should have low relative biological effectiveness. However, the total experimental evidence on the relative biological effectiveness of very fast particles is not very large; in any event, the secondary particles produced in spallation processes, such as occur with

Table 1. Summary of shielding estimates and radiation
doses. The LD_{50} for man is about 500 rem (not rep);
the military tolerance is 25 rem.

| Shield weight (g/cm^2) | Inner belt (D) | | Flares (D) (rep) | |
	rem/hr	rep/hr	Low energy (< 500 Mev)	High energy (< 20 Bev)
2	21	12	2500-25,000	80-400
15	7.5	4.2	18-180	23-80
25	4.5	2.5	6-50	23-50

[From T. Foelsche, "Protection against solar flare protons," a paper presented at the 7th annual meeting of the American Astronautical Society, Dallas, Tex., 16-18 Jan. 1961.]

energetic primaries, are in the binding-energy, not the 100-Mev, region. Finally, the biological effects of extremely energetic heavy particles are not fully understood. Although Curtis's experiments on nerve cells suggest that these particles are not too dangerous (1), the matter is not really settled.

The radiation hazard does not clearly make space an intolerable environment for man; on the other hand, it makes space a much more hostile environment than we had suspected even five years ago. That man can tramp about without shielding for extended times on the moon's surface seems to me quite unlikely. The Lord, so to speak, provided His children with a marvelous radiation shield, the atmosphere, and He did not intend them to poke their heads into His unshielded reactors. The corollary I draw is that, on the basis of what we now know, manned space travel is not definitely feasible in the sense that we can now really place a firm upper limit on the cost of a round trip to the moon; the estimates of $\$20 \times 10^9$ to $\$40 \times 10^9$ for this mission are so large and cover so wide a range as to make the outsider doubt their validity on a priori grounds. May I remind you that about ten years ago the Lexington Project predicted that the cost of the nuclear-powered aircraft would be $\$1 \times 10^9$ and the time required, ten years. As it turned out, after ten years and an expenditure of $\$1 \times 10^9$ we have words, not nuclear airplanes, flying. Just because a project is very big and very expensive does not mean that the project will be very successful.

The other main contender for the position of Number One Event in the scientific Olympics is high-energy physics. It, too, is wonderfully expensive (the Stanford linear accelerator is expected to cost $\$100 \times 10^6$), and we may expect to spend $\$400 \times 10^6$ per year on this area of research by 1970. The issues with which such research deals have greater scientific validity than those dealt with in the *manned* space program, but its remoteness from human affairs is equally great. It has the advantage, from our point of view, that we are ahead of the Russians in high-energy physics.

But even if it were possible to generate around high-energy physics the same popular interest that arises naturally in connection with manned space travel, I am not persuaded that this is the battleground of choice. I personally would much rather choose scientific issues which have more bearing on the world that is part of man's everyday environment, and more bearing on man's welfare, than have either high-energy physics or manned space travel.

There are several such areas, and we are generally very far ahead in them. The most spectacular is molecular biology—a field in which the contribution from the East is minimal. We have learned more about the essential life processes—growth, protein synthesis, and reproduction—during the past decade than during all previous history. In my opinion the probability of our synthesizing living material from nonliving before the end of the century is of the same order as the probability of our making a successful manned round trip to the planets. I suspect that most Americans would prefer to belong to the society which first gave the world a cure for cancer than to the society which put the first astronaut on Mars.

I mention also the group of economic-technical problems which arise from the increasing pressure of population on resources. Of these, nuclear energy is the best known. Here the Western lead is clear, and it is important to consolidate the lead. There are others—the problem of water, or atmospheric pollution, or of chemical contamination of the biosphere, for example. Each of these is a technical issue which can lay claim to our resources—a claim that will have to be heard when we make choices.

But it is presumptuous for me to urge that we study biology on earth rather than biology in space, or physics in the nuclear binding-energy region, with its clear practical applications and its strong bearing on the rest of science, rather than physics in the Bev region, with its absence of practical applications and its very slight bearing on the rest of science. What I am urging is that these choices have become matters of high national policy. We cannot allow our over-all science strategy, when it involves such large sums, to be settled by default, or to be pre-empted by the group with the most skillful publicity department. We should have extensive debate on these over-all questions of scientific choice; we should make a choice, explain it, and then have the courage to stick to a course arrived at rationally.

In making our choices we should remember the experiences of other civilizations. Those cultures which have devoted too much of their talent to monuments which had nothing to do with the real issues of human well-being have usually fallen upon bad days: history tells us that the French Revolution was the bitter fruit of Versailles, and that the Roman Colosseum helped not at all in staving off the barbarians. So it is for us to learn well these lessons of history: we must not allow ourselves, by short-sighted seeking after fragile monuments of Big Science, to be diverted from our real purpose, which is the enriching and broadening of human life.

Reference

1. H. J. Curtis, *Science, 133,* 312 (1961).

The "Two Cultures"

Kenneth E. Boulding

In 1959 C. P. Snow, English scientist, scientific administrator, and novelist, delivered a series of lectures later published under the title *The Two Cultures and the Scientific Revolution.* This book introduced a new phrase—the two cultures—into currency and stimulated widespread discussion of the role of science in modern life. It was Snow's argument that modern culture was becoming increasingly bifurcated between the traditional literary or humanistic culture and the increasingly important scientific culture, in which he included technology. He excoriated the upholders of the humanistic culture for their snobbish refusal to recognize that science itself had, in the modern period, become a valid culture demanding recognition in the present world. Custodians of the literary culture answered, somewhat snippishly, that there was only one culture, and that scientists by and large did not have any culture.

Snow's concept of the polarization of modern society is, of course, oversimplified. There are, in fact, not two but many subcultures with which we must deal, and deciding how to bring about communication among them is a general rather than a specific need. One may know how to make a rocket go up without knowing where it should come down, but to separate completely the two

Kenneth E. Boulding, "The 'Two Cultures,' " in *Technology in Western Civilization,* Vol. II, eds. Melvin Kranzberg and Carrol W. Purcell, Jr. (New York: Oxford University Press, 1967), pp. 686-695. Boulding was born in England and received his B.A. and M.A. degrees at Oxford. He taught at universities in Scotland and Canada before going to the University of Michigan in 1949. He is now professor of economics at the University of Colorado. His many books include *Economic Analyses* (1941) and *The Meaning of the Twentieth Century* (1964).

knowledge systems may be fatal to mankind. Somehow, integration must be achieved.

The Concept of Culture

The word "culture" is itself used in different senses in ordinary speech and in the social sciences, and leads to some confusion. In ordinary speech, we often use it to mean those aspects of human life which involve a cultivated taste, especially in the arts. We think of culture in terms of opera, art galleries, classical music, good taste in architecture, furniture, or dress, and so on. To call a person "uncultured" is a form of abuse, implying that he has unrefined tastes or does not belong to the cultural elite.

In the social sciences, however, and especially in anthropology, the word *culture* is used simply to refer to a social system in all its aspects. The culture of the Hopi Indians, for instance, consists of their language, norms of behavior, forms of organization and community structure, family and kinship patterns, technology and methods of production, and so on. In this sense, then, culture means the general description of a society as a total system, and in this sense everyone is part of a culture of some kind, for no human being can exist in isolation from others. Even Robinson Crusoe carried with him the artifacts, memories, and knowledge of his own culture, though in isolation he began to modify the culture he possessed.

We often use the word "subculture" to mean a subsystem within a larger social system, and we use this term again as a total description. Thus, we find occupational subcultures. Truckers, for instance, have a pattern of life, even of speech, which is very different from that of doctors. There are organizational subcultures. A school, a hospital, a city, or a neighborhood will develop certain patterns of its own, even though it shares patterns of speech, behavior, and organization with other groups in the society in which it is embedded.

Although they all have some apparatus for preventing change and maintaining the old patterns, cultures and subcultures continually change. The very fact that human beings are born, age, and die, forces change; furthermore, some processes of learning, whether a result of inputs of information from outside the culture or the result of internal information generation, likewise lead to change. Where, however, the existing structures and patterns of a culture are highly valued by the persons who belong to it, change will be resisted, and will be interpreted as "bad." Thus the university continually tries to maintain the quality of its staff, its integrity, and academic freedom; a nation resists threats from outside or internal challenges to its legitimacy; a family, too, will resist attempts to undermine the mutual affection of the members; and so on. The overall dynamics of a culture is the result of the interaction of the forces making for change and the countervailing forces making for stability. Perfect stability equilibrium is unknown in nature, though some systems, such as the solar system, approximate it. No biological or social system even comes close to perfect stability. We have to judge the "health" of a system by its ability to maintain desirable patterns of change. What we mean by "desirable," however, raises large issues which cannot be adequately discussed here.

The "Sociosphere"

Social systems, then, consist of people, the roles they occupy (that is, the patterns of behavior they exhibit), and the inputs and outputs which go into these roles and the channels they follow. The inputs and outputs may be material, as when raw materials and people go into a factory and produce automobiles, or they may be inputs and outputs of information. A role in a social system, then, can be thought of as a transformer of inputs into outputs.

The role occupant does not have to be a person; it may be a machine, a combination of a person and a machine, or a group of persons in combination with a group of machines. Some inputs modify the transformation process itself, and create a different input-output relationship. Some material inputs may do this, in which case we think of them as investment. Information inputs also do this when they create new knowledge and new ways of transforming inputs into outputs.

On the whole, the *information* inputs and outputs, and the knowledge they create, dominate social systems, and even biological systems. Though the availability of sources for *material* inputs and outlets for material outputs considerably affects the operation of a system, the role of information and knowledge in social systems can hardly be overestimated. Even something we consider physical capital, such as a machine, is really a knowledge structure imposed on the material world which began as a knowledge structure in the human mind. Material inputs and outputs set limits and boundaries on the system, but information makes the system function.

We can picture the entire social system, then, as a "sociosphere," almost like the biosphere or the atmosphere, which consists at any one moment of all the people in the world, all the roles they are occupying, all the knowledge inside their heads, all the lines of communication among them, all the commodity flows among them, all the material capital (the houses, factories, machines, and so on) with which they work, and the organizations in which they participate. Change in the sociosphere comes partly from the accumulation of material capital, more fundamentally from the accumulation of knowledge, which will determine what people can do. Even when material capital is destroyed it can be recreated if the social system of which it is a part is unimpaired. We see this, for instance, in Japan, where the cities destroyed in World War II are now rebuilt and thriving; we see it in a city such as Leningrad or the central part of Warsaw, which has been rebuilt exactly as it was. These examples show very clearly how the information and knowledge aspects of a culture dominate its material substructure. . . .

The N-Cultures

The "two-cultures" problem arises because within the educated community there seem to be two subcultures, two constellations of communication networks, that do not interact very much with each other—the scientific, engineering, and technological subculture on the one hand and the literary, artistic, and perhaps political subculture on the other. The problem of communication between the two is perhaps more acute in European countries than in the United States because of the nature of the European educational system, which forces specialization at an early age. Even in the United States, however, the problem is real, although it would be more precise to call it the "n-cultures" problem. It is not merely that we have only two non-communicating cultures; we have a great many of them.

It is one of the fundamental principles of economics that specialization without trade is useless, for the farmer would freeze and the tailor would starve. The same principle applies to the world of information and knowledge. Specialization permits greater productivity in a particular field and a particular line of knowledge, but if it is not accompanied by exchange and even by a class of people who specialize in intellectual exchange, the bits of specialized knowledge do not add up to a total knowledge structure for mankind. And within the scientific community, the inability of specialists to communicate with specialists in a different field hampers the progress of the various specialties and also the total growth of knowledge. In part, this problem has been handled in the sciences by the development of what might be called interstitial fields such as physical chemistry or biophysics. It is countered, also, by the development of good scientific journalism, such as we find, for instance, in *Science,* the magazine of the American Association for the Advancement of Science, or in the *Scientific American.* The value of publications of this kind can hardly be overestimated. Nevertheless, the n-culture problem remains, and the fact that politicians, businessmen, artists, writers, poets, musicians, engineers, and scientists, often move in non-intersecting circles means that each may have knowledge and skills that are important to others but which are unavailable because of the lack of communication.

The social sciences can play a crucial role in bridging the gap which exists among the various cultures, and especially the two-culture gap between the humanistic and literary kind of knowledge and scientific knowledge. The social scientist himself is in a key position as a part of the systems he studies. He can not only approach the study of social systems from the point of view of an outside scientific observer—taking careful observations, making careful measurements, making predictions by mathematical or logical inference, and then seeing whether these are confirmed or falsified; but he also has an "inside track." The physicist has never been an atom or an electron; but the social scientist has participated himself in a great many social systems. Genuine knowledge can be derived from the inside track, and indeed provides many of the hypotheses and insights which the social scientists may then proceed to test by more rigorous methods.

Literary and humanistic studies represent a process of reflection and sifting of the accumulated records of folk knowledge. As such they represent a scholarly type of knowledge which is intermediate between the unsophisticated folk knowledge of ordinary life and the more testable images of science. Humanistic knowledge is in no sense to be despised; indeed, if one wants to understand the human being, a reading of Sophocles or Shakespeare may instruct us more than the latest psychological experiments. I have elsewhere defined science as the art of substituting unimportant questions which can be answered for important questions which cannot. This wisecrack clearly belongs to the humanistic subculture and is pretty hard to test. Nevertheless, it contains elements of truth; and as we move from the humanities through the "soft" into the "hard" sciences, we often find that our knowledge becomes less significant as it becomes more exact.

The technologist who is so absorbed in his own technique that he has no time for that expansion of his personal experience and, if we like, folk knowledge, which comes from acquaintance with the great literature of the world, or who has a mind so completely oriented toward verbal and mathematical symbols that he cannot appreciate the messages of art, music, or religion, will fail in his own technique, no matter how good it is. Somewhat in the mood of the former wisecrack, I once defined an engineer as a man who spends his life finding the best way of doing something which shouldn't be done at all. This indeed is always the danger of the technician. It is what is known in the technical language of programming as sub-optimization. The problem is summarized by the story of the engineer who said all he wanted to do was to reduce costs, until it was pointed out that costs could be reduced to zero by the simple process of shutting down the plant and liquidating the enterprise. . . .

Spaceship Earth and the Human Being

There are long-run problems facing the human race which may be very difficult to solve. We do not yet, for instance, have a stable, high-level technology. Our existing technology is based on fossil fuels and ores, and is thus limited; we will be all right for a hundred years, or perhaps two hundred, but within strictly historic time we may face a totally exhausted earth. Fortunately, a technology based on the concept of Earth as a self-contained spaceship is by no means impossible, and indeed seems to be on the way. This would involve placing man in a self-perpetuating cycle, drawing on the atmosphere and the oceans as the only basic resource, and importing energy either from the sun or from nuclear fusion on the earth.

For the spaceship society, we must also achieve population control, which we are a long way from accomplishing. We do not even know how large a population the earth could support in a stable, high-level economy. One hopes for the sake of the unborn that it will be large, for world population is all too likely to go to six billion by the end of this century, and we are not likely to catch it before then.

A final problem related to the problem of the two cultures is that of human development, that is, the full development of human potential in terms of the enjoyment of life, variety of experience, sensitivity of concern, appreciation of beauty, love, affection, community, and so on. The very concept of development implies some ideal or at least some direction of change which we regard as ideal, by which we can measure achievements.

The social sciences can, perhaps, help here by expanding our knowledge of what men have in fact regarded as ideal, and by attempting to explain the circumstances under which one set of ideals become prevalent. Our ideals themselves are derived largely from people we have known, imagined, or encountered in literature, poetry, religion, and art. We can, perhaps, find out something about the relation of prevalent ideals to the survival of societies and subcultures; or we can study the way in which its ideals affect the character of a society. Where, for example, there is an exaggerated ideal of masculinity, where the status of women is low, or where achievement goes into rivalry rather than into production, economic development may be hampered. The social sciences study the relation of these ideals to the nature and development of a society. The ideals themselves, however, come out of the folk culture or out of humanistic culture. This is true even for science itself, which has ideals of objectivity, dispassion, honesty, and so on. These ideals come not from science itself, though they are the prerequisites for the development of science.

A Problem of Choice

There are questions here that the framework of science and technology cannot answer. No matter how far we go in technology, all that technology gives us is power; and power without an objective is meaningless and ultimately self-destructive. This is an area scarcely penetrated as yet by the social sciences. We have, therefore, to rely a great deal on the humanistic vision expressed in poetry, art, and religion. We can grow in knowledge and begin to apply the human mind to the critique of the *ends* of man and his social systems, just as we can to the improvement of *means*.

Thus the increase of power technology produces raises all the more insistently those questions about the "chief end of man" which religion and philosophy, poetry and the arts, have always raised. When we are impotent, the question of whether we want the wrong things hardly arises; we cannot get them anyway. As our power increases, the question of *what* we want to do with it acquires overriding importance. At this point even the social scientist must take a back seat, for such knowledge is perhaps unobtainable, and wisdom is all that we have left.

Section Two

Technology and the Environmental Crisis

The problem of technology in the environment was given a section of its own, not because it transcends all other problems in degree or priority, but because it is both global in extent and related to almost all other major urgent problems such as population, war, and poverty.

To a large degree, the physical and biological aspects of the environmental crisis have been excluded. Overexposure to this part of the problem has resulted in denial of the threat because it appears too large for human intervention and backlash, where the ecologists who are sounding the warning are counter-attacked as prophets of doom or co-opted into futile postures. The essays and articles included all deal, in one way or another, with the social, political, economic, and value aspects of environment—that is to the value we place on the quality of the environment in terms of our choices and priorities. In this way, the issue is integrated to the major themes of the reader.

Pollution is the prime result of technological backlash, the unanticipated and unprecedented ecological hazards introduced by new technologies and the result of technology's anti-ecological and uncontrolled nature. It is also at the crux of our value crisis. To add to our homocidal, suicidal, and genocidal capacities, we are ecocidal and terracidal. Pollution has become a global issue, striking at the heart of our economic and political structures, which seem unable to control it. Almost all pollution, including noise, is technological, and this tends to make the environmental crisis a part of all the issues raised in this book.

The physical and biological aspects of the environmental issue are natural thematic parts of the sections on biology, chemistry, and nuclear power, and these aspects will appear in the appropriate sections, along with the other pertinent problems of those areas. This section will be confined to the sociology of pollution—to the concept that pollution is a direct consequence of the anti-ecological nature of a laissez-faire technology not properly assessed and controlled and designed only to reinforce existing political and economic structures. According to the editor's model of the technological order, these social structures tend to rubberstamp the growth of technology because of its capacity for a rapid pay-off in economic and political power. These social structures allow environmental costs to be paid by society as a whole or deferred to the future. This deficit budgeting is leading us inevitably to catastrophe, unless we can bring technology under control and institute massive pollution abatement and resource management programs. What societies do about this problem reflects the urgency and priority of choices, and these, in turn, reflect what our values are.

The lead article, by Wheeler, presents a sociological overview of the problem of pollution. Eipper's article gives a case history of a specific environmental problem and illustrates the actions and principles through which desirable changes can be created. The now famous articles by Hardin and White are concerned with the ethical issues of the environmental crisis, Hardin being specifically concerned with population while White traces the roots of our ethical crisis in theology.

The Politics of Ecology

Harvey Wheeler

Until little more than six months ago, "new politics" referred to either the protest movement or late-model mass-media campaigning. Today, however, a

Harvey Wheeler, "The Politics of Ecology," from Saturday Review, March 7, 1970. Copyright 1970 Saturday Review, Inc., pp. 51-52, 62-64. Harvey Wheeler is a senior fellow at the Center for the Study of Democratic Institutions, Santa Barbara, California.

third new politics is springing up. It is being given urgency by a growing public alarm over all varieties of pollution. War protest has yielded to demonstrations against the rape of the environment. Youth is turning away from Marxists like Herbert Marcuse and flocking to ecologists like Paul Ehrlich. The message is ecocide, the environment being murdered by mankind. Each day brings to light a new ecological crisis. Our dense, amber air is a noxious emphysema agent; farming—anti-husbandry—turns fertile soil into a poisoned wasteland; rivers are sewers, lakes cesspools, and our oceans are dying.

The early warning signals seemed unrelated and were easily ignored. Five hundred Londoners died of a summer smog attack. New York, blacked out and turned off, became dysfunctional. Union Oil's Platform A sprang a leak and converted Santa Barbara's postcard beaches into a sludge swamp. Traffic congestion made driving slower than walking. Airways threatened to become as dangerous as freeways. Cities, unable to function, closed schools and reduced public services. As power blackouts became seasonal, power demands rose and pushed pollution levels—thermal and hydrocarbon—to higher readings. Mathematical ecologists, such as Kenneth Watt, estimate that the United States is approaching the point where the interstitial energy required to keep the system going is greater than the energy it employs productively: Overhead costs overwhelm output. Our entire social order faces an ecosystem "depression" that will make 1929 look like a shower at a garden party.

It is imperative to correct one common fallacy—one especially popular among the young. Technology is not the culprit. Admittedly, the misuse of technology is part of the problem, but the essence of the real problem is what Watt calls the ecocidal asymptote. It is to the new politics of ecology what $E=mc^2$ was to the thermonuclear era.

The ecocidal asymptote runs as follows: Statistical studies of the pattern of exploitation of every natural resource can be plotted as two curves. One represents the rate of depletion of a resource, the other represents the technological capacity for its exploitation. Both curves are exponential; that is, in the beginning they rise very gradually. But their rate of increase is always rising, pushing their curves up ever more steeply until they reach a vertical explosion. Both follow the same pattern at the same rate, exploding, asymptotically, at the same time.

As an illustration, consider the ocean's fisheries—the blue whale, the salmon, the tuna. In the beginning, the supply is virtually unlimited, and harvesting techniques make little or no dent in the available supply. Soon fishing techniques improve, and, as they do, they gradually overtake reproduction rates; supplies decline as techniques improve. As this situation becomes apparent, it spurs on competition to get more and more while the getting is good. Ever more efficient fishing techniques are invented, and their rate of efficiency rises in direct ratio to the depletion of the resource until the point arrives when the ultimate in fishing technology coincides with the extinction of the species. This "falling together" of the technology and resource depletion curves is the ecocidal asymptote. It is the inimical process that characterizes our age, the enemy of the new politics of ecology. The death of one resource leads to the depletion of another; one technological fix begets another. Each of our ecocidal crises is interconnected with all the others, and none can be solved in isolation. The politics of ecology is architectonic.

The new politics of ecology, however, is not merely an outgrowth of the old politics of conservation. Conservation has a long and revered history, tracing back to such men as John Muir and Clifford Pinchot. This conservationist tradition, somewhat ineffectual in the past, is acquiring a new vitality today. In fact, entire states, largely in the American Northwest, are known for their being officially conservation-minded. Washington, Oregon, and Montana are prominent examples. Conservation slogans gain in popularity each day: "Keep Arizona Clean"; "Preserve Washington's Water" (and keep it out of California); "Stamp Out Billboards"; "Save Lake Tahoe." Rotarians and Yippies unite in "GOO"— "Get Oil Out of Santa Barbara"; and the cry of that great conservationist Howard Hughes is voiced: "Don't let the AEC shake down Caesar's Palace." These are laudable examples of conservationist politics, but all share the basic characteristics of the conservationism of the past; all are local, piecemeal efforts, and all rely upon traditional pressure-group tactics.

Today, we can count approximately 126 Congressmen who have publicly identified themselves as a conservationist bloc. A new bill introduced by Congressman Richard L. Ottinger and others proposes to guarantee all citizens the right to enjoy a healthful environment. Yet, such efforts are still in the mode of the old politics. They have a new twist, a new power base, and a new constituency. This new lease on life for the old mode of conservationist politics is not difficult to understand. It is an outgrowth of the leisure industries spawned by our affluent society. It is, to oversimplify, the politics of tourism. Conservationism is a gut issue in the West. It means preserve our state as an enclave of natural beauty and tourist attractions.

But the new politics of ecology means something quite different. A few examples will sharpen these differences. The essential political problem of the future is, first, to figure out how to preserve general ecological balances, and, second, how to calculate hidden social costs so as to determine how much is really being spent on side effects such as a new freeway, the three-car family, and the SST. Complete ecological harmony is impossible to achieve, but the "trade-offs" necessary to approach it as closely as possible must become known.

There is no such thing as an atmosphere without any pollution. However, it is obvious that certain kinds of air pollution deriving from fossil fuels already have reached perilous levels. This is not merely a question of unsightliness nor even of the threat of a rise in lung cancer and emphysema. Even more serious hazards may develop if pollution particles are carried by superjets from the lower atmosphere into its upper, turbulence-free layers. Scientists warn that these jet contrails may not be dispersed and could act as an insulation layer between Earth and sun, cooling the earth and leading to a new Ice Age. Of course, no one is certain what will really happen. We are in much the same position as when DDT was introduced; nobody knew for certain what its cumulative effects would be. Today, it does not seem inconceivable that pollution particles could quickly clog the upper atmosphere, and before we knew it utter havoc would be upon us.

Obviously, pollution must be reduced, but again we are not dealing in absolutes. We must know what levels are tolerable, and we must know the conveniences or desires that must be sacrificed to maintain these levels. New mass transit systems may be required. Individual desires to own several automobiles will have to be curtailed. And this is but the beginning. Ecologists tell us we shall have to mount a revolution of declining expectations. Gadgets will have to go. Creature comforts will have to give way to culture comforts. Americans today are at 1788. Never again will they or their children enjoy as many material conveniences. This is the real revolution implicit in the new politics of ecology.

What level of public education should we and can we maintain? How much are we willing to pay for it? How can we finance that level? Can we continue to support schools from state land taxes? Is it just to do so? Must we institute a national educational system? To answer these questions we must know the optimum size of an urban community, and how population should be distributed in our clustered communities. In short, we shall have to find out exactly what life in a megalopolis really costs, and whether or not we are getting our money's worth.

What degree of smog is created by population density? Perhaps the same number of people could live in roughly the same area, and even own the same number of cars if they displayed different density patterns with lower ratios of travel between residence and work. Simple freeway tariff schedules could alter traffic patterns immediately by penalizing over-powered and under-occupied vehicles. But we don't know. We don't know how much interstitial overhead energy we waste in a city like New York, merely trying to hold its parts together and keep it operating. We shall have to learn how to calculate the interstitial requirements of cities of different types and sizes to determine the optimum balance between urban amenities and overhead costs. We have no real measures of the price we pay for slums in all sorts of ways—poor health, substandard living conditions, crime, and so on. We do know that slums are high statistics areas; in them are concentrated most of everything bad, and at the end of each statistic lies a dead body.

Automation reduces the number of people required for factory and office operations, making huge cities unnecessary as well as uneconomic. Industrialists have known this for a long time. But what about the city as a cultural center? If we reduced cities to the size of fifty thousand or even a hundred thousand people, wouldn't we have to sacrifice our great cultural centers, our theaters, our museums, our libraries? The answer is no, we would expand them, improve them, and make them more widely available to all. We speak already of the museum without walls, meaning that the treasures of the entire world can now be exhibited everywhere. Microfilm libraries plus computer terminals make it possible for everybody everywhere to use the Library of Congress as well as the British Museum and the Bibliothéque Nationale.

What of the theater, the symphony, the ballet? Of course, recordings and television spread them to all, in one sense. Even great "living" theaters and symphonies are possible in very small cities. Vienna was relatively small when it reached its musical apex. Our greatest cultural traditions have been produced in very small cities. Seventeenth-century London abounded with genius; by modern standards it was but a mini-town. Ancient Athens was even smaller, and Plato and Aristotle thought it far too large at that. There is no reason why the same thing cannot be done again. At least, failure would not be due to smallness. All we really need is to decide to produce the cultural conditions necessary to elicit similarly high achievements. Gross size, far from a prerequisite, is an insuperable hindrance.

To answer such questions and to implement the answers will be one of the chief tasks of the politics of the future. We've never asked these questions of politics in the past. But, today, we can have everything that is really valuable about our large cities, and at the same time avoid the disagreeable and expensive side effects due to size. These are ecological questions, and, even though we may be able to answer them soon, there will still be no way to transmit this ecological wisdom to the average citizen for rational and deliberate application at the polls. Yet, this is exactly what we must be able to do in the near future. We shall require a new kind of party system with a new kind of participational democracy seeking solutions to ecological problems. Finally, we shall require a new kind of deliberation or legislative process to grow out of the new politics of ecology, and we shall have to relate to it in something like the way the existing legislative process related to our traditional party system.

Let us take the second problem first, for although it is generally understood that our party system is inadequate the deficiencies of our legislative system have received scant attention. Reflect for a moment on the fact that our legislatures and our party system are well-tailored to each other. Our parties are, as the textbooks say, loose confederations of state and local boss systems. The key element is "state and local." This means that the representatives selected through our present electoral system arrive at our legislative chambers representing the interests of their local districts. An implicit assumption is that all our primary problems and conflicts will arise from the clash of local interests—conflicts relating to the interests people acquire because they live in one place rather than another. Since before James Madison—the man who provided the underlying rationale for this system of politics—we have trusted that this pluralistic, territorially based expression of interests would produce the general interest, almost as if guided by an unseen hand.

But the issues described earlier are not related to any specific territory as such. Nor are they capable of solution through the expression of local interests. On the contrary, the critical problem—the source of our indictment of the old politics—is that its foundation is too restricted and particularistic to cope with the characteristic problems of our times. Technology-related problems know no territorial bounds, and they defy locally based efforts to deal with them. The same is true for science-related issues. Our present political system is unable to bring all such problems together for resolution within an ecological framework. Yet, this is what we must do.

The characteristic political problems of the present arise from disorders of the entire ecological order. Their solutions are to be found, not through the traditional interaction of local interests and pressure-group politics, but through a new politics of the whole—politics considered architectonically, as the ancients called it. This requires a politics that is more speculative and less mechanistic; it requires us to do our lobbying in the realm of thought as well as in the corridors of power. Our most pressing political problems now have their origins in science and technology. Their solutions will require a new politics especially designed to cope with science and technology, a politics based on what Teilhard de Chardin called the "noösphere," instead of our accustomed politics based on real estate. It follows that entirely new policy-forming institutions will be needed to deal with the ecological politics of the noösphere. Legislatures must be redesigned accordingly. But, of course, before all this can happen, the popular base from which representatives are chosen must be given a new foundation. The scientific-biological-technological revolution that awaits us around the corner of post-industrial time demands entirely new ecological parties. Their outlines are not hard to foresee.

One portent of the new politics occurred in California in 1969. Over the decades, the Sierra Club—a tradition-oriented pressure group of the Pinchot type—had grown into a potent political force. An internal crisis resulted in the defeat of its activist wing. Shortly thereafter, the deposed leadership, forming around the John Muir Society, announced the establishment of a new political movement to be devoted to ecological concerns. Of course, this was not thought of as a new political party, but, nonetheless, it used language that looked ahead to something like the new politics called for above. Whether or not this particular movement prospers, ecological parties promise to be the wave of the future, providing the underpinning required to produce the novel legislative institutions the future will require.

How would such a party system actually operate? How would it differ in essential structure and mode of operation from the electoral and precinct organizations of the past? Again, in California, a technological breakthrough occurred in 1969 that may provide the informational and educational components required to enable voters to make intelligent ecological choices as they function politically in the future.

A team of multidisciplinary experts headed by Kenneth Watt designed a model that would ultimately contain mathematical expressions for almost every conceivable problem concerning the state of California. All these expressions will be programed into a complex computerized analytical system whose formulas alone will run to 5,000 pages. When finished some five years hence, it will be capable of revealing the multifarious interrelationships of each part of the model. The result will be an architectonic mathematical model of California considered as a complete ecological system. Watt calls this the "Model of a Society." Such computer programs will help us to find out how any given problem relates to all others. Suppose we must decide whether to vote for or against a bond issue to raise funds for a new school system. At the present, our choice is determined largely by whether or not we favor public education. But countless other considerations are involved. How would residential patterns be affected? How would traffic on streets and freeways be changed? What new public utilities would be required? How about other services such as fire and police? Would these changes lead to a relocation of shopping centers? What would all these changes add up to? Would they produce the kind of future we want? Computers are not foolproof, and computer models are even less so. We don't expect perfection from either people or machines. All we expect is a device to help us make our decisions on a somewhat more systematic basis. Not only politics would be affected, planning would also change. Those who make our proposals would have to calculate their full ecological consequences well in advance of offering them to the public. The result would be a profound shift in the terms on which political deliberation occurs. The voter would be able to visit computer terminals with multimedia display consoles where the foreseeable implications of alternative policies would be portrayed in pictures, figures, and graphs.

Mathematicians, ecologists, and social scientists working together can lay the beginnings of a new participatory democracy that will be as well-suited to the conditions of the post-industrial era as was the old, grass-roots democracy to the simpler conditions of the nineteenth century, and it can all be realized within a decade. But this is only the beginning. In the more distant future, we shall require even more ingenious innovations to bring our underprivileged and our undereducated back into politics.

The first component will be what systems engineers call the multimedia home: not the home we already know with radio, television, and tape recorders. Rather, what is envisioned is an entirely new assortment of media installations with a revolutionary new domestic architecture to accompany it. All communications media can be integrated into a complete acculturational system. Each family can then "program" the entire "informational" input coming into its home. All the pictorial, the graphic, the sound, and print media can be considered as a whole. All sources of knowledge would become accessible to each home. Every data bank would be a potential reservoir to be drawn upon when needed. Obviously, protection of each person's right of privacy must be insured; appropriate personal safeguards must be perfected before these new systems can be made available. Beyond this, other data access criteria might include need to know, and ability to assimilate, qualifications.

Subscription to separate newspapers, magazines, book clubs, and encyclopedias would continue, but for general acculturational purposes it would no longer be necessary. Indeed, save for amusement and leisure occupations, the "mix" of one's own overall multimedia diet need not be left to impulse or passing whim. On the contrary, each person would have the ability—the possibility—of pre-programing his overall cultural environment for a period reaching far into the future, just as we do now when we embark on a high school or a college degree program. Adjustments in the programing mix would require revision on a regular basis—semiannually, for example—to comport with family and social changes, and in accord with changing individual interests and varying rates of development. Conceivably, we can design individualized programs to realize cultural, educational, and professional goals whose consummation may lie twenty years or more in the future. Variability and change can be imagined as a branching pattern that reaches into the future, just as trees branch upward in ways that can never be predicted at the start.

Certified professional counselors will be required to assist each family select the integrated cultural development programs of its choice, with appropriate variations to account for the special needs of each member. These professional programers will be comparable to the investment brokers who help wealthy clients play their long-range investment portfolios. But once programs are under way, self-motivation can be counted on to take over. This is what happens today with the best of our new programed instruction systems. Students learn at their own pace, but whatever that pace, they do learn. And they so love what they learn that it often becomes necessary to pry them away from their lessons.

In principle, this new system is similar to the original eighteenth-century concept of the encyclopedia, which was designed to "encircle" everything then known, so each man, on his own, could take "all knowledge for his province." At the time of the first encyclopedia, it was very nearly possible to realize both goals, at least if the reader already had a fairly large working vocabulary. By the mid-nineteenth century, however, knowledge in general and science in particular had grown so complex that no encyclopedia could fully encompass everything that was known. And even if it could have, the departments of learning had become too complex to be understood by any but experts. Ph.D.s in botany, for example, were no better off than illiterates, if they tried to read an encyclopedia article on plasma physics or molecular biology. However, multimedia programing systems can now restore the original aim of the encyclopedia. Moreover, neither prior learning, nor even literacy itself, is any longer a precondition to the assimilation of high cultural status. A well-programed system can provide even functional illiterates with the essentials of higher learning. Of course, education and culture are only the civic essentials. Multimedia homes can embrace the entire range of human activities, with leisure, amusement, and frivolity provided according to individual desire. Each part of each program can be tailored to each person's wants, needs, and talents.

All this is technologically possible today. It is only necessary for us to devote our scientific resources to bringing it about. If that is done, we can move toward the realization of one of man's oldest dreams. All our citizens, the most lowly as well as the most favored, can enjoy the highest fruits of civilization. The optimistic conclusion is that we no longer need despair of democracy's future prospects because of the increased complexity of the problems of the post-industrial world. The very technological advances that are bringing about this new world will also make it possible to produce a citizenry able to comprehend and cope with them, ushering in a new era in the history of democracy.

Pollution Problems, Resource Policy, and the Scientist

Alfred W. Eipper

We know that man is degrading his natural environment, but we have no certain knowledge of how much or how fast. In this article I describe some of the salient characteristics of modern water pollution problems, and certain resource management principles that must be recognized in dealing with them. I then consider the implications of these problems and principles to the scientist's role in helping to maintain the quality of the environment.

Population, Technology, and Water Use

The interacting effects of unchecked population growth and industrial and agricultural expansion cause most of our environmental problems. Man has taken some half million years to reach his present population, but he will double this within the next 40 years; the projected 100-million increase in the U.S. population over the next 30 years (1) can be represented as the addition of a new city of 270,000 inhabitants each month between now and A.D. 2000; four of our states now have population densities substantially higher than India's.

Demands on natural resources are increasing much faster than the population is. In the case of water, per capita use in the United States, exclusive of use for transportation and recreation, appears to be doubling every 40 years (2). This

A. W. Eipper, "Pollution Problems, Resource Policy, and the Scientist," *Science,* Vol. 169, No. 3940, July 3, 1970, pp. 11-15. Copyright 1970 by the American Association for the Advancement of Science. Reprinted by permission of the author and publisher. The author is leader of the New York Co-operative Fishery Unit and associate professor of fishery biology at Cornell University, Ithaca, New York 14850.

means that in the 50 years it will take our population to double, *total* water use will quadruple. Hence the 1965 Department of Interior statement (*1*) that, under existing use patterns, the total amount of water needed just to sustain the present U.S. population for the remainder of their lives is greater than all the water that has been used by all people who have occupied the earth to date.

We tend to think of water supplies as fixed. In fact, however, increasing amounts of water are being rendered unusable through various forms of pollution. Although some uses do not make water unfit for certain purposes, our total usable water supplies are being reduced by pollution while demands for water accelerate sharply in response to the combined effects of population increase and technological development.

Case Study

A recent—and still unsettled—controversy over pollution from a proposed power plant on Cayuga Lake, New York (*3*), illustrates a type of pollution management problem that is becoming commonplace. After acquiring the plant site and conducting unpublicized preliminary surveys, the local electric utility company publicly announced its plans to construct an 830-megawatt nuclear-fueled steam turbine electric station next to its small coal-fired plant already operating on the lake. Cayuga Lake has a mean flushing time of 9 years and remains thermally stratified for about 6 months of the year. In the company plan, water at 45°F (7.2°C) for cooling the nuclear plant's condensers would be obtained from a depth of about 100 feet (30 meters) in the hypolimnion (the cold bottom layer), warmed 20° to 25°F, and returned to the epilimnion (the warmer top layer) at a rate of 1100 cubic feet (30.8 cubic meters) per second (500,000 gallons per minute), year-round.

A number of scientists in the area (many of them, but not all, biologists) were concerned about the predictable and the possible ill effects of this operation on the lake. Some of the predictable results would be to increase the volume of the epilimnion, enrich it with nutrients removed from the hypolimnion, and prolong the stratification period, and hence lengthen the "growing season" in the surface waters. Secondary effects such as changes in species composition or numerical relationships in the lake's plant and animal populations, further oxygen depletion in the bottom waters in summer, and increased heat storage in winter were additional possibilities. Small quantities of radionuclides discharged into the condenser cooling water would become concentrated in this slow-flushing lake, and further concentrations could be expected biologically through food chains and physically through local irregularities in water circulation patterns. The concerned scientists based their estimates on the possible magnitudes of these effects on models which they felt utilized the fewest and simplest valid assumptions, coupled with scattered limnological data on Cayuga Lake accumulated over the past 50 years.

Other individuals and groups in the local scientific community arrived at various other estimates—many of them less severe—of the nature and magnitude of the power plant's possible effects on the lake, using different models, assumptions, and interpretations of past data. Few of the individuals or groups, however, seem to have been concerned with seriously challenging the validity of estimates put forward by others. In retrospect, it appears that more critical comparison and discussion of these different views by their proponents would have been productive.

A particularly encouraging by-product of this controversy was a great deal of imaginative thinking on the problem by a wide variety of scientists, engineers, economists, and others. It is the kind of thinking that will ultimately provide significant solutions to pollution problems. One physicist, for example, suggested using some of the generated electricity to remove nutrients from the water in its passage through the cooling cycle, thus reducing the lake's present rate of eutrophication (aging). Other scientists proposed an ingenious scheme for building a pumped-storage cooling pond on the plain several hundred feet above the lakeshore plant site. Company spokesmen said this scheme was not economically feasible; their critics replied that the company's assessment of the plan was prejudiced and superficial.

Perhaps the simplest method for reducing the possibilities of thermal damage to Cayuga Lake from the proposed plant would be to take the cooling water from the lake's upper layer (above a depth of 40 feet) and return it to the surface. This would be equivalent to operating the plant on a river, estuary, or any other unstratified body of water where the temperature of the intake water varies seasonally. It might require only the use of low-profile, mechanical draft cooling units during about 4 months of the year.

The utility company's actions in the Cayuga Lake case seem to illustrate a behavior pattern fairly common in controversies of this general type. The strategy was to announce the proposal *after* plans for implementing it were already well under way, and to keep things moving ahead rapidly thereafter. The substance of the company's numerous publicity releases was that the plant would benefit the community in many ways, and that the company would never allow the plant to "harm" the lake, and was conducting contract research projects which, it said, were expected to demonstrate that its operations would not damage the lake (*4*). That the company did indeed contract with highly qualified independent research teams to make at least two studies is to its credit. (Needless to say, the researchers did not share the company's preconception of what the results might show.) Critics of the company were frankly skeptical of the value of a 1-year research project, in view of the enormous complexity of a large lake ecosystem and the great annual (and other) variations in data already obtained from Cayuga and similar environments.

Company spokesmen tended to be closemouthed, unwilling to debate issues or to discuss alternatives, and generally confined themselves to rather standardized publicity releases and announcements. They were challenged on their lack of receptiveness to the idea of using already available technological safeguards that would eliminate virtually all hazard of thermal and radiological pollution to Cayuga Lake—technology whose cost could be passed on to consumers and would add less than 25 cents a month to the electricity bill of the average household, according to calculations from company data. Company officials, although obviously reluctant to consider adding the safeguards to the plant's proposed design, were equally unwilling to discuss in concrete, meaningful terms, the reasons for their reluctance (5). Their public posture still seems to be that the only feasible way to operate the plant is by the relatively unique method that they have proposed from the outset.

The company proved to have been less than frank in some instances, and indeed appeared cynical. For example, it developed that the company had already (i) invested some $5 million or more in site preparation and (ii) contracted to sell half to three-fourths of its power to Consolidated Edison, in New York City (6), while research to assure that the lake would not be harmed was under way and before even 1 year's data were available for analysis.

Byron Saunders (7) summarizes the Cayuga Lake case as follows:

Oversimplifying the case, then, the position of one group is that because facts are not at hand, the design of the station should be such that all precautions be taken to guarantee as much cooling as necessary so the lake will not be affected in any detrimental way. The position of the company is that to provide for the maximum possible protection would be too costly and unjustified, because absolute knowledge that it would be necessary is not available. I might point out that this is a regulated industry and that any legitimate capital costs that are necessary for generation facilities are proper elements for the rate base, and hence the company's concern cannot be the ability to recover the costs involved. The real reasons appear to me to be political, and the ability of the private utility to compete with comparable rates of some of the public or quasi-public utilities that are reaching into this area. What this example seems to represent is the much too prevalent case of concentrating one's interest and attention on the cost of the primary product or service with insufficient concern for the side effects that the minimum cost concept generally produces.

An active, well-organized, and growing citizens' group concerned with possible effects of the proposed power plant was formed about a year after the utility's first public announcement of its construction plans. Activities of this group, and of others concerned, induced regional political representatives to initiate public hearings on the issue before various state legislative bodies. Subsequently those legislators most directly involved introduced three bills which provided effective and reasonable safeguards against thermal and radionuclide pollution of lakes—in particular, by power plants. Two of these bills were passed virtually unanimously by both arms of the state legislature, but the Governor subsequently vetoed them. The third bill passed the Assembly unanimously, but eventually was killed in Senate committee.

By November 1969 reports from both of the short-term utility-sponsored research projects on Cayuga Lake had been published. It appears that the company will now proceed to apply for a state permit to operate the power plant without cooling devices, and the local Citizens' Committee is girding for another hearing.

Pollution Problems in General

Perhaps the most obvious feature of pollution problems is that new ones are proliferating—in complexity as well as kind—faster than we are able to understand and solve them. Answers seem to accrue at arithmetic rates; pollution problems, at geometric rates.

Two other characteristics of pollution problems are their unpredictability and their persistence. Repeatedly we have proved unable to foresee either the intensity or the scope of pollution effects before they emerge as some form or forms of serious environmental degradation. Also, we are learning from harsh experience that many of these unforeseen effects are largely irreversible, at least within the time span of a human life. Thus, within the past few years we have come to realize that, in the earth's atmosphere, nitrogen oxides, particulate matter, lead, radionuclides, carbon dioxide, and perhaps also heat have increased, and in most cases these increases are continuing. DDT is now distributed throughout soils, waters, and people throughout the world, and it even appears in the body fat of antarctic penguins. It and other durable toxic pesticides have virtually ended reproduction of valuable fishes in bodies of water such as Lake George, New York, possibly for many years to come (8). Each of these is an unanticipated pollution problem for which there is no immediate cure.

Causal relationships between pollutants and environmental degradation are usually much harder to demonstrate than was the case for Lake George. Because all natural systems are highly complex, we cannot quickly or clearly prove even extensive long-term damage to such a system, any more than we can conclusively prove (to the manufacturers' satisfaction) that cigarette smoking is injurious to health. Damage from pollution can seldom, if ever, be predicted with certainty, and, if it can be proved after it has occurred, the proof is likely to be too late, as in the case of Lake Erie.

Typical Attitudes of Polluters

A constructive approach to pollution problems requires more than knowledge of pollution results; we also need to understand the human motives and actions that produce them. Often development plans involve serious threats to water quality and aquatic environments through introductions of heat, radionuclides, nutrients such as phosphorus and nitrogen, toxic chemicals, silt, decomposing organic matter, and so on.

The special-interest groups promoting such developments may be industries that wish to use the water or other resource in a way that will yield them maximum profit, or they may be persons whose welfare or sympathies are more indirectly tied to an industry's success. The latter category includes groups of citizenry primarily concerned with immediate industrial benefits to the local economy, and persons in state or federal agencies who are much concerned with promoting the development of industrial technology. (Unfortunately, many of these agencies are assigned the dual role of promoting *and* regulating an industry.) Technological interest groups often make irrational assertions (based on questionable assumptions) to support programs that will exploit public natural resources. These assertions—or implications—include the following.

The program—as proposed—*has* to be enacted *now*.

The program will be enacted in any event. You can't stop progress.

The program is needed to fill the demand that will be created by the program.

No one opposes the program. It will benefit the majority, and harm no one.

Data used to estimate effects of the program are the only valid, pertinent data available.

Since there is no proof that the development will damage the environment, we can safely assume it will not.

All effects of the program have been considered.

The program, as presented, represents the sum total of the development contemplated for this particular resource.

All applicable alternatives have been considered.

Not only should such assumptions be questioned when they appear in discussions of pollution issues, but other questions should be asked, such as the following.

Who participated in formulating the assumptions and conclusions about this program's desirability?

What lasting social benefits—and costs—will this program produce? Who will derive these benefits?

What environmental problems will, or may, be created?

What alternatives exist? Has the relative desirability of not enacting the program been evaluated?

Resource Management Principles

In light of the ecological, technological, and human aspects of pollution, we can identify certain resource management principles that apply particularly to problems of pollution control.

1. Because almost any decision on management of a natural resource involves the allocation of an essentially fixed (or diminishing) resource among a growing number of competing and expanding uses, it is appropriate to ask first, Who makes such a decision? I believe there is growing evidence and awareness that these decisions must be basically public decisions and cannot be made unilaterally by any particular interest group, be it industrialist or preservationist. One reason for this is that the resources involved are public resources. They concern quality of the environment—quality of life—for all users. Another reason

is that there is an increasing number of widely differing, and often competing, demands on the same resource. Cayuga Lake, for example, is used extensively for boating, water supply (municipal, agricultural, domestic, and industrial), fishing, electric power generation, swimming, residence, flood control, water skiing, waste disposal, camping, hunting, and so on.

2. Narrow, "conventional" economic criteria are at best inadequate and at worst disastrously misleading if used as the sole basis for decisions about natural resources. In deciding what criteria to employ for estimating values and determining priorities in the uses of a natural resource, the governing principle should be to include the widest possible variety of applicable criteria and, above all, to avoid resorting to a single criterion. Resource economists are often the first to point out the severe limitations of dollar values as the only basis for weighing (or justifying) all elements in an allocation complex. As stated by a committee of the Congress (9):

The market approach fails for two reasons: first, it is very difficult to quantify in dollar terms many of the values of environmental quality. Second, the axiom that a unit of profit is more valuable now than at any time in the future leads to short-sightedness in environmental management.

There are other quantitative measures of environmental value that often should be used to supplement dollar criteria, such as priority ranks and environmental diversity indices (10). A decision on a public resource must also take into consideration, through hearings and other media, those wishes of, and values to, the users that can be expressed only through the political process. In the final analysis, decisions on the management of a natural resource are basically political decisions.

3. Another resource management principle involves communication and candor. Impending environmental problems must be promptly recognized and widely discussed as soon as they are perceived. A satisfactory resolution of a conflict over resources can be obtained only when all parties communicate openly, honestly, and freely from the outset, and recognize that the ultimate solution to such a conflict may well be a compromise. If, for example, the Cayuga Lake power plant could be built and operated, but with safeguards to the lake's ecology and would not substantially increase the cost of electricity, this obviously would be an unusually good compromise. But satisfactory compromises, difficult to achieve at best, are even more difficult to achieve without free and open communication. The kind of communication that seems to typify resource management controversies today is generally a com-munication between adversaries. Regulatory agencies must give sincere, serious consideration to the concerns of citizens about environmental hazards from a technology. Failure of such agencies to require that available safeguards be used may force the citizenry into outright opposition of the technology.

4. We cannot disregard impending pollution problems in the belief that science and technology will correct any maladjustments that might subsequently appear in an ecosystem. "Pollution control regulations" that permit discharge of a pollutant, with the stipulation that the polluter must be prepared to correct pollution later (should this "prove" necessary), are usually based on wishful thinking about the availability of proof at some future date.

5. We have an obligation to future generations to maintain the quality of the natural environment. Everyone has a right to a high-quality environment; no one user has a right to pollute without the consent of other users. The burden of proof must be on the potential polluter to demonstrate that he will not pollute, rather than on the public to prove that pollution has occurred.

6. Closely linked to this is the principle that all of us must pay for what we use, whether the use be recreation, sewage disposal, or consumption of electricity, coal, or water. As stressed by Saunders (7), "Let those who dance pay the fiddler. If in our affluent society, we cannot pay the full cost of the products and services we want, do we have the right to expect future generations to pay for our indulgences?" A recent Gallup poll (11) showed that about three-fourths of the total sample from the U.S. population were deeply concerned about the quality of the environment and willing to pay additional taxes to maintain it. Lessons from past mistakes indicate that repair of the environment, even when possible, can seldom be justified economically. Industries should concentrate their expenditures for research and development on (i) devising new technology that will keep conflicts with other resource uses to a minimum, and (ii) helping finance the assessment of new technology before proliferating it.

7. When planning a program that involves exploitation of a natural resource, we must give equal consideration to *each* of the possible means of achieving the program objective, or objectives, using "possible" in the broadest context and including consideration of all possible locations for the program. Electric utilities and their promoters cite the fact that needs for electricity are doubling every 10 years or less, and they protest that conservation groups block them at every turn. Usually, however, the only sites and operating methods considered feasible by power companies are those which are "economical" in a very narrow sense, as in the Cayuga Lake case.

8. The principle of sustained yield, familiar to resource managers as a harvesting concept, has wider applications of growing importance to today's environmental problems. This principle is stated succinctly in "Managing the Environment" (9):

The use of the environment is a necessary and acceptable concept. The difference is that future use must be in the recycle context of perpetual renewal and reuse, not the old pattern of use and discard. A sort of stable state between civilization and the environment is called for—not a balance of nature (for nature is always changing in its own right) but a harmony of society and the environment within natural laws of physics, chemistry, and biology.

9. Last but far from least, we must employ the principle of prevention. As mentioned above, man's adverse influences on natural environments are accelerating and becoming increasingly complex. There is now abundant evidence of severe limitations on our ability to predict, prove, or reverse pollution effects. For these reasons, waiting to measure environmental damage from a technology before taking steps to correct it is no longer a tenable approach. We must place more emphasis on using whatever knowledge is already available to recognize and interpret threats to the environment before they become realities, and must be willing to act on the premise that, when the likelihood of damage can be foreseen, the damage should be forestalled. It is far easier to prevent pollution (or nuclear warfare, or overpopulation) than to correct for it after it has occurred. We should realize that there is at least as much need for safety factors in managing our natural environment as there is in planning a bridge or a boiler. The trial-and-error method is a dangerous one when applied to environmental management. As Senator Edmund Muskie has said of thermal pollution of water (*12*): "You've got to take the point of view that if we don't know enough, we don't know enough to permit the discharge."

The Scientist's Role

Global ecologists point out that our planet is in fact a space vehicle with a mushrooming human population and a balanced, continuously recycling life-support system. Because key elements of this system are increasingly threatened by man's pollution activities, we must develop an effective early-warning process. Scientists must be willing to involve themselves in this process by detecting and publicizing foreseeable threats to the environment (*13*). This is not to suggest any lessened importance of long-term research on the causes and effects of pollution. Our focus here is simply on another dimension of pollution: those impending problems which require preventive action now.

What are some of the functions required of the scientist in this early-warning approach to a potential pollution situation? First, this approach involves ferreting out and analyzing all pertinent data that are available *now*. Frank Di Luzio, former Assistant Secretary of the Interior for Water Pollution Control, stated the concept well (*14*):

. . . all of us would like to know all the facts about the problems we are dealing with. Since we never will know all the facts, we've got to do the best we can with the facts at hand. To a considerable extent we must forego the satisfaction of dealing with incontrovertible scientific data and be guided simply by prima facie evidence.

Next, the scientist must be willing to publicize his tentative conclusions from the data, and his assessment of alternative management measures and the likely effects of each which these conclusions suggest to him. It is not enough to "let the facts speak for themselves." The scientist, as a trained and experienced specialist, has an obligation to give society his professional interpretation of those facts. It is also essential to the validity of the decision-making process that he identify this as *his*—not *the*—interpretation. When scientists disagree in their interpretations, they should discuss and analyze the sources of disagreement, for the ultimate benefit of society.

I suspect a majority of scientists are disquieted by at least some aspects of the role outlined above. It stipulates the unpleasant necessity of going out on a shaky limb of tentative conclusions. It often involves a kind of limelight the scientist would rather avoid, and it may involve him, at least peripherally, in unaccustomed controversy. Nevertheless the scientist must face the fact that he is now living in a different ecosystem, with critical new problems, on a new time scale, that require new approaches. Only the dedicated scientific recluse can totally ignore these new responsibilities. The early-warning approach requires that scientists call the shots as they see them and remember that debate is central to scientific progress. They should recognize that straddling a fence too long can produce sterility, and that when one has reached the point of making all his communications noncontroversial there is no further need for him to communicate.

The role of the scientist, as such should not extend beyond presentation and defense of his estimate of pollution hazards and an assessment of alternatives. He has an obligation to make available information from his profession that will help the voter make a more enlightened decision, but he must scrupulously avoid telling him how to vote. Because decisions on environmental management are so complex, they must represent the best possible reconciliation of many different interests; hence they must be public decisions. The scientist can contribute much to the *basis* for a public decision, but in *making* that decision he has only one vote. He is no more entitled—and no more qualified—than any other citizen to elect which of various alternative courses should be followed.

On the other hand he is no *less* entitled or qualified to choose. The scientist should not, from fear that his professional identity will give him unfair advantage, shrink from exercising the political rights of a private citizen to express his personal views (so identified) on a controversial issue. Although quite properly concerned about his credibility as a scientist, he should not disregard his credibility as a human being and voter with genuine convictions.

Summary

Through exponential increase in population, accompanied by rapid industrial and agricultural expansion, we have reached the point where decisions involving the use of natural resources are much more important and also much more difficult than they were even 10 years ago. The same conditions that make decisions more urgent make them more time-consuming. The Cayuga Lake case illustrates many aspects of a present-day resource management controversy.

Because we are being forced to make increasingly critical decisions about ecosystems for which reliable predictive data are often lacking, we must, collectively, develop a framework of genuinely useful principles to guide our dealings with natural environments. I have suggested a few such principles, and the scientist's role in implementing them.

References and Notes

1. "Quest for Quality," *U.S. Dep. Interior Conserv. Yearb.* (1965), p. 10.

2. "The Nation's Water Resources," *U.S. Water Resources Council Publ.* (1968), p. 4.

3. Accounts of this controversy have appeared in various publications, including the following: A. W. Eipper *et al.*, *Thermal Pollution of Cayuga Lake by a Proposed Power Plant* (Authors, 1968); C. A. Carlson *et al.*, *Radioactivity and a Proposed Power Plant on Cayuga Lake* (Authors, Cornell Univ., Ithaca, 1968); L. J. Carter, *Science* 162, 649 (1968); J. Hampton, *Nat. Observ.* 8, No. 5, 1 (1969).

4. "Bell Station Preliminary Safety Analysis Report," *N.Y. State Elec. Gas Corp. Publ.* (1968), pp. II-4-4, 6, 11.

5. One of the difficulties sometimes associated with such cases is the fact that a utility may fear that the public service regulatory body will not permit a raise in rates that would make it possible to pass on the costs of environmental protection to the consumer. There seems to be no public information on whether such corporate apprehension existed—or was justified—in the Cayuga Lake case.

6. *Nucleonics Week* 1969, 4 (16 Jan. 1969).

7. B. W. Saunders, *J. Eng. Educ.*, in press.

8. G. E. Burdick, E. J. Harris, J. H. Dean, T. M. Walker, J. Skea, D. Colby, *Trans. Amer. Fish. Soc.* 93, 127 (1964).

9. "Managing the Environment," *Publ. Comm. Sci. Astronaut., 90th Congr., 2nd Session, 1968* (Government Printing Office, Washington, D. C., 1968), pp. 14-15.

10. A. W. Eipper, F. W. Howell, R. J. Kalter, R. L. Shelton, B. T. Wilkins. "Aspects of Planning, Evaluation, and Decision-Making in Sport Fishery Management," *Cornell Univ. Conserv. Dept. Publ.* (1970).

11. *Nat. Wildlife* 7, No. 3, 18 (1969).

12. Quoted in *New York Times* 1969, 12E (9 Mar. 1969).

13. It is encouraging to note the growing recognition of this necessity by scientists such as R. S. Morison [*Science* 165, 150 (1969)] and O. M. Solandt [*ibid.*, p. 445].

14. Quoted in "A New Era for America's Waters," *Fed. Water Pollut. Contr. Admin. Publ.* (1967).

15. This article is adapted from a paper presented in August 1969 at the Engineering Foundation Research Conference on Technology Assessment, Andover, N.H. I thank the many colleagues who critically reviewed the manuscript.

The Tragedy of the Commons

Garrett Hardin

At the end of a thoughtful article on the future of nuclear war, Wiesner and York (*1*) concluded that: "Both sides in the arms race are . . . confronted by the dilemma of steadily increasing military power and steadily decreasing national security. *It is our considered professional judgment that this dilemma has no technical solution.* If the great powers continue to look for solutions in the area of science and technology only, the result will be to worsen the situation."

I would like to focus your attention not on the subject of the article (national security in a nuclear world) but on the kind of conclusion they reached, namely that there is no technical solution to the problem. An implicit and almost universal assumption of discussions published in professional and semipopular scientific journals is that the problem under discussion has a technical solution. A technical solution may be defined as one that requires a change only in the techniques of the natural sciences, demanding little or nothing in the way of change in human values or ideas of morality.

In our day (though not in earlier times) technical solutions are always welcome. Because of previous failures in prophecy, it takes courage to assert that a desired technical solution is not possible. Wiesner and York exhibited this

Garrett Hardin, "The Tragedy of the Commons," *Science,* Vol. 162, December 13, 1968, pp. 1243-1248. Copyright 1968 by the American Association for the Advancement of Science. Reprinted by permission of the author and publisher. The author is professor of biology, University of California, Santa Barbara. This article is based on a presidential address presented before the meeting of the Pacific Division of the American Association for the Advancement of Science at Utah State University, Logan, 25 June 1968.

courage; publishing in a science journal, they insisted that the solution to the problem was not to be found in the natural sciences. They cautiously qualified their statement with the phrase, "It is our considered professional judgment. . . ." Whether they were right or not is not the concern of the present article. Rather, the concern here is with the important concept of a class of human problems which can be called "no technical solution problems," and, more specifically, with the identification and discussion of one of these.

It is easy to show that the class is not a null class. Recall the game of tick-tack-toe. Consider the problem, "How can I win the game of tick-tack-toe?" It is well known that I cannot, if I assume (in keeping with the conventions of game theory) that my opponent understands the game perfectly. Put another way, there is no "technical solution" to the problem. I can win only by giving a radical meaning to the word "win." I can hit my opponent over the head; or I can drug him; or I can falsify the records. Every way in which I "win" involves, in some sense, an abandonment of the game, as we intuitively understand it. (I can also, of course, openly abandon the game—refuse to play it. This is what most adults do.)

The class of "No technical solution problems" has members. My thesis is that the "population problem," as conventionally conceived, is a member of this class. How it is conventionally conceived needs some comment. It is fair to say that most people who anguish over the population problem are trying to find a way to avoid the evils of overpopulation without relinquishing any of the privileges they now enjoy. They think that farming the seas or developing new strains of wheat will solve the problem—technologically. I try to show here that the solution they seek cannot be found. The population problem cannot be solved in a technical way, any more than can the problem of winning the game of tick-tack-toe.

What Shall We Maximize?

Population, as Malthus said, naturally tends to grow "geometrically," or, as we would now say, exponentially. In a finite world this means that the per capita share of the world's goods must steadily decrease. Is ours a finite world?

A fair defense can be put forward for the view that the world is infinite; or that we do not know that it is not. But, in terms of the practical problems that we must face in the next few generations with the foreseeable technology, it is clear that we will greatly increase human misery if we do not, during the immediate future, assume that the world available to the terrestrial human population is finite. "Space" is no escape (2).

A finite world can support only a finite population; therefore, population growth must eventually equal zero. (The case of perpetual wide fluctuations above and below zero is a trivial variant that need not be discussed.) When this condition is met, what will be the situation of mankind? Specifically, can Bentham's goal of "the greatest good for the greatest number" be realized?

No—for two reasons, each sufficient by itself. The first is a theoretical one. It is not mathematically possible to maximize for two (or more) variables at the same time. This was clearly stated by von Neumann and Morgenstern (3), but the principle is implicit in the theory of partial differential equations, dating back at least to D'Alembert (1717-1783).

The second reason springs directly from biological facts. To live, any organism must have a source of energy (for example, food). This energy is utilized for two purposes: mere maintenance and work. For man, maintenance of life requires about 1600 kilocalories a day ("maintenance calories"). Anything that he does over and above merely staying alive will be defined as work, and is supported by "work calories" which he takes in. Work calories are used not only for what we call work in common speech; they are also required for all forms of enjoyment, from swimming and automobile racing to playing music and writing poetry. If our goal is to maximize population it is obvious what we must do: We must make the work calories per person approach as close to zero as possible. No gourmet meals, no vacations, no sports, no music, no literature, no art. . . . I think that everyone will grant, without argument or proof, that maximizing population does not maximize goods. Bentham's goal is impossible.

In reaching this conclusion I have made the usual assumption that it is the acquisition of energy that is the problem. The appearance of atomic energy has led some to question this assumption. However, given an infinite source of energy, population growth still produces an inescapable problem. The problem of the acquisition of energy is replaced by the problem of its dissipation, as J. H. Fremlin has so wittily shown (4). The arithmetic signs in the analysis are, as it were, reversed; but Bentham's goal is still unobtainable.

The optimum population is, then, less than the maximum. The difficulty of defining the optimum is enormous; so far as I know, no one has seriously tackled this problem. Reaching an acceptable and stable solution will surely require more than one generation of hard analytical work—and much persuasion.

We want the maximum good per person; but what is good? To one person it is wilderness, to another it is ski lodges for thousands. To one it is estuaries to nourish ducks for hunters to shoot; to another it is factory land. Comparing one good with another is, we usually say, impossible because goods are incommensurable. Incommensurables cannot be compared.

Theoretically this may be true; but in real life incommensurables *are* commensurable. Only a criterion of judgment and a system of weighting are needed. In nature the criterion is survival. Is it better for a species to be small and hideable, or large and powerful? Natural selection commensurates the incommensurables. The compromise achieved depends on a natural weighting of the values of the variables.

Man must imitate this process. There is no doubt that in fact he already does, but unconsciously. It is when the hidden decisions are made explicit that the arguments begin. The problem for the years ahead is to work out an acceptable theory of weighting. Synergistic effects, nonlinear variation, and difficulties in discounting the future make the intellectual problem difficult, but not (in principle) insoluble.

Has any cultural group solved this practical problem at the present time, even on an intuitive level? One simple fact proves that none has: there is no prosperous population in the world today that has, and has had for some time, a growth rate of zero. Any people that has intuitively identified its optimum point will soon reach it, after which its growth rate becomes and remains zero.

Of course, a positive growth rate might be taken as evidence that a population is below its optimum. However, by any reasonable standards, the most rapidly growing populations on earth today are (in general) the most miserable. This association (which need not be invariable) casts doubt on the optimistic assumption that the positive growth rate of a population is evidence that it has yet to reach its optimum.

We can make little progress in working toward optimum population size until we explicitly exorcize the spirit of Adam Smith in the field of practical demography. In economic affairs, *The Wealth of Nations* (1776) popularized the "invisible hand," the idea that an individual who "intends only his own gain" is, as it were, "led by an invisible hand to promote . . . the public interest" (5). Adam Smith did not assert that this was invariably true, and perhaps neither did any of his followers. But he contributed to a dominant tendency of thought that has ever interfered with positive action based on rational analysis, namely, the tendency to assume that decisions reached individually will, in fact, be the best decisions for an entire society. If this assumption is correct it justifies the continuance of our present policy of laissez-faire in reproduction. If it is correct we can assume that men will control their individual fecundity so as to produce the optimum population. If the assumption is not correct, we need to reexamine our individual freedoms to see which ones are defensible.

Tragedy of Freedom in a Commons

The rebuttal to the invisible hand in population control is to be found in a scenario first sketched in a little-known pamphlet (6) in 1833 by a mathematical amateur named William Forster Lloyd (1794-1852). We may well call it "the tragedy of the commons," using the word "tragedy" as the philosopher Whitehead used it (7): "The essence of dramatic tragedy is not unhappiness. It resides in the solemnity of the remorseless working of things." He then goes on to say, "This inevitableness of destiny can only be illustrated in terms of human life by incidents which in fact involve unhappiness. For it is only by them that the futility of escape can be made evident in the drama."

The tragedy of the commons develops in this way. Picture a pasture open to all. It is to be expected that each herdsman will try to keep as many cattle as possible on the commons. Such an arrangement may work reasonably satisfactorily for centuries because tribal wars, poaching, and disease keep the numbers of both man and beast well below the carrying capacity of the land.

Finally, however, comes the day of reckoning, that is, the day when the long-desired goal of social stability becomes a reality. At this point, the inherent logic of the commons remorselessly generates tragedy.

As a rational being, each herdsman seeks to maximize his gain. Explicitly or implicitly, more or less consciously, he asks, "What is the utility *to me* of adding one more animal to my herd?" This utility has one negative and one positive component.

1) The positive component is a function of the increment of one animal. Since the herdsman receives all the proceeds from the sale of the additional animal, the positive utility is nearly +1.

2) The negative component is a function of the additional overgrazing created by one more animal. Since, however, the effects of overgrazing are shared by all the herdsmen, the negative utility for any particular decision-making herdsman is only a fraction of −1.

Adding together the component partial utilities, the rational herdsman concludes that the only sensible course for him to pursue is to add another animal to his herd. And another; and another. . . . But this is the conclusion reached by each and every rational herdsman sharing a commons. Therein is the tragedy. Each man is locked into a system that compels him to increase his herd without limit—in a world that is limited. Ruin is the destination toward which all men rush, each pursuing his own best interest in a society that believes in the freedom of the commons. Freedom in a commons brings ruin to all.

Some would say that this is a platitude. Would that it were! In a sense, it was learned thousands of years ago, but natural selection favors the forces of psychological denial (*8*). The individual benefits as an individual from his ability to deny the truth even though society as a whole, of which he is a part, suffers. Education can counteract the natural tendency to do the wrong thing, but the inexorable succession of generations requires that the basis for this knowledge be constantly refreshed.

A simple incident that occurred a few years ago in Leominster, Massachusetts, shows how perishable the knowledge is. During the Christmas shopping season the parking meters downtown were covered with plastic bags that bore tags reading: "Do not open until after Christmas. Free parking courtesy of the mayor and city council." In other words, facing the prospect of an increased demand for already scarce space, the city fathers reinstituted the system of the commons. (Cynically, we suspect that they gained more votes than they lost by this retrogressive act.)

In an approximate way, the logic of the commons has been understood for a long time, perhaps since the discovery of agriculture or the invention of private property in real estate. But it is understood mostly only in special cases which are not sufficiently generalized. Even at this late date, cattlemen leasing national land on the western ranges demonstrate no more than an ambivalent understanding, in constantly pressuring federal authorities to increase the head count to the point where overgrazing produces erosion and weed-dominance. Likewise, the oceans of the world continue to suffer from the survival of the philosophy of the commons. Maritime nations still respond automatically to the shibboleth of the "freedom of the seas." Professing to believe in the "inexhaustible resources of the oceans," they bring species after species of fish and whales closer to extinction (9).

The National Parks present another instance of the working out of the tragedy of the commons. At present, they are open to all, without limit. The parks themselves are limited in extent—there is only one Yosemite Valley—whereas population seems to grow without limit. The values that visitors seek in the parks are steadily eroded. Plainly, we must soon cease to treat the parks as commons or they will be of no value to anyone.

What shall we do? We have several options. We might sell them off as private property. We might keep them as public property, but allocate the right to enter them. The allocation might be on the basis of wealth, by the use of an auction system. It might be on the basis of merit, as defined by some agreed-upon standards. It might be by lottery. Or it might be on a first-come, first-served basis, administered to long queues. These, I think, are all the reasonable possibilities. They are all objectionable. But we must choose—or acquiesce in the destruction of the commons that we call our National Parks.

Pollution

In a reverse way, the tragedy of the commons reappears in problems of pollution. Here it is not a question of taking something out of the commons, but of putting something in—sewage, or chemical, radioactive, and heat wastes into water; noxious and dangerous fumes into the air; and distracting and unpleasant advertising signs into the line of sight. The calculations of utility are much the same as before. The rational man finds that his share of the cost of the wastes he discharges into the commons is less than the cost of purifying his wastes before releasing them. Since this is true for everyone, we are locked into a system of "fouling our own nest," so long as we behave only as independent, rational, free-enterprisers.

The tragedy of the commons as a food basket is averted by private property, or something formally like it. But the air and waters surrounding us cannot readily be fenced, and so the tragedy of the commons as a cesspool must be prevented by different means, by coercive laws or taxing devices that make it cheaper for the polluter to treat his pollutants than to discharge them untreated. We have not progressed as far with the solution of this problem as we have with the first. Indeed, our particular concept of private property, which deters us from exhausting the positive resources of the earth, favors pollution. The owner of a factory on the bank of a stream—whose property extends to the middle of the stream—often has difficulty seeing why it is not his natural right to muddy the waters flowing past his door. The law, always behind the times, requires elaborate stitching and fitting to adapt it to this newly perceived aspect of the commons.

The pollution problem is a consequence of population. It did not much matter how a lonely American frontiersman disposed of his waste. "Flowing water purifies itself every 10 miles," my grandfather used to say, and the myth was near enough to the truth when he was a boy, for there were not too many people. But as population became denser, the natural chemical and biological recycling processes became overloaded, calling for a redefinition of property rights.

How to Legislate Temperance?

Analysis of the pollution problem as a function of population density uncovers a not generally recognized principle of morality, namely: *the morality of an act is a function of the state of the system at the time it is performed* (10). Using the commons as a cesspool does not harm the general public under frontier conditions, because there is no public; the same behavior in a metropolis is unbearable. A hundred and fifty years ago a plainsman could kill an American bison, cut out only the tongue for his dinner, and discard the rest of the animal. He was not in any important sense being wasteful. Today, with only a few thousand bison left, we would be appalled at such behavior.

In passing, it is worth noting that the morality of an act cannot be determined from a photograph. One does not know whether a man killing an elephant or setting fire to the grassland is harming others until one knows the total system in which his act appears. "One picture is worth a thousand words," said an ancient Chinese; but it may take 10,000 words to validate it. It is as tempting to ecologists as it is to reformers in general to try to persuade others by way of the photographic shortcut. But the essence of an argument cannot be photographed: it must be presented rationally—in words.

That morality is system-sensitive escaped the attention of most codifiers of ethics in the past. "Thou shalt not . . ." is the form of traditional ethical directives which make no allowance for particular circumstances. The laws of our society follow the pattern of ancient ethics, and therefore are poorly suited to governing a complex, crowded, changeable world. Our epicyclic solution is to augment statutory law with administrative law. Since it is practically impossible to spell out all the conditions under which it is safe to burn trash in the back yard or to run an automobile without smog-control, by law we delegate the details to bureaus. The result is administrative law, which is rightly feared for an ancient reason—*Quis custodiet ipsos custodes?*—"Who shall watch the watchers themselves?" John Adams said that we must have "a government of laws and not men." Bureau administrators, trying to evaluate the morality of acts in the total system, are singularly liable to corruption, producing a government by men, not laws.

Prohibition is easy to legislate (though not necessarily to enforce); but how do we legislate temperance? Experience indicates that it can be accomplished best through the mediation of administrative law. We limit possibilities unnecessarily if we suppose that the sentiment of *Quis custodiet* denies us the use of administrative law. We should rather retain the phrase as a perpetual reminder of fearful dangers we cannot avoid. The great challenge facing us now is to invent the corrective feedbacks that are needed to keep custodians honest. We must find ways to legitimate the needed authority of both the custodians and the corrective feedbacks.

Freedom to Breed Is Intolerable

The tragedy of the commons is involved in population problems in another way. In a world governed solely by the principle of "dog eat dog"—if indeed there ever was such a world—how many children a family had would not be a matter of public concern. Parents who bred too exuberantly would leave fewer descendants, not more, because they would be unable to care adequately for their children. David Lack and others have found that such a negative feedback demonstrably controls the fecundity of birds (*11*). But men are not birds, and have not acted like them for millenniums, at least.

If each human family were dependent only on its own resources; *if* the children of improvident parents starved to death; *if*, thus, overbreeding brought its own "punishment" to the germ line—*then* there would be no public interest in controlling the breeding of families. But our society is deeply committed to the welfare state (*12*), and hence is confronted with another aspect of the tragedy of the commons.

In a welfare state, how shall we deal with the family, the religion, the race, or the class (or indeed any distinguishable and cohesive group) that adopts overbreeding as a policy to secure its own aggrandizement (*13*)? To couple the concept of freedom to breed with the belief that everyone born has an equal right to the commons is to lock the world into a tragic course of action.

Unfortunately this is just the course of action that is being pursued by the United Nations. In late 1967, some 30 nations agreed to the following (*14*):

The Universal Declaration of Human Rights describes the family as the natural and fundamental unit of society. It follows that any choice and decision with regard to the size of the family must irrevocably rest with the family itself, and cannot be made by anyone else.

It is painful to have to deny categorically the validity of this right; denying it, one feels as uncomfortable as a resident of Salem, Massachusetts, who denied the reality of witches in the 17th century. At the present time, in liberal quarters, something like a taboo acts to inhibit criticism of the United Nations. There is a feeling that the United Nations is "our last and best hope," that we shouldn't find fault with it; we shouldn't play into the hands of the archconservatives. However, let us not forget what Robert Louis Stevenson said: "The truth that is suppressed by friends is the readiest weapon of the enemy." If we love the truth we must openly deny the validity of the Universal Declaration of Human Rights, even though it is promoted by the United Nations. We should also join with Kingsley Davis (15) in attempting to get Planned Parenthood-World Population to see the error of its ways in embracing the same tragic ideal.

Conscience Is Self-Eliminating

It is a mistake to think that we can control the breeding of mankind in the long run by an appeal to conscience. Charles Galton Darwin made this point when he spoke on the centennial of the publication of his grandfather's great book. The argument is straightforward and Darwinian.

People vary. Confronted with appeals to limit breeding, some people will undoubtedly respond to the plea more than others. Those who have more children will produce a larger fraction of the next generation than those with more susceptible consciences. The difference will be accentuated, generation by generation.

In C. G. Darwin's words: "It may well be that it would take hundreds of generations for the progenitive instinct to develop in this way, but if it should do so, nature would have taken her revenge, and the variety *Homo contracipiens* would become extinct and would be replaced by the variety *Homo progenitivus*" (16).

The argument assumes that conscience or the desire for children (no matter which) is hereditary—but hereditary only in the most general formal sense. The result will be the same whether the attitude is transmitted through germ cells, or exosomatically, to use A. J. Lotka's term. (If one denies the latter possibility as well as the former, then what's the point of education?) The argument has here been stated in the context of the population problem, but it applies equally well to any instance in which society appeals to an individual exploiting a commons to restrain himself for the general good—by means of his conscience. To make such an appeal is to set up a selective system that works toward the elimination of conscience from the race.

Pathogenic Effects of Conscience

The long-term disadvantage of an appeal to conscience should be enough to condemn it, but has serious short-term disadvantages as well. If we ask a man who is exploiting a commons to desist "in the name of conscience," what are we saying to him? What does he hear—not only at the moment but also in the wee small hours of the night when, half asleep, he remembers not merely the words we used but also the nonverbal communication cues we gave him unawares? Sooner or later, consciously or subconsciously, he senses that he has received two communications, and that they are contradictory: (i) (intended communication) "If you don't do as we ask, we will openly condemn you for not acting like a responsible citizen"; (ii) (the unintended communication) "If you *do* behave as we ask, we will secretly condemn you for a simpleton who can be shamed into standing aside while the rest of us exploit the commons."

Every man then is caught in what Bateson has called a "double bind." Bateson and his co-workers have made a plausible case for viewing the double bind as an important causative factor in the genesis of schizophrenia (*17*). The double bind may not always be so damaging, but it always endangers the mental health of anyone to whom it is applied. "A bad conscience," said Nietzsche, "is a kind of illness."

To conjure up a conscience in others is tempting to anyone who wishes to extend his control beyond the legal limits. Leaders at the highest level succumb to this temptation. Has any President during the past generation failed to call on labor unions to moderate voluntarily their demands for higher wages, or to steel companies to honor voluntary guidelines on prices? I can recall none. The rhetoric used on such occasions is designed to produce feelings of guilt in noncooperators.

For centuries it was assumed without proof that guilt was a valuable, perhaps even an indispensable, ingredient of the civilized life. Now, in this post-Freudian world, we doubt it.

Paul Goodman speaks from the modern point of view when he says: "No good has ever come from feeling guilty, neither intelligence, policy, nor compassion. The guilty do not pay attention to the object but only to themselves, and not even to their own interests, which might make sense, but to their anxieties" (*18*).

One does not have to be a professional psychiatrist to see the consequences of anxiety. We in the Western world are just emerging from a dreadful two-centuries-long Dark Ages of Eros that was sustained partly by prohibition laws, but perhaps more effectively by the anxiety-generating mechanisms of education. Alex Comfort has told the story well in *The Anxiety Makers* (*19*); it is not a pretty one.

Since proof is difficult, we may even concede that the results of anxiety may sometimes, from certain points of view, be desirable. The larger question we should ask is whether, as a matter of policy, we should ever encourage the use of a technique the tendency (if not the intention) of which is psychologically pathogenic. We hear much talk these days of responsible parenthood; the coupled words are incorporated into the titles of some organizations devoted to birth control. Some people have proposed massive propaganda campaigns to instill responsibility into the nation's (or the world's) breeders. But what is the meaning of the word responsibility in this context? Is it not merely a synonym for the word conscience? When we use the word responsibility in the absence of substantial sanctions are we not trying to browbeat a free man in a commons into acting against his own interest? Responsibility is a verbal counterfeit for a substantial *quid pro quo*. It is an attempt to get something for nothing.

If the word responsibility is to be used at all, I suggest that it be in the sense Charles Frankel uses it (*20*). "Responsibility," says this philosopher, "is the product of definite social arrangements." Notice that Frankel calls for social arrangements—not propaganda.

Mutual Coercion Mutually Agreed Upon

The social arrangements that produce responsibility are arrangements that create coercion, of some sort. Consider bank-robbing. The man who takes money from a bank acts as if the bank were a commons. How do we prevent such action? Certainly not by trying to control his behavior solely by a verbal appeal to his sense of responsibility. Rather than rely on propaganda we follow Frankel's lead and insist that a bank is not a commons; we seek the definite social arrangements that will keep it from becoming a commons. That we thereby infringe on the freedom of would-be robbers we neither deny nor regret.

The morality of bank-robbing is particularly easy to understand because we accept complete prohibition of this activity. We are willing to say "Thou shalt not rob banks," without providing for exceptions. But temperance also can be created by coercion. Taxing is a good coercive device. To keep downtown shoppers temperate in their use of parking space we introduce parking meters for short periods, and traffic fines for longer ones. We need not actually forbid a citizen to park as long as he wants to; we need merely make it increasingly expensive for him to do so. Not prohibition, but carefully biased options are what we offer him. A Madison Avenue man might call this persuasion; I prefer the greater candor of the word coercion.

Coercion is a dirty word to most liberals now, but it need not forever be so. As with the four-letter words, its dirtiness can be cleansed away by exposure to the light, by saying it over and over without apology or embarrassment. To many, the word coercion implies arbitrary decisions of distant and irresponsible bureaucrats; but this is not a necessary part of its meaning. The only kind of coercion I recommend is mutual coercion, mutually agreed upon by the majority of the people affected.

To say that we mutually agree to coercion is not to say that we are required to enjoy it, or even to pretend we enjoy it. Who enjoys taxes? We all grumble about them. But we accept compulsory taxes because we recognize that voluntary taxes would favor the conscienceless. We institute and (grumblingly) support taxes and other coercive devices to escape the horror of the commons.

An alternative to the commons need not be perfectly just to be preferable. With real estate and other material goods, the alternative we have chosen is the institution of private property coupled with legal inheritance. Is this system perfectly just? As a genetically trained biologist I deny that it is. It seems to me that, if there are to be differences in individual inheritance, legal possession should be perfectly correlated with biological inheritance—that those who are biologically more fit to be the custodians of property and power should legally inherit more. But genetic recombination continually makes a mockery of the doctrine of "like father, like son" implicit in our laws of legal inheritance. An idiot can inherit millions, and a trust fund can keep his estate intact. We must admit that our legal system of private property plus inheritance is unjust—but we put up with it because we are not convinced, at the moment, that anyone has invented a better system. The alternative of the commons is too horrifying to contemplate. Injustice is preferable to total ruin.

It is one of the peculiarities of the warfare between reform and the status quo that it is thoughtlessly governed by a double standard. Whenever a reform measure is proposed it is often defeated when its opponents triumphantly discover a flaw in it. As Kingsley Davis has pointed out (*21*), worshippers of the status quo sometimes imply that no reform is possible without unanimous agreement, an implication contrary to historical fact. As nearly as I can make out, automatic rejection of proposed reforms is based on one of two unconscious assumptions: (i) that the status quo is perfect; or (ii) that the choice we face is between reform and no action; if the proposed reform is imperfect, we presumably should take no action at all, while we wait for a perfect proposal.

But we can never do nothing. That which we have done for thousands of years is also action. It also produces evils. Once we are aware that the status quo is action, we can then compare its discoverable advantages and disadvantages with the predicted advantages and disadvantages of the proposed reform, discounting as best we can for our lack of experience. On the basis of such a comparison, we can make a rational decision which will not involve the unworkable assumption that only perfect systems are tolerable.

Recognition of Necessity

Perhaps the simplest summary of this analysis of man's population problems is this: the commons, if justifiable at all, is justifiable only under conditions of low-population density. As the human population has increased, the commons has had to be abandoned in one aspect after another.

First we abandoned the commons in food gathering, enclosing farm land and restricting pastures and hunting and fishing areas. These restrictions are still not complete throughout the world.

Somewhat later we saw that the commons as a place for waste disposal would also have to be abandoned. Restrictions on the disposal of domestic sewage are widely accepted in the Western world; we are still struggling to close the commons to pollution by automobiles, factories, insecticide sprayers, fertilizing operations, and atomic energy installations.

In a still more embryonic state is our recognition of the evils of the commons in matters of pleasure. There is almost no restriction on the propagation of sound waves in the public medium. The shopping public is assaulted with mindless music, without its consent. Our government is paying out billions of dollars to create supersonic transport which will disturb 50,000 people for every one person who is whisked from coast to coast 3 hours faster. Advertisers muddy the airwaves of radio and television and pollute the view of travelers. We are a long way from outlawing the commons in matters of pleasure. Is this because our Puritan inheritance makes us view pleasure as something of a sin, and pain (that is, the pollution of advertising) as the sign of virtue?

Every new enclosure of the commons involves the infringement of somebody's personal liberty. Infringements made in the distant past are accepted because no contemporary complains of a loss. It is the newly proposed infringements that we vigorously oppose; cries of "rights" and "freedom" fill the air. But what does "freedom" mean? When men mutually agreed to pass laws against robbing, mankind became more free, not less so. Individuals locked into the logic of the commons are free only to bring on universal ruin; once they see the necessity of mutual coercion, they become free to pursue other goals. I believe it was Hegel who said "Freedom is the recognition of necessity."

The most important aspect of necessity that we must now recognize is the necessity of abandoning the commons in breeding. No technical solution can rescue us from the misery of overpopulation. Freedom to breed will bring ruin to all. At the moment, to avoid hard decisions many of us are tempted to propagandize for conscience and responsible parenthood. The temptation must be resisted, because an appeal to independently acting consciences selects for the disappearance of all conscience in the long run, and an increase in anxiety in the short.

The only way we can preserve and nurture other and more precious freedoms is by relinquishing the freedom to breed, and that very soon. "Freedom is the recognition of necessity"—and it is the role of education to reveal to all the necessity of abandoning the freedom to breed. Only so, can we put an end to this aspect of the tragedy of the commons.

References

1. J. B. Wiesner and H. F. York, *Sci. Amer.* **211** (No. 4), 27 (1964).

2. G. Hardin, *J. Hered.* **50**, 68 (1959); S. von Hoernor, *Science* **137**, 18 (1962).

3. J. von Neumann and O. Morgenstern, *Theory of Games and Economic Behavior* (Princeton Univ. Press, Princeton, N.J., 1947), p. 11.

4. J. H. Fremlin, *New Sci.,* No. 415 (1964), p. 285.

5. A. Smith, *The Wealth of Nations* (Modern Library, New York, 1937), p. 423.

6. W. F. Lloyd, *Two Lectures on the Checks to Population* (Oxford Univ. Press, Oxford, England, 1833), reprinted (in part) in *Population, Evolution, and Birth Control,* G. Hardin, Ed. (Freeman, San Francisco, 1964), p. 37.

7. A. N. Whitehead, *Science and the Modern World* (Mentor, New York, 1948), p. 17.

8. G. Hardin, Ed., *Population, Evolution, and Birth Control* (Freeman, San Francisco, 1964), p. 56.

9. S. McVay, *Sci. Amer.* **216** (No. 8), 13 (1966).

10. J. Fletcher, *Situation Ethics* (Westminster, Philadelphia, 1966).

11. D. Lack, *The Natural Regulation of Animal Numbers* (Clarendon Press, Oxford, 1954).

12. H. Girvetz, *From Wealth to Welfare* (Stanford Univ. Press, Stanford, Calif., 1950).

13. G. Hardin, *Perspec. Biol. Med.* **6**, 366 (1963).

14. U. Thant, *Int. Planned Parenthood News*, No. 168 (February 1968), p. 3.

15. K. Davis, *Science* **158**, 730 (1967).

16. S. Tax, Ed., *Evolution after Darwin* (Univ. of Chicago Press, Chicago, 1960), vol. 2, p. 469.

17. G. Bateson, D. D. Jackson, J. Haley, J. Weakland, *Behav. Sci.* **1**, 251 (1956).

18. P. Goodman, *New York Rev. Books* **10** (8), 22 (23 May 1968).

19. A. Comfort, *The Anxiety Makers* (Nelson, London, 1967).

20. C. Frankel, *The Case for Modern Man* (Harper, New York, 1955), p. 203.

21. J. D. Roslansky, *Genetics and the Future of Man* (Appleton-Century-Crofts, New York, 1966), p. 177.

The Historical Roots of Our Ecologic Crisis

Lynn White, Jr.

A conversation with Aldous Huxley not infrequently put one at the receiving end of an unforgettable monologue. About a year before his lamented death he was discoursing on a favorite topic: Man's unnatural treatment of nature and its sad results. To illustrate his point he told how, during the previous summer, he

Lynn White, Jr., "The Historical Roots of Our Ecologic Crisis," *Science*, Vol. 155, No. 3767, March 10, 1967, pp. 1203-1207. Copyright 1967 by the American Association for the Advancement of Science. Reprinted by permission of the author and publisher. The author is professor of history at the University of California, Los Angeles. This is the text of a lecture delivered 26 December 1966 at the Washington meeting of the AAAS.

had returned to a little valley in England where he had spent many happy months as a child. Once it had been composed of delightful grassy glades; now it was becoming overgrown with unsightly brush because the rabbits that formerly kept such growth under control had largely succumbed to a disease, myxomatosis, that was deliberately introduced by the local farmers to reduce the rabbits' destruction of crops. Being something of a Philistine, I could be silent no longer, even in the interests of great rhetoric. I interrupted to point out that the rabbit itself had been brought as a domestic animal to England in 1176, presumably to improve the protein diet of the peasantry.

All forms of life modify their contexts. The most spectacular and benign instance is doubtless the coral polyp. By serving its own ends, it has created a vast undersea world favorable to thousands of other kinds of animals and plants. Ever since man became a numerous species he has affected his environment notably. The hypothesis that his fire-drive method of hunting created the world's great grasslands and helped to eliminate the monster mammals of the Pleistocene from much of the globe is plausible, if not proved. For 6 millennia at least, the banks of the lower Nile have been a human artifact rather than the swampy African jungle which nature, apart from man, would have made it. The Aswan Dam, flooding 5000 square miles, is only the latest stage in a long process. In many regions terracing or irrigation, overgrazing, the cutting of forests by Romans to build ships to fight Carthaginians or by Crusaders to solve the logistics problems of their expeditions, have profoundly changed some ecologies. Observation that the French landscape falls into two basic types, the open fields of the north and the *bocage* of the south and west, inspired Marc Bloch to undertake his classic study of medieval agricultural methods. Quite unintentionally, changes in human ways often affect nonhuman nature. It has been noted, for example, that the advent of the automobile eliminated huge flocks of sparrows that once fed on the horse manure littering every street.

The history of ecologic change is still so rudimentary that we know little about what really happened, or what the results were. The extinction of the European aurochs as late as 1627 would seem to have been a simple case of overenthusiastic hunting. On more intricate matters it often is impossible to find solid information. For a thousand years or more the Frisians and Hollanders have been pushing back the North Sea, and the process is culminating in our own time in the reclamation of the Zuider Zee. What, if any, species of animals, birds, fish, shore life, or plants have died out in the process? In their epic combat with Neptune have the Netherlanders overlooked ecological values in such a way that the quality of human life in the Netherlands has suffered? I cannot discover that the questions have ever been asked, much less answered.

People, then, have often been a dynamic element in their own environment, but in the present state of historical scholarship we usually do not know exactly when, where, or with what effects man-induced changes came. As we enter the last third of the 20th century, however, concern for the problem of ecologic backlash is mounting feverishly. Natural science, conceived as the effort to understand the nature of things, had flourished in several eras and among several peoples. Similarly there had been an age-old accumulation of technological skills, sometimes growing rapidly, sometimes slowly. But it was not until about four generations ago that Western Europe and North America arranged a marriage between science and technology, a union of the theoretical and the empirical approaches to our natural environment. The emergence in widespread practice of the Baconian creed that scientific knowledge means technological power over nature can scarcely be dated before about 1850, save in the chemical industries, where it is anticipated in the 18th century. Its acceptance as a normal pattern of action may mark the greatest event in human history since the invention of agriculture, and perhaps in nonhuman terrestrial history as well.

Almost at once the new situation forced the crystallization of the novel concept of ecology; indeed, the word *ecology* first appeared in the English language in 1873. Today, less than a century later, the impact of our race upon the environment has so increased in force that it has changed in essence. When the first cannons were fired, in the early 14th century, they affected ecology by sending workers scrambling to the forests and mountains for more potash, sulfur, iron ore, and charcoal, with some resulting erosion and deforestation. Hydrogen bombs are of a different order: a war fought with them might alter the genetics of all life on this planet. By 1285 London had a smog problem arising from the burning of soft coal, but our present combustion of fossil fuels threatens to change the chemistry of the globe's atmosphere as a whole, with consequences which we are only beginning to guess. With the population explosion, the carcinoma of planless urbanism, the now geological deposits of sewage and garbage, surely no creature other than man has ever managed to foul its nest in such short order.

There are many calls to action, but specific proposals, however worthy as individual items, seem too partial, palliative, negative: ban the bomb, tear down the billboards, give the Hindus contraceptives and tell them to eat their sacred cows. The simplest solution to any suspect change is, of course, to stop it, or, better yet, to revert to a romanticized past: make those ugly gasoline stations look like Anne Hathaway's cottage or (in the Far West) like Ghost-town saloons. The "wilderness area" mentality invariably advocates deep-freezing an ecology, whether San Gimignano or the High Sierra, as it was before the first Kleenex was dropped. But neither atavism nor prettification will cope with the ecologic crisis of our time.

What shall we do? No one yet knows. Unless we think about fundamentals, our specific measures may produce new backlashes more serious than those they are designed to remedy.

As a beginning we should try to clarify our thinking by looking, in some historical depth, at the presuppositions that underlie modern technology and science. Science was traditionally aristocratic, speculative, intellectual in intent; technology was lower-class, empirical, action-oriented. The quite sudden fusion of these two, towards the middle of the 19th century, is surely related to the slightly prior and contemporary democratic revolutions which, by reducing social barriers, tended to assert a functional unity of brain and hand. Our ecologic crisis is the product of an emerging, entirely novel, democratic culture. The issue is whether a democratized world can survive its own implications. Presumably we cannot unless we rethink our axioms.

The Western Traditions of Technology and Science

One thing is so certain that it seems stupid to verbalize it: both modern technology and modern science are distinctively *Occidental*. Our technology has absorbed elements from all over the world, notably from China; yet everywhere today, whether in Japan or in Nigeria, successful technology is Western. Our science is the heir to all the sciences of the past, especially perhaps to the work of the great Islamic scientists of the Middle Ages, who so often outdid the ancient Greeks in skill and perspicacity: al-Rāzī in medicine, for example; or ibn-al-Haytham in optics; or Omar Khayyám in mathematics. Indeed, not a few works of such geniuses seem to have vanished in the original Arabic and to survive only in medieval Latin translations that helped to lay the foundations for later Western developments. Today, around the globe, all significant science is Western in style and method, whatever the pigmentation or language of the scientists.

A second pair of facts is less well recognized because they result from quite recent historical scholarship. The leadership of the West, both in technology and in science, is far older than the so-called Scientific Revolution of the 17th century or the so-called Industrial Revolution of the 18th century. These terms are in fact outmoded and obscure the true nature of what they try to describe—significant stages in two long and separate developments. By A.D. 1000 at the latest—and perhaps, feebly, as much as 200 years earlier—the West began to apply water power to industrial processes other than milling grain. This was followed in the late 12th century by the harnessing of wind power. From simple beginnings, but with remarkable consistency of style, the West rapidly expanded its skills in the development of power machinery, labor-saving devices, and automation. Those who doubt should contemplate that most monumental achievement in the history of automation: the weight-driven mechanical clock, which appeared in two forms in the early 14th century. Not in craftsmanship but in basic technological capacity, the Latin West of the later Middle Ages far outstripped its elaborate, sophisticated, and esthetically magnificent sister cultures, Byzantium and Islam. In 1444 a great Greek ecclesiastic, Bessarion, who had gone to Italy, wrote a letter to a prince in Greece. He is amazed by the superiority of Western ships, arms, textiles, glass. But above all he is astonished by the spectacle of waterwheels sawing timbers and pumping the bellows of blast furnaces. Clearly, he had seen nothing of the sort in the Near East.

By the end of the 15th century the technological superiority of Europe was such that its small, mutually hostile nations could spill out over all the rest of the world, conquering, looting, and colonizing. The symbol of this technological superiority is the fact that Portugal, one of the weakest states of the Occident, was able to become, and to remain for a century, mistress of the East Indies. And we must remember that the technology of Vasco da Gama and Albuquerque was built by pure empiricism, drawing remarkably little support or inspiration from science.

In the present-day vernacular understanding, modern science is supposed to have begun in 1543, when both Copernicus and Vesalius published their great works. It is no derogation of their accomplishments, however, to point out that such structures as the *Fabrica* and the *De revolutionibus* do not appear overnight. The distinctive Western tradition of science, in fact, began in the late 11th century with a massive movement of translation of Arabic and Greek scientific works into Latin. A few notable books—Theophrastus, for example—escaped the West's avid new appetite for science, but within less than 200 years effectively the entire corpus of Greek and Muslim science was available in Latin, and was being eagerly read and criticized in the new European universities. Out of criticism arose new observation, speculation, and increasing distrust of ancient authorities. By the late 13th century Europe had seized global scientific leadership from the faltering hands of Islam. It would be as absurd to deny the profound originality of Newton, Galileo, or Copernicus as to deny that of the 14th century scholastic scientists like Buridan or Oresme on whose work they built. Before the 11th century, science scarcely existed in the Latin West, even in Roman times. From the 11th century onward, the scientific sector of Occidental culture has increased in a steady crescendo.

Since both our technological and our scientific movements got their start, acquired their character, and achieved world dominance in the Middle Ages, it would seem that we cannot understand their nature of their present impact upon ecology without examining fundamental medieval assumptions and developments.

Medieval View of Man and Nature

Until recently, agriculture has been the chief occupation even in "advanced" societies; hence, any change in methods of tillage has much importance. Early plows, drawn by two oxen, did not normally turn the sod but merely scratched it. Thus, cross-plowing was needed and fields tended to be squarish. In the fairly light soils and semiarid climates of the Near East and Mediterranean, this worked well. But such a plow was inappropriate to the wet climate and often sticky soils of northern Europe. By the latter part of the 7th century after Christ, however, following obscure beginnings, certain northern peasants were using an entirely new kind of plow, equipped with a vertical knife to cut the line of the furrow, a horizontal share to slice under the sod, and a moldboard to turn it over. The friction of this plow with the soil was so great that it normally required not two but eight oxen. It attacked the land with such violence that cross-plowing was not needed, and fields tended to be shaped in long strips.

In the days of the scratch-plow, fields were distributed generally in units capable of supporting a single family. Subsistence farming was the presupposition. But no peasant owned eight oxen: to use the new and more efficient plow, peasants pooled their oxen to form large plow-teams, originally receiving (it would appear) plowed strips in proportion to their contribution. Thus, distribution of land was based no longer on the needs of a family but, rather, on the capacity of a power machine to till the earth. Man's relation to the soil was profoundly changed. Formerly man had been part of nature; now he was the exploiter of nature. Nowhere else in the world did farmers develop any analogous agricultural implement. Is it coincidence that modern technology, with its ruthlessness toward nature, has so largely been produced by descendants of these peasants of northern Europe?

This same exploitive attitude appears slightly before A.D. 830 in Western illustrated calendars. In older calendars the months were shown as passive personifications. The new Frankish calendars, which set the style for the Middle Ages, are very different: they show men coercing the world around them—plowing, harvesting, chopping trees, butchering pigs. Man and nature are two things, and man is master.

These novelties seem to be in harmony with larger intellectual patterns. What people do about their ecology depends on what they think about themselves in relation to things around them. Human ecology is deeply conditioned by beliefs about our nature and destiny—that is, by religion. To Western eyes this is very evident in, say, India or Ceylon. It is equally true of ourselves and of our medieval ancestors.

The victory of Christianity over paganism was the greatest psychic revolution in the history of our culture. It has become fashionable today to say that, for better or worse, we live in "the post-Christian age." Certainly the forms of our thinking and language have largely ceased to be Christian, but to my eye the substance often remains amazingly akin to that of the past. Our daily habits of action, for example, are dominated by an implicit faith in perpetual progress which was unknown either to Greco-Roman antiquity or to the Orient. It is rooted in, and is indefensible apart from, Judeo-Christian teleology. The fact that Communists share it merely helps to show what can be demonstrated on many other grounds: that Marxism, like Islam, is a Judeo-Christian heresy. We continue today to live, as we have lived for about 1700 years, very largely in a context of Christian axioms.

What did Christianity tell people about their relations with the environment?

While many of the world's mythologies provide stories of creation, Greco-Roman mythology was singularly incoherent in this respect. Like Aristotle, the intellectuals of the ancient West denied that the visible world had had a beginning. Indeed, the idea of a beginning was impossible in the framework of their cyclical notion of time. In sharp contrast, Christianity inherited from Judaism not only a concept of time as nonrepetitive and linear but also a striking story of creation. By gradual stages a loving and all-powerful

God had created light and darkness, the heavenly bodies, the earth and all its plants, animals, birds, and fishes. Finally, God had created Adam and, as an afterthought, Eve to keep man from being lonely. Man named all the animals, thus establishing his dominance over them. God planned all of this explicitly for man's benefit and rule: no item in the physical creation had any purpose save to serve man's purposes. And, although man's body is made of clay, he is not simply part of nature: he is made in God's image.

Especially in its Western form, Christianity is the most anthropocentric religion the world has seen. As early as the 2nd century both Tertullian and Saint Irenaeus of Lyons were insisting that when God shaped Adam he was foreshadowing the image of the incarnate Christ, the Second Adam. Man shares, in great measure, God's transcendence of nature. Christianity, in absolute contrast to ancient paganism and Asia's religions (except, perhaps, Zoroastrianism), not only established a dualism of man and nature but also insisted that it is God's will that man exploit nature for his proper ends.

At the level of the common people this worked out in an interesting way. In Antiquity every tree, every spring, every stream, every hill had its own *genius loci*, its guardian spirit. These spirits were accessible to men, but were very unlike men; centaurs, fauns, and mermaids show their ambivalence. Before one cut a tree, mined a mountain, or dammed a brook, it was important to placate the spirit in charge of that particular situation, and to keep it placated. By destroying pagan animism, Christianity made it possible to exploit nature in a mood of indifference to the feelings of natural objects.

It is often said that for animism the Church substituted the cult of saints. True; but the cult of saints is functionally quite different from animism. The saint is not *in* natural objects; he may have special shrines, but his citizenship is in heaven. Moreover, a saint is entirely a man; he can be approached in human terms. In addition to saints, Christianity of course also had angels and demons inherited from Judaism and perhaps, at one remove, from Zoroastrianism. But these were all as mobile as the saints themselves. The spirits *in* natural objects, which formerly had protected nature from man, evaporated. Man's effective monopoly on spirit in this world was confirmed, and the old inhibitions to the exploitation of nature crumbled.

When one speaks in such sweeping terms, a note of caution is in order. Christianity is a complex faith, and its consequences differ in differing contexts. What I have said may well apply to the medieval West, where in fact technology made spectacular advances. But the Greek East, a highly civilized realm of equal Christian devotion, seems to have produced no marked technological innovation after the late 7th century, when Greek fire was invented. The key to the contrast may perhaps be found in a difference in the tonality of piety and thought which students of comparative theology find between the Greek and the Latin Churches. The Greeks believed that sin was intellectual blindness, and that salvation was found in illumination, orthodoxy—that is, clear thinking. The Latins, on the other hand, felt that sin was moral evil, and that salvation was to be found in right conduct. Eastern theology has been intellectualist. Western theology has been voluntarist. The Greek saint contemplates; the Western saint acts. The implications of Christianity for the conquest of nature would emerge more easily in the Western atmosphere.

The Christian dogma of creation, which is found in the first clause of all the Creeds, has another meaning for our comprehension of today's ecologic crisis. By revelation, God had given man the Bible, the Book of Scripture. But since God had made nature, nature also must reveal the divine mentality. The religious study of nature for the better understanding of God was known as natural theology. In the early Church, and always in the Greek East, nature was conceived primarily as a symbolic system through which God speaks to men: the ant is a sermon to sluggards; rising flames are the symbol of the soul's aspiration. This view of nature was essentially artistic rather than scientific. While Byzantium preserved and copied great numbers of ancient Greek scientific texts, science as we conceive it could scarcely flourish in such an ambience.

However, in the Latin West by the early 13th century natural theology was following a very different bent. It was ceasing to be the decoding of the physical symbols of God's communication with man and was becoming the effort to understand God's mind by discovering how his creation operates. The rainbow was no longer simply a symbol of hope first sent to Noah after the Deluge: Robert Grosseteste, Friar Roger Bacon, and Theodoric of Frieberg produced startlingly sophisticated work on the optics of the rainbow, but they did it as a venture in religious understanding. From the 13th century onward, up to and including Leibnitz and Newton, every major scientist, in effect, explained his motivations in religious terms. Indeed, if Galileo had not been so expert an amateur theologian he would have got into far less trouble: the professionals resented his intrusion. And Newton seems to have regarded himself more as a theologian than as a scientist. It was not until the late 18th century that the hypothesis of God became unnecessary to many scientists.

It is often hard for the historian to judge, when men explain why they are doing what they want to do, whether they are offering real reasons or merely culturally acceptable reasons. The consistency with which scientists during the long formative centuries of Western science said that the task and the reward of the scientist was "to think God's thoughts after him" leads one to believe that this was their real motivation. If so, then modern Western science was cast in a matrix of Christian theology. The dynamism of religious devotion, shaped by the Judeo-Christian dogma of creation, gave it impetus.

An Alternative Christian View

We would seem to be headed toward conclusions unpalatable to many Christians. Since both *science* and *technology* are blessed words in our contemporary vocabulary, some may be happy at the notions, first, that, viewed historically, modern science is an extrapolation of natural theology and, second, that modern technology is at least partly to be explained as an Occidental, voluntarist realization of the Christian dogma of man's transcendence of, and rightful mastery over, nature. But, as we now recognize, somewhat over a century ago science and technology—hitherto quite separate activities—joined to give mankind powers which, to judge by many of the ecologic effects, are out of control. If so, Christianity bears a huge burden of guilt.

I personally doubt that disastrous ecologic backlash can be avoided simply by applying to our problems more science and more technology. Our science and technology have grown out of Christian attitudes toward man's relation to nature which are almost universally held not only by Christians and neo-Christians but also by those who fondly regard themselves as post-Christians. Despite Copernicus, all the cosmos rotates around our little globe. Despite Darwin, we are *not*, in our hearts, part of the natural process. We are superior to nature, contemptuous of it, willing to use it for our slightest whim. The newly elected Governor of California, like myself a churchman but less troubled than I, spoke for the Christian tradition when he said (as is alleged), "when you've seen one redwood tree, you've seen them all." To a Christian a tree can be no more than a physical fact. The whole concept of the sacred grove is alien to Christianity and to the ethos of the West. For nearly 2 millennia Christian missionaries have been chopping down sacred groves, which are idolatrous because they assume spirit in nature.

What we do about ecology depends on our ideas of the man-nature relationship. More science and more technology are not going to get us out of the present ecologic crisis until we find a new religion, or rethink our old one. The beatniks, who are the basic revolutionaries of our time, show a sound instinct in their affinity for Zen Buddhism, which conceives of the man-nature relationship as very nearly the mirror image of the Christian view. Zen, however, is as deeply conditioned by Asian history as Christianity is by the experience of the West, and I am dubious of its viability among us.

Possibly we should ponder the greatest radical in Christian history since Christ: Saint Francis of Assisi. The prime miracle of Saint Francis is the fact that he did not end at the stake, as many of his left-wing followers did. He was so clearly heretical that a General of the Franciscan Order, Saint Bonaventura, a great and perceptive Christian, tried to suppress the early accounts of Franciscanism. The key to an understanding of Francis is his belief in the virtue of humility—not merely for the individual but for man as a species. Francis tried to depose man from his monarchy over creation and set up a democracy of all God's creatures. With him the ant is no longer simply a homily for the lazy, flames a sign of the thrust of the soul toward union with God: now they are Brother Ant and Sister Fire, praising the Creator in their own ways as Brother Man does in his.

Later commentators have said that Francis preached to the birds as a rebuke to men who would not listen. The records do not read so: he urged the little birds to praise God, and in spiritual ecstasy they flapped their wings and chirped rejoicing. Legends of saints, especially the Irish saints, had long told of their dealings with animals but always, I believe, to show their human dominance over creatures. With Francis it is different. The land around Gubbio in the

Apennines was being ravaged by a fierce wolf. Saint Francis, says the legend, talked to the wolf and persuaded him of the error of his ways. The wolf repented, died in the odor of sanctity, and was buried in consecrated ground.

What Sir Steven Ruciman calls "the Franciscan doctrine of the animal soul" was quickly stamped out. Quite possibly it was in part inspired, consciously or unconsciously, by the belief in reincarnation held by the Cathar heretics who at that time teemed in Italy and southern France, and who presumably had got it originally from India. It is significant that at just the same moment, about 1200, traces of metempsychosis are found also in western Judaism, in the Provencal *Cabbala*. But Francis held neither to transmigration of souls nor to pantheism. His view of nature and of man rested on a unique sort of pan-psychism of all things animate and inanimate, designed for the glorification of their transcendent Creator, who, in the ultimate gesture of cosmic humility, assumed flesh, lay helpless in a manger, and hung dying on a scaffold.

I am not suggesting that many contemporary Americans who are concerned about our ecologic crisis will be either able or willing to counsel with wolves or exhort birds. However, the present increasing disruption of the global environment is the product of a dynamic technology and science which were originating in the Western medieval world against which Saint Francis was rebelling in so original a way. Their growth cannot be understood historically apart from distinctive attitudes toward nature which are deeply grounded in Christian dogma. The fact that most people do not think of these attitudes as Christian is irrelevant. No new set of basic values has been accepted in our society to displace those of Christianity. Hence we shall continue to have a worsening ecologic crisis until we reject the Christian axiom that nature has no reason for existence save to serve man.

The greatest spiritual revolutionary in Western history, Saint Francis, proposed what he thought was an alternative Christian view of nature and man's relation to it: he tried to substitute the idea of the equality of all creatures, including man, for the idea of man's limitless rule of creation. He failed. Both our present science and our present technology are so tinctured with orthodox Christian arrogance toward nature that no solution for our ecologic crisis can be expected from them alone. Since the roots of our trouble are so largely religious, the remedy must also be essentially religious, whether we call it that or not. We must rethink and refeel our nature and destiny. The profoundly religious, but heretical, sense of the primitive Franciscans for the spiritual autonomy of all parts of nature may point a direction. I propose Francis as a patron saint for ecologists.

Section Three

Biology and Society

The major new frontier of science seems to be the biochemedical revolution—the complex developments in biochemistry, molecular biology, and medical technology. The media and the popular publications have made DNA, genetic engineering, and planned evolution into household phrases. Periodically and with greater frequency, we read about new inroads into molecular biology and the ability to synthesize and understand the basic units of living matter. Together these new fields of biology have created a new dominant area of science and technology and comprise the realm of Big Biology, analogous to Big Science. The outlines of a biological order tending to fulfill the anatomy of the Ellulian model are now discernible. In the fulfillment of this order is a tendency for present means to become future ends—realizing planned evolution, sex determination, population control, genetic and brain manipulation, and so forth. The "biological time bomb," like the population and nuclear bombs, presents serious threats to human individuality and freedom while promising production of superior beings and the control of disease.

The problem of food and population falls into this area. The "green revolution" has been greeted by some as the ultimate technological panacea, an end to the Malthusian threat of population exceeding food supply. Others have been extremely critical of any present technological solutions to the population crisis, be it fertility control or food production.

This section on biology and society is followed by the section on chemical technology that recognizes the areas of biochemistry which are common to both. There is a natural and synthetic progression from mastery of giant molecules that are not part of living matter to those, such as proteins and nucleic acids, that are essential to life. The former are dealt with in the next section.

The selections in this section cover the range of themes discussed in the preface. Weinberg's article deals with the emergence of Big Biology, analogous to Big Science. The articles by Lederberg, Dobzhansky, and Etzioni deal with various aspects of the new biology and the genetic prospect with its potential to control and direct the hereditary nature of humans and animals. The article by Ehrlich and Holdren is concerned with the problem of population. Torrey's article deals with emerging ethical issues in medicine, such as transplants, while Taylor's selection from the *Biological Time Bomb* seeks answers concerning the future of the new genetics.

The Coming Age of Biomedical Science

Alvin M. Weinberg

The Urgency of Biomedical Research

In this essay I shall expand on a conclusion I reached in "Criteria for Scientific Choice": that of all the sciences now supported by our society, biomedical science ought to stand first. My purpose therefore is to illustrate how the criteria developed in that essay can be applied in a specific, concrete way.

We are, or ought to be, entering an age of biomedical science and biomedical technology that could rival in magnitude and richness the present age of physical science and physical technology. Whether we shall indeed enter this age will depend upon the attitude toward Big Biology adopted by biomedical scientists and government agencies that support biology. Whether the age of Big Biology will be truly rewarding will depend on the common sense and integrity of all who participate in this adventure.

Alvin M. Weinberg, "The Coming Age of Biomedical Science," in *Reflections on Big Science* (Boston: M.I.T. Press, 1967), pp. 101-109. Most of this essay originally appeared in *Minerva*, Vol. IV, pp. 3-14, Autumn 1965. Reprinted by permission of the author.

Of all the bases for claiming large-scale public support for a scientific activity, the possibility of alleviating human disease through such activity is obviously one of the most compelling. Of all the sciences, the biomedical sciences are the only ones specifically aimed at, and relevant to, alleviation of man's elementary sufferings, disease and premature death. There is urgency of the most excruciating kind in getting on with this job. The assault on human disease, insofar as it may result in alleviation of immediate everyday human suffering, has an urgency comparable to the urgency with which a nation prosecutes a war. Indeed, I would draw an analogy in this regard between wartime research in physics and present-day research in the biomedical sciences.

This claim to urgency hardly can be matched by any of the other great fields of natural science. Certainly those fields that base their claims to support primarily on the promise of enlarging the human spirit have, to my mind, a less valid case for *urgency* than do those fields that base their claim on the possibility of curing or preventing human disease. SU(n) symmetry is magnificent and soul-satisfying to those who understand it; a cure for leukemia is more immediate in its benefit to mankind.

Are the biomedical sciences that relevant to the conquest of disease? To an applied scientist like me, this question seems absurd. What strikes an observer most about modern biology is how the new viewpoints have unified the subject. The genetic code appears to be universal. The dogma of protein synthesis—DNA, messenger RNA, transfer RNA, protein—seems to be valid in almost every life form. The same twenty-odd amino acids build proteins in bacteria, in mice, and in men. This unity suggests that most of what we learn about biological mechanisms in almost any animal is likely to have ultimate medical applications, whereas the same degree of relevance to application cannot be claimed for large parts of modern physics, or astronomy, or mathematics.

Derek de Solla Price has stressed that applied science tends to be older science, the science that excited the basic scientist of a previous generation.[1] Though I agree with his general thesis that applied science is older science, I think the characteristic time lag varies from science to science. The "basic" biological sciences are so strongly connected with medicine, in my view, that I would *a priori* expect findings in basic biological science to move into experimental medicine with great rapidity, so rapidly that the distinction between applied and basic is very blurred. For example, the work on suppression of immunological mechanisms by radiation and the limited use of this technique in organ transplantation came almost simultaneously. The bulk of the basic work on the enhancement of radio-sensitivity caused by oxygen and the application of this technique to hyperbaric x-ray therapy were separated by hardly five years. Because in the biomedical sciences the distinction between pure and applied is rather irrelevant, as a matter of tactics I have argued that all of biomedical

[1] "Is Technology Historically Independent of Science; A Study in Statistical Historiography," *Technology and Culture* 6, 553-568 (1965).

science be viewed as applied science. This hardly endears me to some of my good friends who consider themselves to be basic biological scientists. Yet from the point of view I am discussing here—the validity of the biomedical sciences' claim to urgency and therefore the validity of their claim to large-scale support from society—the position of biology is far stronger if it regards itself as fighting the war against disease rather than the war to enlarge the human spirit, worthy as is the latter.

If the biomedical sciences are viewed as applied sciences, aimed at alleviating disease, then in assessing their priority they should be judged not so much against other pure sciences but rather against alternative means of alleviating disease. The most obvious such alternative is medical practice, including treatment centers, hospitals, medical education, nursing care, and so on. I have already alluded to the competition between the demands of medical practice and the demands of medical research. I expect this competition, which presently favors research, to shift toward practice now that a study such as that by the President's Commission on Heart Disease, Cancer and Stroke[2] is bringing our country's attention to the need for more medical practice. My own view is that we need more biomedical science *and* more medical practice, and that the two, taken together, deserve very high priority in our society's allocation of resources.

The Ripeness of Biomedical Research

Relevant as is the aim of a science to achievement of a recognized human value—in the case of biology, to the elimination of human disease—this can only be a partial justification for large-scale public support. Before any scientific field can expect support on a very large scale it must be at a stage where large-scale public support is likely to produce useful results. Anyone who claims that biomedical science should become our number-one scientific priority must show that this field is likely to give fair return for support received.

In this respect the situation in the biomedical sciences at first sight seems to stand between certain of the physical sciences and the behavioral sciences. Judging by the criterion of direct relevance to human welfare, any ordering would almost surely place the behavioral sciences at least on a par with, if not above, the biomedical sciences; the more abstract physical sciences would almost surely rate below these. Judging by the criterion of ripeness for exploitation—that is, whether lack of large-scale support is mainly what is holding up progress—abstract physical science, like elementary particle physics or astronomy, is probably ahead of biomedical sciences, and behavioral sciences are much farther behind. This at least is the view one would gather from the strength of the plea for support made by the physical scientists,

---

[2] The President's Commission on Heart Disease, Cancer and Stroke, "A National Program to Conquer Heart Disease, Cancer and Stroke," U. S. Government Printing Office, Washington, D. C. (December 1964).

compared with the relative weakness of the plea we hear from the biomedical scientists. I think, however, that the biomedical scientists understate their case.

To begin with, as I have said, the war on human disease is a tangible war—more tangible, say, than our efforts to enlarge the human spirit—and it should be fought with the same attitudes we adopt when fighting a shooting war. We expect less return per dollar expended when fighting a war than when carrying on a less crucially important activity. So I would argue that, because of the importance of each victory in the battle against disease, we ought to be willing to get less per dollar spent on biomedical research than we are willing to get from expenditures on the more remote fields of science. We should stop putting more resources into the enterprise only when we have reached a stage of negative return—when more resources *reduce* the total useful output, not merely raise the unit cost of an increased total output. My attitude in this respect resembles that of one of our country's larger chemical companies. The president of this company once told me that where something very important like the design of a new plant was at stake, the company did not hesitate to put more than enough scientists and engineers on the job. Even though this led to duplication of effort, not to speak of a sense of frustration on the part of some of the men, this technical redundancy has paid off very well indeed.

I believe the biomedical sciences are not near the stage where additional large-scale support will *reduce* the over-all output of the entire enterprise. It is apparent even to the most casual observer that we are beginning to understand many of the life processes which for so long had been mysteries: the revolution in molecular biology; or the beautiful elucidation of the mechanism of nerve action; or the new insights into the genetic control of immune mechanisms; or the implication of viruses in some cancers, notably animal leukemia, although the role of viruses had long been suspected. One can hardly believe that the many fruitful points of departure uncovered during the past decade are any-where close to being exploited, or that, if more well-trained, well-supported investigators are set to work, new and startling points of departure will not be found.

Moreover, I think the biomedical sciences can be force-fed, even more than they are now being force-fed. More money for biology has raised the salaries of biologists, at least in the United States, so that presently biologists enjoy an unaccustomed affluence. Though this state of affairs annoys administrators, particularly of multidisciplinary laboratories where disciplines use each other's salary schedules as ratchets, the over-all effect as far as biomedical science is concerned is, on balance, good. More bright youngsters are attracted to well-paid careers than to poorly paid ones. In the United States such force-feeding of a discipline in the past has produced results. For example, the Atomic Energy Commission, by pouring money into nuclear research, caused it to flourish, and encouraged many young science students to go into nuclear research. Or again, the AEC and the U.S. Department of Defense deliberately established about a dozen interdisciplinary materials research laboratories; though it is too early to say positively, my impression is that materials research in the United States has profited by this action.

The New Style of Biomedical Research

There are other reasons, intrinsic to the changing style of research in biology, why more money will be needed. Most obvious is the growing cost of equipment. A modern electron microscope now costs $40,000, and more and more, cellular biology seems to depend on the electron microscope. Even now attempts are being made, both at Oak Ridge National Laboratory and at Argonne National Laboratory, to develop an electron microscope with a resolution of 1 Å. Such a device, if successful, would enable one to identify individual atoms in biological molecules. It might cost several million dollars.

But there are other, possibly subtler, reasons why biological research is becoming more expensive and is requiring more people. In earlier times, when biology was par excellence Little Science, biologists were content to look only at those problems that could be handled in the manner of Little Science. Genetics was done with fruit flies, with their large chromosomes, because fruit flies are inexpensive, not because fruit flies are as much like man as are mammals. Those questions that required large protocols of expensive animals were answered poorly or not at all, not because the questions were unimportant, but because to answer them was expensive and required the style of Big Science, which was so foreign to the biologists' tradition.

But this is changing, in part at least, because the Big Scientists from neighboring fields have taught the habit of Big Science to the biologists. Perhaps the best-known example of the drastically changed style of some biological research is the large-scale mouse genetics experiment of W. L. Russell at Oak Ridge. For the past sixteen years Russell has been studying the genetic effects of ionizing radiation in a mammal, the mouse. Since mutations even at high dose rates are so rare, Russell uses colonies containing 100,000 mice. To perform such experiments takes much money and many people, and yet it seems impossible to visualize any other way of obtaining the data.

The problem of large protocols that Russell faced, and the AEC solved (at a cost of a million dollars per year for this single experiment), is one which arises in many other situations. The increasingly important matter of low-level physical and chemical insults to the biosphere, or of subtle environmental factors in general, will require many large experiments if we are to assess accurately the various hazards that now bombard us. Or take old age, the commonest "disease" of all. Merely because the effects are subtle and often appear haphazardly, the study of aging requires large and expensive protocols. The tradition of the biologists has been to scrimp; biomedical research avoided expensive experiments even if expensive experiments were required to obtain reliable statistics. Biology, while continuing its tradition of Little Science, will have to accept also the style of Big Science. Even though this is expensive, the biologists will find the public willing to support them.

There is another trend in the style of biology which will add to its expense. I refer to the increasingly interdisciplinary character of modern biology, and particularly its increasing dependence on the techniques and methods of the physical sciences and even of the engineering sciences. A few examples, taken from our experience at Oak Ridge, will illustrate these points. For instance, in attacking the problem of radiation insult, we have mobilized biochemists, cytologists, geneticists, pathologists, and biophysicists. Our dependence on disciplines even farther removed from biology is growing. Thus, our biochemists need large quantities of transfer-RNA, preferably separated into unique fractions, to study how amino acids are assembled into proteins. The problem in many ways is one in chemical engineering, and some of the chemical engineers at Oak Ridge have pitched in to help. What the chemical engineers already have done strikes me as being rather impressive. They have been able to extract as much as 600 grams of pure t-RNA from 300 kilograms of *E. coli* by fractionating crude nucleic acids and then separating the extract into specific transfer-RNA's by using a liquid ion-exchange system of the general sort developed in refining uranium ores. The resulting separations are superior to any that have been achieved by older methods.

Second, I mention, again from our Oak Ridge experience, the exciting developments in zonal centrifugation applied to biology. For many years very high-speed, very large, continuously fed centrifuges have been developed for separating the isotopes of uranium. Much of this work has been carried out at the K-25 Gaseous Diffusion Plant. Around 1959, N. G. Anderson of the ORNL Biology Division realized that such centrifuges, suitably modified, might separate cellular moieties on a larger scale than could be done with any other technique. And indeed, with the generous support of the National Cancer Institute and the AEC, this is exactly what has happened. With these centrifuges Anderson has been able to detect virus-like particles in leukemic blood more consistently than have most other investigators who do not have this tool. I would expect Anderson's centrifuges to become widely used in biomedical research, even though some of his centrifuges cost as much as $45,000.

I could list many other instances of the growing interaction between the biological sciences and the physical and engineering sciences—for example, the technique of medical scintillation spectrometry, which has become a medical specialty in its own right, or the wide use of computers in biomedical science, or, for that matter, the application of the methods of quantum chemistry to the attempts to understand the carcinogenic action of aromatic hydrocarbons. But I believe I have given enough examples to bring out the main points: that biomedical science is becoming ever more interdisciplinary, that the disciplines and techniques it draws upon are expensive, and that this will add to the expense of biomedical science.

The New Biomedical Institutes

The changing style of biomedical research and its great and urgent expansion will affect the future organization of such research. At present, a very large part of biomedical research is carried out at universities, institutions that are, or should be, committed to education at least as strongly as they are committed to research. University biomedical research must flourish and must grow. We shall have to maintain Little Biology as well as Big Biology, and we shall have to produce many more trained biomedical scientists if we are to attack, with both styles, the problem of human disease.

Human Implications of Biological Discovery

Joshua Lederberg

Recent advances in medical and biological science, such as the heart transplantation technique by Norman Shumway and DNA replication in vitro by Arthur Kornberg, my colleagues at the Stanford Medical School, are indeed fabulous scientific advances. Without question these events hold great promise for the future of mankind. In the not too distant future, we will be able to artificially create and sustain life. And serious discussions continue in regard to our potential ability to use biochemistry to alter genetic structure and thereby change the minds and bodies of men. These dramatic possibilities and others as yet unmentioned promise the steady lengthening and improving of human life. However, I believe they also raise profound questions for our society: What is life? What is death? Who shall live and who shall die? Whose genes shall be altered and for what purpose? How long and under what conditions shall we prolong life? How far shall we go in creating artificial life, and what will be its status once it has been created?

Extracted from Chapter 4, Joshua Lederberg, "Human Complications of Biological Discovery," in *Toward Century 21* edited by C. S. Wallia, © 1970 by Basic Books, Inc., Publishers, New York. Lederberg is a professor of genetics at Stanford University Medical School. In 1958, he was awarded the Nobel Prize for Medicine for his research in microbial genetics. He has many publications in the area of immunology, microbial genetics, and more recently exobiology.

A National Commission for Controlling
Biological Sciences?

Recently, Senator Walter F. Mondale, a Democrat from Minnesota, placed a rather sharp emphasis on the recent heart transplant operations:

Because I believe it is imperative to deal with these crucial considerations as rationally and as publicly as possible, I intend to introduce a resolution early in the coming session of the United States Senate to establish a national commission on the ethical and social implications on health science research and development. This committee would study the meaning of health science development for this nation and the world, explore its moral and ethical implications and formulate ethical guidelines for its application, and make recommendations to the President and to the Congress for actions to insure that our social policies reflect and influence our technological advances. The Commission and its staff should represent a broad cross-section of disciplines: scientists, health practitioners, administrators, economists, educators, theologians, sociologists, philosophers, and attorneys.

In addition, if there is anyone left, the general American public must be heard if meaningful recommendations are to be made.

I quote this, because it represents the appearance in the legislative consciousness of the impact of current biological advance and its potential relationship to the human condition, to a degree that is unprecedented in our cultural history. In fact, these kinds of remarks lead me to a near reversal on the fundamental stance that I would have taken previously. Six months ago I would be exhorting giving some concern to the way in which the quality of life is likely to be influenced by biology, and asking you to think about biology as one of the politically oriented, socially scientific disciplines. The newspapers have done a very good job of wresting that job from my hands, and I now propose to do almost exactly the opposite: namely, to attempt to quiet some of the unwarranted and unnecessarily extreme extrapolations that might be made even beyond Senator Mondale's statement.

Let me say at the outset, by the way, that I do not think his commission is a good idea if it is going to address itself to the ethical and moral guidelines for applications of medicine. Congress is an excellent organization to the extent that it is representative of our society for the promulgation of laws, but I don't see how in the world any creature of the legislature can lay down moral and ethical guidelines and prescriptions. I would wonder, for example, how it would deal with such matters as private choices in areas such as abortion or contraception or any of a number of things that some people still regard as controversial.

On the other hand, there are urgent matters of law to which Congress should be addressing itself that have to do with at least some of the questions mentioned here. If there is to be an intelligent approach to them, we must particularize. We must get past the stage of throwing up our hands in awe or horror against the vague possibilities of future developments and try to isolate those concerns that we can frame in realistic terms and that represent real challenges to our existing legal system, if we are to have a healthy society.

"Creation" of Life in Test Tube

Now the event that has focused so much attention on these concerns—or these events—has been the transplantation of the heart, as practiced in Capetown and at Stanford; and perhaps at a much more fundamental level, the announcements that have appeared in the scientific literature and have been widely echoed in the press concerning the accomplishments of my colleague, Arthur Kornberg, in the Department of Biochemistry. This has been described as the creation of life in the test tube, and has evoked all kinds of images of the way in which science is now going to modify our genes in the not too distant future. We wonder who will decide whose genes will be altered, in what condition, and so on.

Statements have also been made to the effect that we were about to learn how to make supermen by the application of biochemical genetic principles. Senator Mondale was rather alarmed about that, and I think most of us might be if we were faced with the reality.

Recent Genetics Research

I think perhaps I should first review the actual significance of these epochal contributions from the laboratory, as they do come from the work of one of my close friends and one of my most admired colleagues. I regard the experimental replication of DNA to be one of the most astounding intellectual achievements of the century. I think there has been a certain distortion of emphasis in the newspaper accounts of this work. It is not incorrect to speak about it as the creation of life, but I think we would have to be very careful in our definition of terms if we were to justify that description.

Almost 15 years ago Kornberg began to study the question of the way in which the cell replicates its DNA. At that time it was already reasonably clear—although the final evidence was perhaps not quite in—that DNA was the genetic material. That is to say, the information that prescribes the way in which an organism should develop, and which is present in the nucleus, in the chromosomes of every cell—there being a copy of the original nucleus that was in the original egg cell from which each one of us was derived—was in the form of a very complex organic molecule, deoxyribonucleic acid, or DNA.

Now geneticists have been studying DNA without knowing it for quite a few years. They have been dealing with "genes" at a much higher level of abstraction since their first recognition about 100 years ago in the pioneering work of Mendel, work that was actively ignored by his contemporaries for about 35 years; it had too mathematical and numerological a flavor to be convincing to a generation of biologists who refused to believe that rules of number could have any part of all in the workings of life. The view that living organisms must have rules of their own, and that we cannot apply the simple laws of chemistry and physics or mathematics, is one that has been stubbornly held by a certain fraction of biologists but one that has been constantly retreating against the onslaught of scientific advance. The resistance to the adoption of the theory of evolution and the resistance to the adoption of Mendel's account of the behavior of the genetic material were last century's contributions to that particular struggle. Much more recently we found geneticists working on the rules of inheritance in numerical terms and quite unwilling to discuss the actual material basis of the genetic material, and at least some geneticists stubbornly resisting some of the evidence that showed them that there were actually substantial molecules that could be invoked to account for the behavior of the genetic system. And that stubbornness, that unwillingness to reduce living systems to a materialistic framework, more than anything else accounts for the delay in the development of a chemistry of life. There were traces of it even in well-intentioned and hard-thinking biologists in the thirties and forties that were expressed not so much in a studious opposition to new thought and new experimentation trying to find the biochemical basis of genetics, but more in ignoring it. Kornberg's major contribution—his major intellectual insight—was to regard the problem as soluble: One could discover an enzyme to account for the replication of genetic material, and one could attack that problem by the existing techniques of enzymology—that if one developed a biochemical assay for some steps in the replication of DNA, one could just track this down in the cell, try to purify the enzyme, try to determine the conditions under which it operated, and so on, and that such a program would have some hope of success. Very few of his contemporaries had the confidence that such a program was possible. I think most geneticists would have regarded him as hopelessly ambitious in attempting to perform a task such as the replication of a gene in the test tube.

In fact, it is quite remarkable that this feat was accomplished well before what for a long time had been regarded as a much more inevitable result: the artificial reproduction of proteins by an enzymatic system. The DNA preliminaries were worked out 5 to 10 years before a real understanding of the mechanisms of protein synthesis. However, about 11 or 12 years ago Kornberg reached the point in his investigations where he was able to publish a report on the isolation of an enzyme that he called DNA-polymerase, which had the essential properties of accepting a primer specimen of DNA that could be isolated from any particular kinds of cells, and that in the presence of the appropriate starting materials, new molecules of a DNA-like material would appear resembling that of the primer that was put in. This is quite unlike most enzymatic systems whose whole information with regard to what kind of product they make is inherent in the enzyme. If I begin with starch and one enzyme, I know I am going to obtain glucose-phosphate; if I put in one kind of starch-destroying enzyme, I know I will obtain maltose; if I put in another kind of enzyme, I will obtain dextrin, and so on. But, of course, a replicating system is by definition one that takes some copies of a specimen of the material that has to be copied and makes another copy of it, so the substrate has to determine what the final result is going to be if it is going to meet those conditions.

Twelve years ago, Kornberg had ample evidence that DNA-polymerase had these properties: that it was producing a product material whose properties were determined in great detail by the properties of the DNA that was used as the primer. This was about the time that he and I came to Stanford. I felt a great sense of excitement in having the opportunity to be able to look over his shoulder in the further development of this kind of biochemical investigation. I was confident that it was going to be a very short period of time before the use of Kornberg's polymerase on DNA, of the kind that I was accustomed to working with, which provided genetic information for the development and behavior of bacteria, would enable one to replicate bacterial genes in the test tube. From there one might go to the genetic material of higher organisms, and all kinds of interesting experiments would be possible.

It has been rather surprising that it has taken 10 years from that date to actually accomplish the kind of result that was only recently published. The main methodological gap was the failure to recognize that there was another enzyme, whose existence was at the start not suspected, and which then had to be teased out and simultaneously studied by several different laboratories. This *repair* enzyme is capable of healing the nicks that appear in a growing molecule of DNA even if the DNA is by and large accurately replicated by the DNA-polymerase. These nicks are probably not accidental but are inherent in the detailed mechanism of DNA replication that result in small breaks in the growing DNA chain. If these breaks are not healed, the product DNA, which is obtained as a result of the action of DNA-polymerase on some primer DNA, will have most of the properties of the primer but will be a damaged copy. It will have breaks every few dozen or few hundred nucleotides down the chain. These are the elements of the DNA chain, and as a result, the copy DNA will not have biological activity when you test it for its genetic information; the sentences are broken.

Until this was recognized, it was quite a frustrating experience to attempt experiment after experiment, to obtain excellent chemical evidence that there had been a very neat replication of the primer information, to find that the new DNA that was synthesized depended on the primer DNA for its over-all composition, for its proportion of the bases, for the statistics of which element was placed next to which element, and that all of the low order chemistry of the product was exactly what you would expect in terms of the chemistry of the input material. But then when you test its biological activity, you find that it is essentially inactive.

About 2 years ago some of Kornberg's associates, and at Stanford I. R. Lehman's name must be especially mentioned, and a number of other laboratories elsewhere made almost simultaneous findings in this direction. They delineated the healing enzyme, polynucleotide-"ligase," the enzyme that can tie together broken strands, and can heal them together into one large continuous chain. In addition, a particularly appropriate experimental system was chosen: the genetic material of a very small virus that could be obtained in pure form and has a number of other technical properties that make these experiments much easier to do. The result was the demonstration that one could start with a specimen of the DNA of a certain virus phi-X-174, which happens to occur in nature in the form of a closed ring (and that represents one more reason why the healing enzyme was necessary, because in order to copy a ring, it has to be a string first and then finally closed up by the healing enzyme working at the head and the tail of it). To reuse that copy to make something exactly like the original would demonstrate that this had the biological activity of the original virus DNA. One of the technical properties that makes that virus particularly suitable for this kind of experimentation is that under special conditions the virus DNA, by itself, is an infectious agent. Ordinarily, the virus is released in the natural course of events with the DNA wrapped up inside a protein overcoat. This protects the DNA in its transit from the cell that it has infected and destroyed. It has been known for some time, however, that one could artificially strip off this protein overcoat and if one were extremely cautious in treating the free DNA, it could be allowed to unwrap itself. It is quite tightly wound up inside the virus coat, and under special conditions this isolated, purified, DNA is itself infectious and can start the process of virus infection. In that sense we can refer to the virus DNA by itself as being a living particle. It will initiate a life cycle of the virus when it is allowed to enter an appropriately sensitive bacterial cell.

A. T. Ganesan, in the Stanford genetics department has been pursuing similar lines of investigation, inspired by Kornberg's work. Ganesan reached substantially similar endpoints a few months behind Kornberg, with respect to the replication of other kinds of DNA. Thus, while the viral system is quite a specialized one, it really does represent an opening of the door into a very general application of the use of isolated enzymes for the replication of biologically active DNA of any kind. That means that the copied material, the newly synthesized material, will have the same kind of biological activity that was represented in the specimen of DNA originally placed in the test tube.

"Creation" or Replication of Life. Many of the discussions center on this point, quibbling at the phrase "creation of life" (you know, is it really "living"?). Kornberg replied to that by saying that he had never given that question very much thought; there wasn't any great operational significance in whether one defined viral DNA as living or not, and I know this is correct. When he says he's not given much thought to it, I don't mean that he's thoughtless about it. Rather it is essentially a matter of taste at what level of complexity one wishes to draw the line in the definition of a living organism; my tastes happen to agree with his. I would have no hesitation whatever in describing a virus as a living organism, one that has very special nutritional requirements and only functions by being able to subvert the metabolism of another living cell that has a higher degree of autonomy.

However, I think there is a more appropriate point on which to quibble with those newspaper headlines. The title of Kornberg's paper in the proceedings of the National Academy of Sciences is not "Creation of Life in the Test Tube," but "Enzymatic Replication of the DNA of Bacteria Phage phi-X-174." The quibble is perhaps on the expression "creation" because the appropriate work is "replication." DNA has been put into the test tube, and the purpose of these investigations has been to discover the mechanism whereby DNA is replicated inside of living cells. Considerable insight had been achieved into this question by the investigations of 10 years ago. But at the time it was thought that the answer was in hand, whereas the crucial test was "Can you make an effective replication of DNA information in a purified system, in the test tube, using the components that you think account for it inside the cell?" That didn't work. As long as it didn't, one was entitled to be quite skeptical about whether one had indeed accounted for the mechanism whereby DNA is replicated inside the cell. We now know that there was a very important missing ingredient: the DNA-polymerase. This enzyme that could be extracted and would accomplish the copying job certainly is the crux of the matter. However, without the ligase and without certain other conditions, it is unable to function effectively in completing the cycle of replication of that information. I don't need to belabor the importance of this kind of insight in the most fundamental of biological mechanisms. There is now an enzymatic explanation for the way in which genetic information is copied from one generation to another. On the other hand, it is not quite appropriate to call it a creation. It is a replication. It is similar to the way in which the printing press works when it's making a number of copies of Shakespeare's sonnets. It is not the creation of those sonnets. The poetry in our analogy comes from the process of evolution during a period of a few billion years, to reach where all of us are today.

Khorana's Approach. What are the prospects for a creation in the more restricted sense that I have just discussed? The most active investigations along these lines are being pursued in the laboratories of Gobind Khorana at the University of Wisconsin in Madison.[1] He is an organic chemist, whereas Kornberg is an enzymologist. Khorana has been working on techniques for dealing with nucleic acids as organic molecules. He works with nonaqueous systems, with organic reagents, with the painful and plodding adding of one unit at a time to those long chains. When Khorana makes a polynucleotide, he is "creating" it because he starts out with a statement of the message that he wants to see represented in a DNA-like molecule. By dint of an enormous tour-de-force he ends up getting it. Now, we have a long way to go before the University of Wisconsin work can be regarded as a model of the creation of a gene. The longest chains that he has published on so far are about 30 units long, whereas the ones that the enzyme replicates many times a minute, are several thousand units long. But he is getting there.

---

[1] Nobel Laureate awarded December 1968.

Now, in fact, the smallest nucleic acids that have a recognizable biological activity, that have a specificity that enables one to do a really interesting experiment with them involving a role in life, are about 80 units long. These are the nucleic acids, called transfer RNA, that are involved in transferring amino acid residues to the growing protein chain. They are not quite typical genes in the kind of specificity that they have, but they do represent a very attractive way station to motivate the work of the organic chemical laboratory. They help to prove that you can do it, that is to test out the precision with which you have copied the information that was in a certain sentence, in a certain book, in a certain encyclopedia, which is the blueprint of a large organism. And by being one of the smallest sentences in that book, and by having a specific biological activity, they represent something more nearly feasible than some of the other tasks that you might set yourself to.

Khorana has divided the transfer RNA for phenylalanine into four parts, and he has set up four factories to attempt the assembly of the nucleotides needed for each of those four parts. He has worked out the methods with which those four parts can be grafted together; so I have no doubt that within the next few years he will have accomplished in vitro the organic chemical creation of a biological nucleic acid. This is perhaps a fifth of the size of the stretch of DNA that would be necessary to make a respectable gene, and those problems grow geometrically with the size of the product you are trying to make.

One might ask, "Is that creation?" Khorana has used not an existing DNA or RNA molecule and copied it with an enzyme, but he has gone through another step of abstraction. He has done a job similar to that which Holley was the first to report on, in working out the exact nucleotide sequence of a specimen of transfer RNA.[2] Then he wrote that down in a book, and now he is going to copy what he wrote down in a book rather than copy the original molecule. He is going to proceed by design rather than by direct impression. The contrast is a bit like getting one of Shakespeare's handwritten sonnets and using a photographic method to copy it in its original form, as opposed to having someone recite it over the radio as you write it down and then attempt to write or type it out again before putting it through the printing press. It will have been a symbolic transformation of the information that was in the original message, preceding the step of the organic chemist in assembling the characters of the message and putting the sentence together again.

That quibble, I think, is a reasonable one and should be thought about. The step of creation will arrive because once a chemist knows how to assemble *any* meaningful sentence, he can then really start creating. He can start putting together his own words, his own characters, and his own sentences. Most of them are going to be garbage in terms of some biological activity; even at the level of the transfer RNA there are some 4^{80} possible combinations. That

[2] Nobel Laureate awarded December 1968.

number is rather larger than the size of the universe expressed in electron diameters, so it is not likely he'll get around to making all of them. But he will make a few, and I have no doubt that Khorana himself, one of these days, is going to create another transfer RNA molecule, a nucleic acid molecule that will have interesting properties, different from those of the naturally occurring material.[3] He will have studied nature closely; he will perhaps not like the sound of what he heard in the original poet's rendition of the sonnet and he will try to make up another one that does, perhaps, some closely related job.

This clearly is a creation; it is based on some insight into the way that nature has worked, but we are certainly on the way there for messages of this size. From this one can guess that some brave soul is going to bludgeon the federal government into giving him $4 or $5 billion in order to proceed with the task of synthesizing an even larger DNA sequence. Now, the job of manufacturing a polynucleotide sequence of the kind that we are describing, with the necessary precision at every step of the line (and you can't tolerate a 1 per cent error at each step or you'll have absolute garbage before you've gone 10 to 20 steps along), is a little bit like deciding that if I have a pick and shovel I know how to dig a hole, and therefore I'm going to start making the Grand Canyon. In principle that is absolutely right; but how many engineers are going to be motivated to want to participate in this particular kind of a program? I really have some doubts about it. I think it is necessary to parody this because I think there has been a lack of perspective about the actual significance of the results that have been achieved, which tends to obscure what really is going to happen.

Another analogy that I could give to the story would be to remark that I can still recall a headline announcement "Alchemists' Dream Achieved—Gold Synthesized in the Laboratory." That had something to do with the fact that a few atoms of the element gold had been fabricated in the cyclotron and someone had actually managed to produce enough of one of the radioactive isotopes of gold to be quite sure that that was his product so that he could justify the statement "creation of new forms of matter" as a legitimate headline. I don't think if that headline were to appear today it would allay the concerns of the United States government about our gold reserves. In principle, we could solve the problem of our external balance of payments by diverting our internal economic resources to the manufacture of gold by nucleonic methods, but I don't think that is likely to happen. It is extraordinarily important to distinguish the important leaps of insight that are represented by the things that can be done in principle because of the kind of understanding that they give. We have learned a great deal about gold by having manufactured it in the cyclotron and about the kind of practical utilities that are represented by saying, "This is the way that we're going to go about solving this or that technical problem."

---

[3]Chemical modification of existing RNA molecules have recently been studied and have interesting properties.

Changing Man

Theodosius Dobzhansky

Optimists believe that ours is the best of all possible worlds. And pessimists are those who fear that the optimists are right. This is a flippant, but valid, statement of a truth. Optimism is often a result of ignorance of cold and unwelcome realities. There is, however, another kind of optimism, which is pessimism surmounted. The world is far from perfect, but it is not unalterable. I am tempted to call this evolutionary optimism.

The clash of optimistic and pessimistic world views is nowhere more poignant than in the evaluation of the prospects of mankind. Human nature has flaws too evident to be shrugged off. What is the outlook for the future? Prophets of doom are not in short supply, and they receive strong support from some eminent biologists. It is alleged that the genetic endowment of the human species is deteriorating. The evolutionary future is consequently bleak. A catastrophe may be avoided only by drastic measures, applied without delay. Regardless of whether they may be effective biologically, these measures are not likely to gain rapid acceptance psychologically and sociologically.

Mankind is exposed to some biological dangers. Ways to avoid them, or to minimize their effects, must be found. Yet cogent arguments may be adduced in favor of the view that man's evolution is still ascending, rather than going downhill. Rapid advances of the biological sciences, though not in themselves sufficient to solve all problems, may make evolutionary progress easier to achieve.

Darwin versus Copernicus

Two crucial discoveries were decisive in shaping modern man's image of himself. The names of Copernicus and Darwin stand as symbols of these

T. Dobzhansky, "Changing Man," *Science* Vol. 155, No. 3761, January 27, 1967, pp. 409-415. Copyright 1967 by the American Association for the Advancement of Science. Reprinted by permission of the author and publisher. The author is professor of biology and genetics at Rockefeller University, New York, N.Y. 10021. This article is the basis of a lecture presented 26 December 1966 at the Washington meeting of the AAAS.

discoveries, although others anticipated them or contributed to their validation. It is often held that the Copernican and Darwinian ideas make a pessimistic world view compelling. I wish to argue that this is a mistaken judgment. The post-Copernican and post-Darwinian man would not like to find himself back in the childhood of the pre-Darwinian and pre-Copernican world. Childhood memories may be pleasing indeed, but we have simply outgrown them.

Man is not the center of a snug little world created expressly to serve as his abode. Our earth is a second-rate planet, and our sun is only one among myriads of suns in the universe. This universe runs according to precise and inexorable laws; the more comprehensible of these were discovered by Newton, while Einstein and other modern physicists and cosmologists added some less comprehensible ones. And finally, man himself is very much a newcomer; he inhabits a vanishingly small bit of the cosmic scene, for at most 2 million years, while the scene itself is somewhere between 5 and 10 billion years old.

Man's smallness and recency are undeniable. Are these valid grounds for regarding him as no more than a bit of slime with a capacity for self-deception? This seems to be the opinion of some avant-garde writers, painters, and musicians. Even a theologian has recently published a book entitled *The Lord of the Absurd*. What these sages overlook can be summed up in a single word: evolution.

An evolutionist need not be a Pangloss or a Pollyanna; he may recognize that the absurd is widespread. Evolution is not predestined to promote always the good and the beautiful. Nevertheless, evolution is a process which has produced life from non-life, which has brought forth man from an animal, and which may conceivably continue doing remarkable things in the future. In giving rise to man, the evolutionary process has, apparently for the first and only time in the history of the Cosmos, become conscious of itself. This opens at least a possibility that evolution may some day be directed by man, and that the prevalence of the absurd may be cut down.

Evolution comprises all the stages of the development of the universe: the cosmic, biological, and human or cultural developments. Attempts to restrict the concept of evolution to biology are gratuitous. Life is a product of the evolution of inorganic nature, and man is a product of the evolution of life. In a sense, the discovery of evolution reinstates man in the station from which he was demoted by Copernicus: man is again the center of the stage—at least of the planetary, and quite possibly of the cosmic, one. Most important of all, the stage and the actor not only have evolved but are evolving.

Man Continues to Evolve

Mankind evolves. For perhaps as long as 100,000 years the most rapid and radical changes have been cultural ones. Man is a product of his cultural development as well as of his biological nature. The preponderance of cultural over biological evolution will continue or increase in the foreseeable future. We would not wish this to be otherwise; adaptation to the environment by culture is more rapid and efficient than biological adaptation. Moreover, control of the cultural evolution is achievable probably more easily than control of the biological evolution.

And yet mankind has not ceased to evolve biologically. Cultural evolution is superimposed on, it has not supplanted, biological evolution. The claim that something called "man's intrinsic intelligence" has remained constant at least since Paleolithic times is most likely erroneous, although a proof one way or the other is difficult to come by. The cranial capacity of the Neanderthal race of *Homo sapiens* was, on the average, equal to or even greater than that in modern man. Cranial capacity and brain size are, however, not reliable criteria of "intelligence" or intellectual abilities of any kind. The painters of the Altamira and Lascaux caves may have been no less talented than Picasso, and the intellectual powers of Aristotle were at least equal to those of the Nobel prize winners. But it does not follow that all the contemporaries of Aristotle were his intellectual equals, or that all inhabitants of Altamira could paint equally well.

The argument in favor of the view that mankind continues to evolve biologically is deductive and inferential, but it seems strong enough nevertheless. There are but two necessary and sufficient conditions for the occurrence of evolutionary change. First, there must be available genetic variance affecting different traits, and, second, this variance must be relevant to Darwinian fitness in different available environments which change in time and in space. Both conditions are fulfilled: many human traits, including intellectual and behavioral ones, are genetically variable; at least some of these variations affect the chances of survival and of reproductive success; and human environments, most of all cultural environments, are changing constantly and rapidly. Cultural and biological evolution are linked by feedback relationships (1).

If, then, mankind changes biologically, are the changes beneficial or detrimental? Cassandras prophesying doom attract public attention more easily than do those who hold the unspectacular view that a disaster is not around the corner, and not even inevitable. The alarmist argument is by now so well known that a brief summary will suffice here. Mankind's distinctive attributes and capacities arose in evolution under the control of natural selection. Natural selection makes the evolutionary changes usually adaptive in the environments in which the species lives. It fosters the gene patterns which enable their carriers to survive and to reproduce, and it fails to perpetuate the patterns less well attuned to the demands of the environments. Genetic variants of low fitness constantly arise in all living species, owing to the pressure of mutation. Some generations may elapse between the origin of a harmful mutant by mutation and its elimination by selection; therefore, the populations of every living species carry genetic loads of relatively unfit or downright inviable or sterile variants.

Mankind, like any other biological species, has carried a genetic load since the dawn of time. It is claimed, however, that man's genetic load grows rapidly heavier. Civilized living, technology, medicine, help to the handicapped, protection of the weak—all these factors are blamed for the relaxation of natural selection. Pessimists go even further and declare that natural selection and civilization are incompatible. On the other hand, the mutation rates have, if anything, increased, owing to radiation exposure and to chemical mutagens. A vision is thus conjured of mankind's degenerating rather than improving biologically, of his sliding downhill rather than rising upward.

Negative Eugenics

If, in developing culture and civilization, mankind has somehow managed to imperil its genetic endowment, the situation can be corrected only by more and better civilization. Even if one does not accept the pessimist rendering of the situation as accurate, one may well ponder the ways and means for possible control of the evolution of the human species. Any deliberate measures to improve genetic endowment belong to the province of eugenics. Euthenics and "euphenics" (2, 3) are concerned with amelioration of the manifestation of existing genetic endowments. Eugenics, euthenics, and euphenics are complementary rather than alternative. It is in the highest degree unlikely that an "optimal" genotype will be found that could produce excellent physical and mental health and vigor in all environments, and equally unlikely that environments could be devised to elicit satisfactory products from any and all genotypes. Environmental engineering, education, and social betterment are not made any less necessary by eugenics; the converse is also true, at least in the long run.

There is no agreement as to which eugenical measures may be effective and, at the same time, in good taste and ethically acceptable. The measures proposed are roughly classifiable into negative and positive, and range from persuasion to coercion. Nobody (outside Hitler's Germany) advocates killing the weak and the defective. Sterilization, optional or mandatory, is legal in some states. There is nothing cruel about eugenic sterilization, and, hedged with proper medical and legal guarantees, it may be acceptable in some circumstances. Its overall effectiveness in reducing the load of major genetic defects in the human species is, however, inadequate. Recessive defects are carried mainly in heterozygotes and escape detection, while the dominant ones are due mostly to new mutations.

I am inclined to favor a more tender-minded form of negative eugenics, which is the spread of elementary knowledge of genetics and of genetic counseling. The carriers of genetic defects must be assured that their condition is not their fault, or sin, or shame. They may also be informed of the probable consequences of their begetting children. It is perhaps not silly optimism to hope that some of such prospective parents would draw the proper conclusions from the information made available to them. Nobody is more competent than the carrier of a genetic defect to decide whether he wants to pass it on to descendants.

Positive Eugenics

Some eugenicists are skeptical about the good judgment of their fellow men. Indeed, the carriers of certain genetic defects are patently incapable of exercising such judgment. One may also feel that negative eugenics is not enough. In addition to keeping down the incidence of major genetic defects, one may aspire to attain a vastly more ambitious goal—no less a goal than to reform the genetic endowment of the human species and to engineer the genetic foundation of a New Man. This is positive eugenics. The difficulty of this enterprise should be obvious. There is, unfortunately, more than a grain of truth in Lederberg's remark (3) that "positive eugenic programs can be defended roughly in proportion to their ineffectiveness."

Perhaps the boldest of all such programs, one which certainly would be effective if it were put into operation, has been outlined in numerous popular and technical writings of H. J. Muller and Sir Julian Huxley (see, for example, 4 and 5). We shall restrict our consideration here to the first stage of the Muller-Huxley program, which is relatively "modest" and would seem to be technically feasible at present.

This first stage relies on a "germinal choice" of the male parents. Semen of selected donors (or of all healthy males) is to be collected and stored at low temperatures in "sperm banks." After a time sufficient for reaching a dispassionate judgment concerning the biological and other virtues of the donors, the sperm will be withdrawn from the banks, unfrozen, and utilized for artificial insemination of as many women as the supply permits, or of as many as may wish to have it. The application of germinal choice may, however, start on a relatively less ambitious scale immediately. Artificial insemination of women whose husbands produce no functional sperm is practiced at present, the donors not being selected with genetic considerations in view and remaining unknown to the prospective mothers. Muller gives 10,000 per year as an estimate of the number of artificial inseminations in the United States. Make the selection eugenically motivated and you have an entering wedge for the more ambitious schemes.

Many objections can be made to Muller-Huxley eugenical schemes. Not all the objections are, of course, equally serious. The recommended techniques will be branded by some as "unnatural," with as much or as little justification as in the case of family planning. In my opinion there is nothing wrong in this "unnaturalness," or in letting women who must or who wish to produce children by artificial insemination have a choice of sperm donors, and thus of the biological father of their offspring. Keeping human semen for long periods in deep-frozen state is not to be accepted so lightly, since there is no evidence to rule out the possibility that such treatment may cause mutational changes, and thus increase rather than decrease man's genetic load.

What Should the Selection Select?

Even if we had safe and dependable *means* of selection, very difficult questions would arise regarding the *ends*. As with other ambitious schemes of positive eugenics, that of Muller and Huxley is likely to be shipwrecked on attempts to decide what sort of man is the ideal to be striven for. Does anyone know what will be best for mankind centuries or millennia hence? Muller wants man to be intelligent, compassionate, altruistic. This is unexceptionable, but shall we endeavor to breed a race of brawny athletes, or brainy intellectuals, or sensitive esthetes, or some combination of these qualities, or a population containing certain proportions of each kind? Negative eugenics meets fewer difficulties in this regard. It is easier to reach a consensus on which defects man would be better off without than on which traits and abilities he should possess.

In general, dominant defects give rise to the fewest doubts. One can hardly imagine circumstances in which such disorders as dominant muscular distrophy, aniridia, epiloia, multiple polyposis of the colon, fragile bones, and neurofibromatosis may be useful. However, these conditions lower the fitness of their carriers so greatly that almost the only measure to be considered for their control is minimization of the rates of their origin by mutation. With recessive defects the thorny question has to be faced of whether they are maintained in populations only by the mutation pressure or also by increased fitness of the heterozygous carriers—that is, by hybrid vigor, or heterosis.

The classic example of this sort is, of course, the sickle-cell condition, which is almost completely lethal when homozygous but which confers some protection against falciparum malaria when heterozygous. Increased Darwinian fitness of heterozygotes appears, however, in most unexpected places: Myrianthopoulos and Aronson (6) have published fairly convincing evidence that the heterozygous carriers of the Tay-Sachs disease (infantile amaurotic idiocy) may show a reproductive advantage of about 6 percent in Ashkenazic Jewish populations. How widespread such situations are in human, or for that matter in *Drosophila* populations is one of the outstanding still-unsolved problems of population genetics. Some authorities have declared them to be negligibly rare, but this only shows a cavalier disregard of increasingly substantial evidence to the contrary.

The average and above-average fitness and vigor in populations of sexually reproducing organisms, including man, are quite possibly the result of multiple heterozygosis for many genetic variants which decrease the fitness in homozygous condition. This does not quite mean that we should perpetuate recessive hereditary diseases in human populations, even if they do have heterozygous heterotic effects. It means that the problem is too complex for a simple-minded approach. The ideal of mankind free of all forms of genetic loads may be not only unattainable but also unacceptable, owing to the adaptively ambivalent effects of some of these load forms. Such a load-free mankind may turn out to be a dull stereotype, with no particular physical or mental vigor. At present we simply do not know enough to be sure either way, and more research, both in man and with animals, is needed.

Possible Antagonisms of Old and New Adaptations

Civilization has often been blamed for diverting human biological evolution from its "natural" and beneficial to its present and allegedly pernicious course.

Pampered by civilization, medicine, technology, and growing security, the human species, or at least the pampered part of it, is losing its physical and mental stamina and its resistance to environmental shocks of various kinds. It is becoming flabby and vulnerable. It is indeed possible, though not proved, that even if we were brought up to lead the life of our Paleolithic ancestors we would be less efficient in their environments than they were.

Is this, however, a terrible loss? Except for "roughing it" during summer vacations, most of mankind, or at least the inhabitants of technologically advanced countries, rarely face these ancient environments; nor, barring a breakdown of civilization, are our descendants likely to face them. What is needed is, rather, the strength and energy to face the ever more complex, and chiefly psychological, problems with which our industrial civilization is confronting us. If this strength and the primitive ruggedness were genetically one and the same, or if they were compatible, we would of course like to have them both. The process of adaptation by natural selection frequently works out, however, in such ways that a high adaptedness in some respects has to be paid for by a lesser development of other adaptive traits, or even by toleration of some downright harmful features. This is a part of what is sometimes referred to as the opportunism of natural selection. The Darwinian fitness is a property of a genotype as a whole, in relation to its environment, and not of this or that genetic factor in isolation. Now, if forced to make a choice, we must certainly prefer an adaptedness to the present environments, not to those long defunct.

The choice may be clearest in the case of resistance to certain diseases. As pointed out first, apparently, by Haldane (7), until very recent times, selection for resistances to multifarious infectious diseases was probably one of the major factors in the biological evolution of man. With the infections more and more under control, this selection is relaxed and possibly reversed. Genetic resistance to a disease may have to be paid for by disadvantages in other respects. The sickle-cell condition mentioned above is a paradigm: a resistance of the population to falciparum malaria is bought by the death of the anemic homozygotes, and possibly by a slight anemia in the heterozygotes as well. When a population learns to combat malaria by mosquito control or by chemotherapy, must it strive at all costs to retain the genetic resistance as well? The answer evidently depends on one's confidence that our civilization is here to stay. Although Dubos (8) has, with good reason, warned against overconfidence in this matter, it is a fact that an increasingly large part of mankind now lives in environments in which infectious diseases and old environmental hazards are being gradually brought under control. For this part of mankind, a source of genetic improvement may be, paradoxical as this may sound, a weakening or elimination of resistances to environmental hazards, resistances which were indispensable to our not-so-remote ancestors.

Euthenics, Euphenics, and Algeny

There is considerable distrust of eugenics, especially among some social scientists. The reason is that the name, though of course not the substance, of eugenics has often been exploited by those who want to obstruct social change. They claim that social ills stem from bad heredity and cannot be corrected by anything in the environment (9). The fallacy is evident. No heredity is "good" regardless of the environment. Genetic improvements are worthless if the improved genotypes have no access to environments which elicit their strong and inhibit their weak qualities. Man adapts his environments to his genes more often than he adapts his genes to his environments. Euthenics—environmental engineering, ranging all the way from control of infectious diseases to education and to social and political reforms—is not an alternative but is an indispensable partner of eugenics. Osborn (10) has pointed out not only the need of this partnership but also the possibility that positive eugenics—selection of superior genetic endowments—may result from properly directed social change. I return to this idea below.

Lederberg (2) has suggested "euphenics" as a designation for that part of euthenics concerned particularly with "the engineering of human development." Euphenics can compensate for, or redeem, certain genetic defects. The simplest example is the provision of eyeglasses to those with weak eyesight. Some forms of weak eyesight are genetically conditioned. There exist treatments to relieve the symptoms of, and in this sense to "cure," certain genetic defects. Among these defects are some otherwise fatal, or at any rate crippling, hereditary diseases. Galactosemia is an example. Children homozygous for a certain recessive gene lack an enzyme that converts the milk sugar galactose into glucose; if the condition is discovered sufficiently early, galactose-free diets permit fairly normal development; otherwise the homozygotes suffer severe liver damage and mental retardation. There is every reason to hope that treatments will be discovered for many other genetic defects.

Spectacular achievements of molecular biology have raised the hopes for euphenics very high. According to Lederberg (2), we are witnessing a "medical revolution" which may lead to the invention of such new techniques as construction of artificial organs; synthesis of hormones, enzymes, antigens, and structural proteins; and breeding of suitable laboratory animals to serve as donors of organs or tissues that could be transplanted to human bodies. Finally, he thinks, we may come to "more confidently design genotypically programmed reactions, in place of evolutionary pressures, and search for further innovations."

Distant vistas equally alluring seem to be opened by the discovery that the functioning of genes or gene groups in the development of the individual is subject to repression or to stimulation at the intracellular level. If one learns the art of "switching" on or off at will the action of desirable and undesirable genes at specified periods of development, the possibilities of controlling realization of the heredity in the treated individuals would be impressive indeed (11).

Still another array of conceivable techniques is called genetic engineering by Tatum (12), genetic surgery by Muller (4), and "algeny" by Lederberg (3). This concept is the altering of genes in the body cells or in germinal tissues, or the introduction of desired genes from outside. In Luria's words (13), "If the code sequence of a given gene can be deciphered, it might then be feasible to synthesize in vitro a segment of DNA with a desired 'improved' sequence, but with enough similarity to the recognized sequence of the gene in question to be able to replace it in the genetic apparatus." These techniques would, then, straddle the dividing line between euphenics and eugenics and would represent an instrument of scarcely imaginable power for guidance of the evolution of the human species.

Is this "Brave New World" of algeny more than a daydream? Some biologists talk and write about it as though all the wonderful techniques are as good as ready to be applied tomorrow. It would be very unwise for a scientist to maintain that some inventions (short of *perpetuum mobile*) will never be made. Such claims have too often been belied by subsequent discoveries. It is permissible, however, to doubt that genetic surgery would easily solve all problems. I am forced to agree with Muller (4) that, even if the needed techniques were available, "it would be a task of transcendent magnitude, intricacy, and reconditeness to do all this by genetic surgery for any one individual. Moreover, every individual to be operated on would present his own unique complex of labyrinthine problems. . . ."

Translation of the existing genetic knowledge into social practice may give man considerable powers to make Man. New discoveries will doubtless enhance these powers incalculably. This obviously raises many thorny questions which cannot be dealt with here. A biologist should have the humility to recognize that these questions are more sociological than biological. Are we to have, in place of Plato's philosopher-king a geneticist-king? And who will be the president of the National Sperm Bank and of the National DNA Bank? What checks and balances are to be imposed on the genetic legislative and the genetic executive powers? Who will guard the guardians?

Genetic Consequences of Equality of Opportunity

While eugenic and euphenic projects are being framed, evolutionary changes, cultural and biological, are going on. On the biological side, insufficient attention has been given to these changes. They are discussed mostly from the point of view of the alleged relaxation or stoppage of natural selection, which is at most a half truth. Natural selection is operating, although in modern man it does not always select the same gene patterns which it selected in the past. Its operation is conditioned by the tremendous social changes which are taking place throughout the world. We may consider here briefly the genetic effects of social mobility and of equality, versus inequality, of opportunity, a topic which I discussed in *Science* earlier from a different point of view (14).

None other than President Dwight D. Eisenhower proclaimed that "humanity shall one day achieve the unity of freedom to which all men have aspired from the dawn of time." Herbert J. Muller, the historian, comments (15) that this idea "truly reflects the history of Western civilization, especially in recent centuries. It points to a significant change in the basic mentality of ordinary men, or to some extent their 'nature.' Today it reflects the extraordinary stir all over the world, as 'backward' peoples are beginning to realize possibilities and demand opportunities that through ages they scarcely dreamed of. With this stir the revolutionary doctrine of the Rights of Men . . . has swept the world as has no other idea, or no religion. If it is still widely violated in practice, it is now universally accepted in theory as the bill of "human rights' affirmed by the United Nations."

In caste and rigid class societies the ascription of status and the assignment of occupation is made according to the social position of the parents. In-group marriage maintains the genetic as well as the social stratification. The explicit, or more often implied, justification is the belief that the different estates concentrate genes for different aptitudes. The truth of this is questionable. What is, however, undeniable is the fact that individual differences within each class have remained greater than any possible average differences between the classes. This is true even of the most rigorous and most enduring caste system, that of India.

The transition, taking place at different rates in different countries, from closed to open class systems increases the social mobility and the consequent gene exchange. As equality of opportunity is approached, will the significance of the genetic differences among men be reduced to naught? The truth is the exact opposite. Equality of opportunity should not be confused with genetic identity. More than one eminent biologist has been hailed in the popular press for having discovered that "men are not equal," when all he wanted to say was that men are not genetically alike. Equality and inequality are social, identity and diversity biological, phenomena. Equality may be bestowed upon diverse people, and identical twins may have unequal opportunities.

Social mobility does not lead to genetic uniformity. Neither does interracial marriage. The genetic differences between populations are transmuted into genetic variability of individuals. The variety of genetic constitutions increases. The greater the diversity of environments—of social, economic, and educational opportunities—the fewer the genetic differences manifested in the observable variety of personalities and abilities. In exactly uniform environments all differences would be genetically determined. Environmental uniformity is a theoretically thinkable condition, not realized anywhere. The existing societal arrangements form a spectrum, ranging from very restricted to relatively free social mobility and from inequality to equality of opportunity. The trend is, however, toward the equality side; this is acknowledged by those who welcome this trend and by those who oppose it.

If all humans had the same genetic endowment, if man were born a *tabula rasa*, if every individual had the same potentialities for intelligence, for special abilities, and for all other socially significant traits, then the differences between most rigid caste societies and societies providing equality for their members would be inconsequential. With "equality," different occupations could be distributed by lot, or according to the day of the week on which one was born. Equality is invaluable because it enables people to be different and to follow their diverse inclinations.

The genetic variety of capacities and aptitudes is partly concealed and smothered under rigid caste and class systems. A son of a peasant, of an artisan, or of a musician is encouraged, and sometimes even pressured or forced, to become a peasant, an artisan, or a musician, as the case may be. If his tastes or abilities, no matter whether genetically conditioned or otherwise, make him attracted to or suited for a social role or a profession different from that of his parents, he may encounter a resistance severe enough to frustrate his plans. The situation would be equally unpropitious for individual self-actualization in a society so compulsively egalitarian that it would insist on reducing the diversity of abilities to a uniform level by differential treatment and education. It is in open class societies that genetic diversity can be most fully utilized for social good.

According to Gardner (16), "our devotion to equality does not ignore the fact that individuals differ greatly in their talents and motivations. It simply asserts that each should be enabled to develop to the full, in his own style and to his own limit. Each is worthy of respect as a human being. This means that there must be diverse programs within the educational system to take care of the diversity of individuals; and that each of these programs should be accorded respect and stature." I believe that Gardner gives here what amounts to a concise statement of a program of both positive eugenics and euthenics.

Assortative Mating

Equality of opportunity and social mobility are not unidimensional but are pluridimensional. They should not be envisaged solely in terms of individuals becoming members of wealthier classes or of less-privileged groups. The diversity of human abilities cannot be accommodated in so simple a model. What is significant to a biologist is the fact that people not only rise upward or fall downward on a scale of social status and emoluments but also choose among a great variety of occupations. Man's outstanding evolutionary adaptation is his trainability and behavioral plasticity; most people can become competent in any one of many vocations and employments. This does not preclude the existence of genetically conditioned aptitudes, preferences, and special abilities. And it is a reasonable generalization to say that people do best in what they find congenial and where they feel they are most likely to pass muster. A practical recognition of the diversity of abilities can be seen in the fact that between 150 and 250 million standardized aptitude tests of various types are now administered per year in the United States (17). Although the usefulness of these tests has been questioned, they are apparently here to stay. The Russian poet Voznesensky has been quoted as follows: "Talent cannot be grown like potatoes. It is a national resource, like radium deposits, healing springs, or autumn in Sigulda [a resort]."

Given something close to freedom of social mobility, the most significant genetic consequence of the occupational diversity is the fact that it almost necessarily leads to assortative mating. An old saying has it that "birds of a feather flock together." A mathematician may marry a ballerina, and a boxer a philosopher. Yet mathematicians meet mathematicians and members of their families on the average more often than they meet ballerinas, and boxers do not as a rule spend their leisure time in the company of philosophers. Positive assortative mating, marriage of persons with similar genetic abilities and preferences, has greater freedom to operate in open class societies than in societies with rigid class boundaries. This is a matter of probability, not an inflexible rule. Assortative mating operates more freely among people of higher than of lower educational levels, and more freely in urban than in rural communities.

The genetic consequences of assortative mating in man have not been adequately studied [Spuhler (18) is one of the pioneers in this field]. It does not of itself change the gene frequencies in the populations in which it occurs. It may nevertheless be a genetic and evolutionary agent of appreciable importance. Spassky and I (19) made experiments, with Drosophila flies, which may simulate the processes of assortative mating in human societies. The experimental results show that genetically different moieties may differentiate out of a formerly random breeding, but, of course, genetically variable, population. In these experiments the gene exchange between the moieties in a measure simulates the social mobility in human populations. Without going into technical details, one may state that the assortative mating, although it created no new genes, permitted the formation of gene combinations which would have been unlikely to arise in a randomly breeding population.

Equality of opportunity and assortative mating are not alternatives to other eugenics programs. As pointed out particularly by Osborn (10), they are, rather, necessary conditions for the success of such programs. Equality of opportunity promotes formation of professional and occupational aggregations of people; the genes which predispose for, or enhance the chances of, success in certain lines of endeavor may be concentrated in such aggregations. And yet such aggregations have, in at least their biological aspects, no resemblance to traditional class societies. They promote, rather than impede, social mobility, and make it genetically meaningful. They further positive assortative mating, and thus increase the likelihood that gene combinations propitious for particular kinds of achievement will appear.

Conclusions

The human condition is changing both culturally and biologically. Although the cultural evolution overshadows the biological, the two are connected by feedback relationships; culture has a biological foundation. Natural selection continues to operate in modern mankind, but its action ought to be supplemented by artificial selection. The problems of the management of human evolution are, however, as much sociological as they are biological. The success of any eugenical program depends on the creation of favorable conditions for human development and self-actualization. In particular, the urgency of the problem of uncontrolled overpopulation exceeds at present that of genetic improvement. Contrary to the alarmist views of some biologists, the evolutionary perspectives for the human species may be regarded as favorable, although, of course, subject to improvement. Man should be the maker of his history, including his evolutionary history. The trend toward increasing social mobility and equality of opportunity may have desirable genetic effects because of the positive assortative mating which it encourages. It makes possible the realization of many hitherto concealed genetically conditioned talents and aptitudes. Rapid progress of both molecular and organismic, Cartesian and Darwinian, biology gives hope of development of new and powerful methods of genetic engineering, control of gene action, betterment of the environment, and improved understanding of the evolutionary processes in the living world, including man.

References and Notes

1. T. Dobzhansky, *Mankind Evolving* (Yale Univ. Press, New Haven, Conn., 1962).

2. J. Lederberg, in *Man and His Future,* G. Wolstenholme, Ed. (Little, Brown, Boston, 1963).

3. _____, *Amer. Naturalist* **100**, 519 (1966).

4. H. J. Muller, *Amer. J. Human Genet.* 2, 111 (1950); *Perspectives Biol. Med.* 3, 1 (1959); in *Man and His Future,* G. Wolstenholme, Ed. (Little, Brown, Boston, 1963); in *The Control of Human Heredity and Evolution,* T. M. Sonneborn, Ed. (Macmillan, New York, 1965).

5. _____, an address given at the 3rd International Congress on Human Genetics; J. Huxley. *The Humanist Frames* (Allen & Unwin, London, 1961); *Eugenics in Evolutionary Perspectives* (Eugenics Society, London, 1962); *Essays of a Humanist* (Harper & Row, New York, 1964).

6. N. C. Myrianthopoulos and S. M. Aronson, *Amer. J. Human Genet.* **18**, 313 (1966)

7. J. B. S. Haldane, *Ric. Sci. Suppl.* **19**, 68 (1949).

8. R. Dubos, *Man Adapting* (Yale Univ. Press, New Haven, Conn. 1965).

9. M. H. Haller, *Eugenics, Hereditarian Attitudes in American Thought* (Rutgers Univ. Press, New Brunswick, N.J., 1963).

10. F. Osborn, *Preface to Eugenics* (Harper, New York, 1951).

11. I am obligated to Professor A. E. Mirsky for pointing out to me some of these possibilities.

12. E. L. Tatum, in *The Control of Human Heredity and Evolution,* T. M. Sonneborn, Ed. (Macmillan, New York, 1965).

13. S. E. Luria, *ibid.*

14. T. Dobzhansky, *Science* **126**, 191 (1957); *ibid.* **137**, 112 (1962).

15. H. J. Muller, *Freedom in the Modern World* (Harper & Row, New York, 1966).

16. J. W. Gardner, in *Goals for Americans* (Prentice-Hall, Englewood Cliffs, N.J., 1960), p. 81.

17. D. A. Goslin, *The Search for Ability* (Russell Sage Foundation, New York, 1963).

18. J. N. Spuhler, in *The Use of Vital and Health Statistics for Genetic and Radiation Studies* (United Nations, New York, 1962), p. 241.

19. T. Dobzhansky and B. Spassky, *Proc. Roy. Soc. London Ser. B,* in press.

20. M. Lerner, *America as a Civilization* (Simon & Schuster, New York, 1957).

21. Variants of parts of this article have been included in lectures given at the University of Maryland, at Wittenberg University, at the New York Academy of Medicine, and at a conference on Biology and Behavior Genetics held under the auspices of the Russell Sage Foundation, the Rockefeller University, and the Social Science Research Council. I am greatly obliged to the colleagues who made suggestions, comments, and criticisms of the ideas and arguments presented.

Population and Panaceas:
A Technological Perspective

Paul R. Ehrlich and John P. Holdren

Today more than one billion human beings are either undernourished or malnourished, and the human population is growing at a rate of 2% per year. The existing and impending crises in human nutrition and living conditions are well-documented but not widely understood. In particular, there is a tendency among the public, nurtured on Sunday-supplement conceptions of technology, to believe that science has the situation well in hand—that farming the sea and the tropics, irrigating the deserts, and generating cheap nuclear power in abundance hold the key to swift and certain solution of the problem. To espouse this belief is to misjudge the present severity of the situation, the disparate time scales on which technological progress and population growth operate, and the vast complexity of the problems beyond mere food production posed by population pressures. Unfortunately, scientists and engineers have themselves often added to the confusion by failing to distinguish between that which is merely theoretically feasible, and that which is economically and logistically practical.

As we will show here, man's present technology is inadequate to the task of maintaining the world's burgeoning billions, even under the most optimistic assumptions. Furthermore, technology is likely to remain inadequate until such time as the population growth rate is drastically reduced. This is not to assert that present efforts to "revolutionize" tropical agriculture, increase yields of fisheries, desalt water for irrigation, exploit new power sources, and implement

Paul R. Ehrlich and John P. Holdren, "Population and Panaceas: A Technological Perspective," *BioScience,* December, 1969, Vol. 19, No. 12, pp. 1065-1071. Reprinted by permission of the publisher. We thank the following individuals for reading and commenting on the manuscript: J. H. Brownell (Stanford University); P. A. Cantor (Aerojet General Corp.); P. E. Cloud (University of California, Santa Barbara); D. J. Eckstrom (Stanford University); R. Ewell (State University of New York at Buffalo); J. L. Fisher (Resources for the Future, Inc.); J. A. Hendrickson, Jr. (Stanford University); J. H. Hessel (Stanford University); R. W. Holm (Stanford University); S. C. McIntosh, Jr. (Stanford University); K. E. F. Watt (University of California, Davis). This work was supported in part by a grant from the Ford Foundation. The co-authors are affiliated, respectively, with the department of biological sciences, and with the Institute for Plasma Research and department of aeronautics and astronautics, Stanford University.

related projects are not worthwhile. They may be. They could also easily produce the ultimate disaster for mankind if they are not applied with careful attention to their effects on the ecological systems necessary for our survival (Woodwell, 1967; Cole, 1968). And even if such projects are initiated with unprecedented levels of staffing and expenditures, without population control they are doomed to fall far short. No effort to expand the carrying capacity of the Earth can keep pace with unbridled population growth.

To support these contentions, we summarize briefly the present lopsided balance sheet in the population/food accounting. We then examine the logistics, economics, and possible consequences of some technological schemes which have been proposed to help restore the balance, or, more ambitiously, to permit the maintenance of human populations much larger than today's. The most pertinent aspects of the balance are:

1. The world population reached 3.5 billion in mid-1968, with an annual increment of approximately 70 million people (itself increasing) and a doubling time on the order of 35 years (Population Reference Bureau, 1968).

2. Of this number of people, at least one-half billion are undernourished (deficient in calories or, more succinctly, slowly starving), and approximately an additional billion are malnourished (deficient in particular nutrients, mostly protein) (Borgstrom, 1965; Sukhatme, 1966). Estimates of the number actually perishing annually from starvation begin at 4 million and go up (Ehrlich, 1968) and depend in part on official definitions of starvation which conceal the true magnitude of hunger's contribution to the death rate (Lelyveld, 1968).

3. Merely to maintain present inadequate nutrition levels, the food requirements of Asia, Africa, and Latin America will, conservatively, increase by 26% in the 10-year period measured from 1965 to 1975 (Paddock and Paddock, 1967). World food production must double in the period 1965-2000 to stay even; it must triple if nutrition is to be brought up to minimum requirements.

Food Production

That there is insufficient additional, good quality agricultural land available in the world to meet these needs is so well documented (Borgstrom, 1965) that we will not belabor the point here. What hope there is must rest with increasing yields on land presently cultivated, bringing marginal land into production, more efficiently exploiting the sea, and bringing less conventional methods of food production to fruition. In all these areas, science and technology play a dominant role. While space does not permit even a cursory look at all the proposals on these topics which have been advanced in recent years, a few representative examples illustrate our points.

Conventional Agriculture.   Probably the most widely recommended means of increasing agricultural yields is through the more intensive use of fertilizers. Their production is straightforward, and a good deal is known about their effective application, although, as with many technologies we consider here, the environmental consequences of heavy fertilizer use are ill understood and potentially dangerous[1] (Wadleigh, 1968). But even ignoring such problems, we find staggering difficulties barring the implementation of fertilizer technology on the scale required. In this regard the accomplishments of countries such as Japan and the Netherlands are often cited as offering hope to the underdeveloped world. Some perspective on this point is afforded by noting that if India were to apply fertilizer at the per capita level employed by the Netherlands, her fertilizer needs would be nearly half the present world output (United Nations, 1968).

On a more realistic plane, we note that although the goal for nitrogen fertilizer production in 1971 under India's fourth 5-year plan is 2.4 million metric tons (Anonymous, 1968a), Raymond Ewell (who has served as fertilizer production adviser to the Indian government for the past 12 years) suggests that less than 1.1 million metric tons is a more probable figure for that date.[2] Ewell cites poor plant maintenance, raw materials shortages, and power and transportation breakdowns as contributing to continued low production by existing Indian plants. Moreover, even when fertilizer is available, increases in productivity do not necessarily follow. In parts of the underdeveloped world lack of farm credit is limiting fertilizer distribution; elsewhere, internal transportation systems are inadequate to the task. Nor can the problem of educating farmers on the advantages and techniques of fertilizer use be ignored. A recent study (Parikh et al., 1968) of the Intensive Agriculture District Program in the Surat district of Gujarat, India (in which scientific fertilizer use was to have been a major ingredient) notes that "on the whole, the performance of adjoining districts which have similar climate but did not enjoy relative preference of input supply was as good as, if not better than, the programme district. . . . A particularly disheartening feature is that the farm production plans, as yet, do not carry any educative value and have largely failed to convince farmers to use improved practices in their proper combinations."

As a second example of a panacea in the realm of conventional agriculture, mention must be given to the development of new high-yield or high-protein strains of food crops. That such strains have the potential of making a major contribution to the food supply of the world is beyond doubt, but this potential is limited in contrast to the potential for population growth, and will be realized too slowly to have anything but a small impact on the immediate crisis. There are major difficulties impeding the widespread use of new high-yield grain varieties. Typically, the new grains require high fertilizer inputs to realize their full potential, and thus are subject to all the difficulties mentioned above. Some other problems are identified in a recent address by Lester R. Brown, administrator of the International Agricultural Development Service: the limited amount of irrigated land suitable for the new varieties, the fact that a farmer's

---

[1] Barry Commoner, address to 135th Meeting of the AAAS, Dallas, Texas (28 December 1968).
[2] Raymond Ewell, private communication (1 December 1968).

willingness to innovate fluctuates with the market prices (which may be driven down by high-yield crops), and the possibility of tieups at market facilities inadequate for handling increased yields.[3]

Perhaps even more important, the new grain varieties are being rushed into production without adequate field testing, so that we are unsure of how resistant they will be to the attacks of insects and plant diseases. William Paddock has presented a plant pathologist's view of the crash programs to shift to new varieties (Paddock, 1967). He describes India's dramatic program of planting improved Mexican wheat, and continues: "Such a rapid switch to a new variety is clearly understandable in a country that tottered on the brink of famine. Yet with such limited testing, one wonders what unknown pathogens await a climatic change which will give the environmental conditions needed for their growth." Introduction of the new varieties creates enlarged monocultures of plants with essentially unknown levels of resistance to disaster. Clearly, one of the prices that is paid for higher yield is a higher risk of widespread catastrophe. And the risks are far from local: since the new varieties require more "input" of pesticides (with all their deleterious ecological side effects), these crops may ultimately contribute to the defeat of other environment-related panaceas, such as extracting larger amounts of food from the sea.

A final problem must be mentioned in connection with these strains of food crops. In general, the hungriest people in the world are also those with the most conservative food habits. Even rather minor changes, such as that from a rice variety in which the cooked grains stick together to one in which the grains fall apart, may make new foods unacceptable. It seems to be an unhappy fact of human existence that people would rather starve than eat a nutritious substance which they do not recognize as food.[4]

Beyond the economic, ecological, and sociological problems already mentioned in connection with high-yield agriculture, there is the overall problem of time. We need time to breed the desired characteristics of yield and hardiness into a vast array of new strains (a tedious process indeed), time to convince farmers that it is necessary that they change their time-honored ways of cultivation, and time to convince hungry people to change the staples of their diet. The Paddocks give 20 years as the "rule of thumb" for a new technique or plant variety to progress from conception to substantial impact on farming (Paddock and Paddock, 1967). They write: "It is true that a *massive* research attack on the problem could bring some striking results in less than 20 years. But I do not find such an attack remotely contemplated in the thinking of those officials capable of initiating it." Promising as high-yield agriculture may be, the funds, the personnel, the ecological expertise, and the necessary years are unfortunately not at our disposal. Fulfillment of the promise will come too late for many of the world's starving millions, if it comes at all.

---

[3] Lester R. Brown, address to the Second International Conference on the War on Hunger, Washington, D.C. (February 1968).

[4] For a more detailed discussion of the psychological problems in persuading people to change their dietary habits, see McKenzie, 1968.

Bringing More Land Under Cultivation. The most frequently mentioned means of bringing new land into agricultural production are farming the tropics and irrigating arid and semiarid regions. The former, although widely discussed in optimistic terms, has been tried for years with incredibly poor results, and even recent experiments have not been encouraging. One essential difficulty is the unsuitability of tropical soils for supporting typical foodstuffs instead of jungles (McNeil, 1964; Paddock and Paddock, 1964). Also, "the tropics" are a biologically more diverse area than the temperate zones, so that farming technology developed for one area will all too often prove useless in others. We shall see that irrigating the deserts, while more promising, has serious limitations in terms of scale, cost, and lead time.

The feasible approaches to irrigation of arid lands appear to be limited to large-scale water projects involving dams and transport in canals, and desalination of ocean and brackish water. Supplies of usable ground water are already badly depleted in most areas where they are accessible, and natural recharge is low enough in most arid regions that such supplies do not offer a long-term solution in any case. Some recent statistics will give perspective to the discussion of water projects and desalting which follows. In 1966, the United States was using about 300 billion gal of water per day, of which 135 billion gal were consumed by agriculture and 165 billion gal by municipal and industrial users (Sporn, 1966). The bulk of the agricultural water cost the farmer from 5 to 10 cents/1000 gal; the highest price paid for agricultural water was 15 cents/1000 gal. For small industrial and municipal supplies, prices as high as 50 to 70 cents/1000 gal were prevalent in the U. S. arid regions, and some communities in the Southwest are paying on the order of 1.00/1000 gal for "project" water. The extremely high cost of the latter stems largely from transportation costs, which have been estimated at 5 to 15 cents/1000 gal per 100 miles (International Atomic Energy Agency, 1964).

We now examine briefly the implications of such numbers in considering the irrigation of the deserts. The most ambitious water project yet conceived in this country is the North American Water and Power Alliance, which proposes to distribute water from the great rivers of Canada to thirsty locations all over the United States. Formidable political problems aside (some based on the certainty that in the face of expanding populations, demands for water will eventually arise at the source), this project would involve the expenditure of $100 billion in construction costs over a 20-year completion period. At the end of this time, the yield to the United States would be 69 million acre feet of water annually (Kelly, 1966), or 63 billion gal per day. If past experience with massive water projects is any guide, these figures are overoptimistic; but if we assume they are not, it is instructive to note that this monumental undertaking would provide for an increase of only 21% in the water consumption of the United States, during a period in which the population is expected to increase by between 25 and 43% (U. S. Dept. of Commerce, 1966). To assess the possible contribution to the *world* food situation, we assume that all this water could be devoted to agriculture, although extrapolation of present consumption patterns indicates that only about one-half would be. Then using the rather optimistic figure of 500 gal per day to grow the food to feed one person, we find that this project could feed 126 million additional people. Since this is less than 8% of the projected world population growth during the construction period (say 1970 to 1990), it should be clear that even the most massive water projects can make but a token contribution to the solution of the world food problem in the long term. And in the crucial short term—the years preceding 1980—*no* additional people will be fed by projects still on the drawing board today.

In summary, the cost is staggering, the scale insufficient, and the lead time too long. Nor need we resort to such speculation about the future for proof of the failure of technological "solutions" in the absence of population control. The highly touted and very expensive Aswan Dam project, now nearing completion, will ultimately supply food (at the present miserable diet level) for less than Egypt's population growth during the time of construction (Borgstrom, 1965; Cole, 1968). Furthermore, its effect on the fertility of the Nile Delta may be disastrous, and, as with all water projects of this nature, silting of the reservoir will destroy the gains in the long term (perhaps in 100 years).

Desalting for irrigation suffers somewhat similar limitations. The desalting plants operational in the world today produce water at individual rates of 7.5 million gal/day and less, at a cost of 75 cents/1000 gal and up, the cost increasing as the plant size decreases (Bender, 1969). The most optimistic firm proposal which anyone seems to have made for desalting with present or soon-to-be available technology is a 150 million gal per day nuclear-powered installation studied by the Bechtel Corp. for the Los Angeles Metropolitan Water District. Bechtel's early figures indicated that water from this complex would be available at the site for 27-28 cents/1000 gal (Galstann and Currier, 1967). However, skepticism regarding the economic assumptions leading to these figures (Milliman, 1966) has since proven justified—the project was shelved after spiralling construction cost estimates indicated an actual water cost of 40-50 cents/1000 gal. Use of even the original figures, however, bears out our contention that the *most* optimistic assumptions do not alter the verdict that technology is losing the food/population battle. For 28 cents/1000 gal is still approximately twice the cost which farmers have hitherto been willing or able to pay for irrigation water. If the Bechtel plant had been intended to supply agricultural needs, which it was not, one would have had to add to an already unacceptable price the very substantial cost of transporting the water inland.

Significantly, studies have shown that the economies of scale in the distillation process are essentially exhausted by a 150 million gal per day plant (International Atomic Energy Agency, 1964). Hence, merely increasing desalting capacity further will not substantially lower the cost of the water. On purely economic grounds, then, it is unlikely that desalting will play a major role in food production by conventional agriculture in the short term.[5] Technological "break-throughs" will presumably improve this outlook with the passage of time, but world population growth will not wait.

Desalting becomes more promising if the high cost of the water can be offset by increased agricultural yields per gallon and, perhaps, use of a single nuclear installation to provide power for both the desalting and profitable on-site industrial processes. This prospect has been investigated in a thorough and well-documented study headed by E. S. Mason (Oak Ridge National Laboratory, 1968). The result is a set of preliminary figures and recommendations regarding nuclear-powered "agro-industrial complexes" for arid and semiarid regions, in which desalted water and fertilizer would be produced for use on an adjacent, highly efficient farm. In underdeveloped countries incapable of using the full excess power output of the reactor, this energy would be consumed in on-site production of industrial materials for sale on the world market. Both near-term (10 years hence) and far-term (20 years hence) technologies are considered, as are various mixes of farm and industrial products. The representative near-term case for which a detailed cost breakdown is given involves a seaside facility with a desalting capacity of 1 billion gal/day, a farm size of 320,000 acres, and an industrial electric power consumption of 1585 Mw. The initial investment for this complex is estimated at $1.8 billion, and annual operating costs at $236 million. If both the food and the industrial materials produced were sold (as opposed to giving the food, at least, to those in need who could not pay),[6] the estimated profit for such a complex, before subtracting financing costs, would be 14.6%.

The authors of the study are commendably cautious in outlining the assumptions and uncertainties upon which these figures rest. The key assumption is that 200 gal/day of water will grow the 2500 calories required to feed one person. Water/calorie ratios of this order or less have been achieved by the top 20% of farmers specializing in such crops as wheat, potatoes, and tomatoes; but more water is required for needed protein-rich crops such as peanuts and soybeans. The authors identify the uncertainty that crops usually raised separately can be grown together in tight rotation on the same piece of land. Problems of water storage between periods of peak irrigation demand, optimal patterns of crop rotation, and seasonal acreage variations are also mentioned. These "ifs" and assumptions, and those associated with the other technologies involved, are unfortunately often omitted when the results of such painstaking studies are summarized for more popular consumption (Anonymous, 1968b, 1968c). The

---

[5] An identical conclusion was reached in a recent study (Clawson et al;, 1969) in which the foregoing points and numerous other aspects of desalting were treated in far more detail than was possible here.

[6] Confusing statements often are made about the possibility that food supply will outrun food demand in the future. In these statements, "demand" is used in the economic sense, and in this context many millions of starving people may generate no demand whatsoever. Indeed, one concern of those engaged in increasing food production is to find ways of increasing demand.

result is the perpetuation of the public's tendency to confuse feasible and available, to see panaceas where scientists in the field concerned see only potential, realizable with massive infusions of time and money.

It is instructive, nevertheless, to examine the impact on the world food problem which the Oak Ridge complexes might have if construction were to begin today, and if all the assumptions about technology 10 years hence were valid *now*. At the industrial-agricultural mix pertinent to the sample case described above, the food produced would be adequate for just under 3 million people. This means that 23 such plants per year, at a cost of $41 billion, would have to be put in operation merely to keep pace with world population growth, to say nothing of improving the substandard diets of between one and two billion members of the present population. (Fertilizer production beyond that required for the on-site farm is of course a contribution in the latter regard, but the substantial additional costs of transporting it to where it is needed must then be accounted for.) Since approximately 5 years from the start of construction would be required to put such a complex into operation, we should commence work on at least 125 units post-haste, and begin at least 25 per year thereafter. If the technology *were* available now, the investment in construction over the next 5 years, prior to operation of the first plants, would be $315 billion—about 20 times the total U.S. foreign aid expenditure during the past 5 years. By the time the technology *is* available the bill will be much higher, if famine has not "solved" the problem for us.

This example again illustrates that scale, time, and cost are all working against technology in the short term. And if population growth is not decelerated, the increasing severity of population-related crises will surely neutralize the technological improvements of the middle and long terms.

Other Food Panaceas.   "Food from the sea" is the most prevalent "answer" to the world food shortage in the view of the general public. This is not surprising, since estimates of the theoretical fisheries productivity of the sea run up to some 50-100 times current yields (Schmitt, 1965; Christy and Scott, 1965). Many practical and economic difficulties, however, make it clear that such a figure will never be reached, and that it will not even be approached in the foreseeable future. In 1966, the annual fisheries harvest was some 57 million metric tons (United Nations, 1968). A careful analysis (Meseck, 1961) indicates that this might be increased to a world production of 70 million metric tons by 1980. If this gain were realized, it would represent (assuming no violent change in population growth patterns) a small per capita *loss* in fisheries yield.

Both the short- and long-term outlooks for taking food from the sea are clouded by the problems of overexploitation, pollution (which is generally ignored by those calculating potential yields), and economics. Solving these problems will require more than technological legerdemain; it will also require unprecedented changes in human behavior, especially in the area of international cooperation. The unlikelihood that such cooperation will come about is reflected in the recent news (Anonymous, 1968d) that Norway has dropped out of the whaling industry because overfishing has depleted the stock below the level at which it may economically be harvested. In that industry, international controls were tried—and failed. The sea is, unfortunately, a "commons" (Hardin, 1968), and the resultant management problems exacerbate the biological and technical problems of greatly increasing our "take." One suspects that the return per dollar poured into the sea will be much less than the corresponding return from the land for many years, and the return from the land has already been found wanting.

Synthetic foods, protein culture with petroleum, saline agriculture, and weather modification all may hold promise for the future, but all are at present expensive and available only on an extremely limited scale. The research to improve this situation will also be expensive, and, of course, time-consuming. In the absence of funding, it will not occur at all, a fact which occasionally eludes the public and the Congress.

Domestic and Industrial Water Supplies

The world has water problems, even exclusive of the situation in agriculture. Although total precipitation should in theory be adequate in quantity for several further doublings of population, serious shortages arising from problems of quality, irregularity, and distribution already plague much of the world. Underdeveloped countries will find the water needs of industrialization staggering: 240,000 gal of water are required to produce a ton of newsprint; 650,000 gal, to produce a ton of steel (International Atomic Energy Agency, 1964). Since maximum acceptable water costs for domestic and industrial use are higher than for agriculture, those who can afford it are or soon will be using desalination (40-100 + cents/1000 gal) and used-water renovation (54-57 cents/1000 gal [Ennis, 1967]). Those who cannot afford it are faced with allocating existing supplies between industry and agriculture, and as we have seen, they must choose the latter. In this circumstance, the standard of living remains pitifully low. Technology's only present answer is massive externally financed complexes of the sort considered above, and we have already suggested there the improbability that we are prepared to pay the bill rung up by present population growth.

The widespread use of desalted water by those who *can* afford it brings up another problem only rarely mentioned to date, the disposal of the salts. The product of the distillation processes in present use is a hot brine with salt concentration several times that of seawater. Both the temperature and the salinity of this effluent will prove fatal to local marine life if it is simply exhausted to the ocean. The most optimistic statement we have seen on this problem is that *"smaller plants* (our emphasis) at seaside locations may return the concentrated brine to the ocean if proper attention is paid to the design of the outfall, and to the effect on the local marine ecology" (McIlhenny, 1966). The same writer identifies the major economic uncertainties connected with extracting the salts for sale (to do so is straightforward, but often not profitable).

Nor can one simply evaporate the brine and leave the residue in a pile. The 150 million gal/day plant mentioned above would produce brine bearing 90 million lb of salts daily (based on figures by Parker, 1966). This amount of salt would cover over 15 acres to a depth of one foot. Thus, every year a plant of the billion gallon per day, agro-industrial complex size would produce a pile of salt over 52 ft deep and covering a square mile. The high winds typical of coastal deserts would seriously aggravate the associated soil contamination problem.

Energy

Man's problems with energy supply are more subtle than those with food and water: we are not yet running out of energy, but we are being forced to use it faster than is probably healthy. The rapacious depletion of our fossil fuels is already forcing us to consider more expensive mining techniques to gain access to lower-grade deposits, such as the oil shales, and even the status of our high-grade uranium ore reserves is not clear-cut (Anonymous, 1968e).

A widely held misconception in this connection is that nuclear power is "dirt cheap," and as such represents a panacea for developed and underdeveloped nations alike. To the contrary, the largest nuclear-generating stations now in operation are just competitive with or marginally superior to modern coal-fired plants of comparable size (where coal is not scarce); at best, both produce power for on the order of 4-5 mills (tenths of a cent) per kilowatt-hour. Smaller nuclear units remain less economical than their fossil-fueled counterparts. Under-developed countries can rarely use the power of the larger plants. Simply speaking, there are not enough industries, appliances, and light bulbs to absorb the output, and the cost of industrialization and modernization exceeds the cost of the power required to sustain it by orders of magnitude, regardless of the source of the power. (For example, one study noted that the capital requirement to consume the output of a 70,000 kilowatt plant—about $1.2 million worth of electricity per year at 40% utilization and 5 mills/kwh—is $111 million per year if the power is consumed by metals industries, $270 million per year for petróleum product industries [E. A. Mason, 1957].) Hence, at least at present, only those underdeveloped countries which are short of fossil fuels or inexpensive means to transport them are in particular need of nuclear power.

Prospects for major reductions in the cost of nuclear power in the future hinge on the long-awaited breeder reactor and the still further distant thermo-nuclear reactor. In neither case is the time scale or the ultimate cost of energy a matter of any certainty. The breeder reactor, which converts more nonfissile uranium (^{238}U) or thorium to fissionable material than it consumes as fuel for itself, effectively extends our nuclear fuel supply by a factor of approximately 400 (Cloud, 1968). It is not expected to become competitive economically with conventional reactors until the 1980's (Bump, 1967). Reductions in the unit energy cost beyond this date are not guaranteed, due both to the probable continued high capital cost of breeder reactors and to increasing costs for the ore which the breeders will convert to fuel. In the latter regard, we mention that although crushing granite for its few parts per million of uranium and thorium is possible in theory, the problems and cost of doing so are far from resolved.[7] It is too soon to predict the costs associated with a fusion reactor (few who work in the field will predict whether such a device will work at all within the next 15-20 years). One guess puts the unit energy cost at something over half that for a coal or fission power station of comparable size (Mills, 1967), but this is pure speculation. Quite possibly the major benefit of controlled fusion will again be to extend the energy supply rather than to cheapen it.

A second misconception about nuclear power is that it can reduce our dependence on fossil fuels to zero as soon as that becomes necessary or desirable. In fact, nuclear power plants contribute only to the electrical portion of the energy budget; and in 1960 in the United States, for example, electrical energy comprised only 19% of the total energy consumed (Sporn, 1963). The degree to which nuclear fuels can postpone the exhaustion of our coal and oil depends on the extent to which that 19% is enlarged. The task is far from a trivial one, and will involve transitions to electric or fuel-cell powered transportation, electric heating, and electrically powered industries. It will be extremely expensive.

Nuclear energy, then, is a panacea neither for us nor for the underdeveloped world. It relieves, but does not remove, the pressure on fossil fuel supplies; it provides reasonably priced power where these fuels are not abundant; it has substantial (but expensive) potential in intelligent applications such as that suggested in the Oak Ridge study discussed above; and it shares the propensity of fast-growing technology to unpleasant side effects (Novick, 1969). We mention in the last connection that, while nuclear power stations do not produce conventional air pollutants, their radioactive waste problems may in the long run prove a poor trade. Although the AEC seems to have made a good case for solidification and storage in salt mines of the bulk of the radioactive fission products (Blanko et al., 1967), a number of radioactive isotopes are released to the air, and in some areas such isotopes have already turned up in potentially harmful concentrations (Curtis and Hogan, 1969). Projected order of magnitude increases in nuclear power generation will seriously aggravate this situation. Although it has frequently been stated that the eventual advent of fusion reactors will free us from such difficulties, at least one authority, F. L. Parker, takes a more cautious view. He contends that losses of radioactive tritium from fusion power plants may prove even more hazardous than the analogous problems of fission reactors (Parker, 1968).

A more easily evaluated problem is the tremendous quantity of waste heat generated at nuclear installations (to say nothing of the usable power output, which, as with power from whatever source, must also ultimately be dissipated as heat). Both have potentially disastrous effects on the local and world ecological and climatological balance. There is no simple solution to this problem, for, in general, "cooling" only moves heat; it does not *remove* it from the

---

[7]A general discussion of extracting metals from common rock is given by Cloud, 1968.

environment viewed as a whole. Moreover, the Second Law of Thermodynamics puts a ceiling on the efficiency with which we can do even this much, i.e., concentrate and transport heat. In effect, the Second Law condemns us to aggravate the total problem by generating still *more* heat in any machinery we devise for local cooling (consider, for example, refrigerators and air conditioners).

The only heat which actually leaves the whole system, the Earth, is that which can be radiated back into space. This amount steadily is being diminished as combustion of hydrocarbon fuels increases the atmospheric percentage of CO_2 which has strong absorption bands in the infrared spectrum of the outbound heat energy. (Hubbert, 1962, puts the increase in the CO_2 content of the atmosphere at 10% since 1900.) There is, of course, a competing effect in the Earth's energy balance, which is the increased reflectivity of the upper atmosphere to incoming sunlight due to other forms of air pollution. It has been estimated, ignoring both these effects, that man risks drastic (and perhaps catastrophic) climatological change if the amount of heat he dissipates in the environment on a global scale reaches 1% of the incident solar energy at the Earth's surface (Rose and Clark, 1961). At the present 5% rate of increase in world energy consumption,[8] this level will be reached in less than a century, and in the immediate future the direct contribution of man's power consumption will create serious local problems. If we may safely rule out circumvention of the Second Law or the divorce of energy requirements from population size, this suggests that, whatever science and technology may accomplish, population growth must be stopped.

Transportation

We would be remiss in our offer of a technological perspective on population problems without some mention of the difficulties associated with transporting large quantities of food, material, or people across the face of the Earth. While our grain exports have not begun to satisfy the hunger of the underdeveloped world, they already have taxed our ability to transport food in bulk over large distances. The total amount of goods of *all* kinds loaded at U.S. ports for external trade was 158 million metric tons in 1965 (United Nations, 1968). This is coincidentally the approximate amount of grain which would have been required to make up the dietary shortages of the underdeveloped world in the same year (Sukhatme, 1966). Thus, if the United States *had* such an amount of grain to ship, it could be handled only by displacing the entirety of our export trade. In a similar vein, the gross weight of the fertilizer, in excess of present consumption, required in the underdeveloped world to feed the additional population there in 1980 will amount to approximately the same figure—150 million

---

[8]The rate of growth of world energy consumption fluctuates strongly about some mean on a time scale of only a few years, and the figures are not known with great accuracy in any case. A discussion of predicting the mean and a defense of the figure of 5% are given in Gueron et al., 1957.

metric tons (Sukhatme, 1966). Assuming that a substantial fraction of this fertilizer, should it be available at all, will have to be shipped about, we had best start building freighters! These problems, and the even more discouraging one of internal transportation in the hungry countries, coupled with the complexities of international finance and marketing which have hobbled even present aid programs, complete a dismal picture of the prospects for "external" solutions to ballooning food requirements in much of the world.

Those who envision migration as a solution to problems of food, land, and water distribution not only ignore the fact that the world has no promising place to put more people, they simply have not looked at the numbers of the transportation game. Neglecting the fact that migration and relocation costs would probably amount to a minimum of several thousand dollars per person, we find, for example, that the entire long-range jet transport fleet of the United States (about 600 planes [Molloy, 1968] with an average capacity of 150), averaging two round trips per week, could transport only about 9 million people per year from India to the United States. This amounts to about 75% of that country's annual population *growth* (Population Reference Bureau, 1968). Ocean liners and transports, while larger, are less numerous and much slower, and over long distances could not do as well. Does anyone believe, then, that we are going to compensate for the world's population growth by sending the excess to the planets? If there were a place to go on Earth, financially and logistically we could not send our surplus there.

Conclusion

We have not attempted to be comprehensive in our treatment of population pressures and the prospects of coping with them technologically; rather, we hope simply to have given enough illustrations to make plausible our contention that technology, without population control, cannot meet the challenge. It may be argued that we have shown only that any one technological scheme taken individually is insufficient to the task at hand, whereas *all* such schemes applied in parallel might well be enough. We would reply that neither the commitment nor the resources to implement them all exists, and indeed that many may prove mutually exclusive (e.g., harvesting algae may diminish fish production).

Certainly, an optimum combination of efforts exists in theory, but we assert that no organized attempt to find it is being made, and that our examination of its probable eventual constituents permits little hope that even the optimum will suffice. Indeed, after a far more thorough survey of the prospects than we have attempted here, the President's Science Advisory Committee Panel on the world food supply concluded (PSAC, 1967): "The solution of the problem that will exist after about 1985 *demands* that programs of population control be initiated now." We most emphatically agree, noting that "now" was 2 years ago!

Of the problems arising out of population growth in the short, middle, and long terms, we have emphasized the first group. For mankind must pass the first hurdles—food and water for the next 20 years—to be granted the privilege of confronting such dilemmas as the exhaustion of mineral resources and physical space later.[9] Furthermore, we have not conveyed the extent of our concern for the environmental deterioration which has accompanied the population explosion, and for the catastrophic ecological consequences which would attend many of the proposed technological "solutions" of the population/food crisis. Nor have we treated the point that "development" of the rest of the world to the standards of the West probably would be lethal ecologically (Ehrlich and Ehrlich, 1970). For even if such grim prospects are ignored, it is abundantly clear that in terms of cost, lead time, and implementation on the scale required, technology without population control will be too little and too late.

What hope there is lies not, of course, in abandoning attempts at technological solutions; on the contrary, they must be pursued at unprecedented levels, with unprecedented judgment, and above all with unprecedented attention to their ecological consequences. We need dramatic programs now to find ways of ameliorating the food crisis—to buy time for humanity until the inevitable delay accompanying population control efforts has passed. But it cannot be emphasized enough that if the population control measures are *not* initiated immediately and effectively, all the technology man can bring to bear will not fend off the misery to come.[10] Therefore, confronted as we are with limited resources of time and money, we must consider carefully what fraction of our effort should be applied to the cure of the disease itself instead of to the temporary relief of the symptoms. We should ask, for example, how many vasectomies could be performed by a program funded with the 1.8 billion dollars required to build a single nuclear agro-industrial complex, and what the relative impact on the problem would be in both the short and long terms.

The decision for population control will be opposed by growth-minded economists and businessmen, by nationalistic statesmen, by zealous religious leaders, and by the myopic and well-fed of every description. It is therefore incumbent on all who sense the limitations of technology and the fragility of the environmental balance to make themselves heard above the hollow, optimistic chorus—to convince society and its leaders that there is no alternative but the cessation of our irresponsible, all-demanding, and all-consuming population growth.

---

[9]Since the first draft of this article was written, the authors have seen the manuscript of a timely and pertinent forthcoming book, *Resources and Man,* written under the auspices of the National Academy of Sciences and edited by Preston E. Cloud. The book reinforces many of our conclusions in such areas as agriculture and fisheries and, in addition, treats both short- and long-term prospects in such areas as mineral resources and fossil fuels in great detail.

[10]This conclusion has also been reached within the specific context of aid to underdeveloped countries in a Ph.D. thesis by Douglas Daetz: "Energy Utilization and Aid Effectiveness in Nonmechanized Agriculture: A Computer Simulation of a Socioeconomic System" (University of California, Berkeley, May 1968).

References

Anonymous. 1968a. India aims to remedy fertilizer shortage. *Chem. Eng. News,* 46 (November 25): 29.

_____. 1968b. Scientists Studying Nuclear-Powered Agro-Industrial Complexes to Give Food and Jobs to Millions. *New York Times,* March 10, p. 74.

_____. 1968c. Food from the atom. *Technol. Rev.,* January, p. 55.

_____. 1968d. Norway—The end of the big blubber. *Time,* November 29, p. 98.

_____. 1968e. Nuclear fuel cycle. *Nucl. News,* January, p. 30.

Bender, R. J. 1969. Why water desalting will expand. *Power,* 113 (August): 171.

Blanko, R. E., J. O. Blomeke, and J. T. Roberts. 1967. Solving the waste disposal problem. *Nucleonics,* 25: 58.

Borgstrom, Georg. 1965. *The Hungry Planet.* Collier-Macmillan, New York.

Bump, T. R. 1967. A third generation of breeder reactors. *Sci. Amer.,* May, p. 25.

Christy, F. C., Jr., and A. Scott. 1965. *The Commonwealth in Ocean Fisheries.* Johns Hopkins Press, Baltimore.

Clawson, M., H. L. Landsberg, and L. T. Alexander. 1969. Desalted seawater for agriculture: Is it economic? *Science,* 164: 1141.

Cloud, P. R. 1968. Realities of mineral distribution. *Texas Quart.,* Summer, p. 103.

Cole, LaMont C. 1968. Can the world be saved? *BioScience,* 18: 679.

Curtis, R., and E. Hogan. 1969. *Perils of the Peaceful Atom.* Doubleday, New York, pp. 135, 150-152.

Ennis, C. E. 1967. Desalted water as a competitive commodity. *Chem. Eng. Progr.,* 63 (1): 64.

Ehrlich, P. R. 1968. *The Population Bomb.* Sierra Club/Ballantine, New York.

Ehrlich, P. R., and Anne H. Ehrlich. 1970. *Population, Resources, and Environment.* W. H. Freeman, San Francisco (in press).

Galstann, L. S., and E. L. Currier. 1967. The Metropolitan Water District desalting project. *Chem. Eng. Progr.,* 63 (1): 64.

Gueron, J., J. A. Lane, I. R. Maxwell, and J. R. Menke. 1957. *The Economics of Nuclear Power. Progress in Nuclear Energy.* McGraw-Hill Book Co., New York. Series VIII, p. 23.

Hardin, G. 1968. The tragedy of the commons. *Science,* 162: 1243.

Hubbert, M. K. 1962. Energy resources. A report to the Committee on Natural Resources. National Research Council Report 1000-D, National Academy of Sciences.

International Atomic Energy Agency. 1964. Desalination of water using conventional and nuclear energy. Technical Report 24, Vienna.

Kelly, R. P. 1966. North American water and power alliance. In: *Water Production Using Nuclear Energy*, R. G. Post and R. L. Seale (eds.). University of Arizona Press, Tucson, p. 29.

Lelyveld, D. 1968. Can India survive Calcutta? *New York Times Magazine*, October 13, p. 58.

Mason, E. A. 1957. Economic growth and energy consumption. In: *The Economics of Nuclear Power. Progress in Nuclear Energy*, Series VIII. J. Gueron et al. (eds.). McGraw-Hill Book Co., New York, p. 56.

McIlhenny, W. F. 1966. Problems and potentials of concentrated brines. In: *Water Production Using Nuclear Energy*, R. G. Post and R. L. Seale (eds.). University of Arizona Press, Tucson, p. 187.

McKenzie, John. 1968. Nutrition and the soft sell. *New Sci.*, **40**: 423.

McNeil, Mary. 1964. Lateritic soils. *Sci. Amer.*, November, p. 99.

Meseck, G. 1961. Importance of fish production and utilization in the food economy. Paper R11.3, presented at FAO Conference on Fish in Nutrition, Rome.

Milliman, J. W. 1966. Economics of water production using nuclear energy. In: *Water Production Using Nuclear Energy*. R. G. Post and R. L. Seale (eds). University of Arizona Press, Tucson, p. 49.

Mills, R. G. 1967. Some engineering problems of thermonuclear fusion. *Nucl. Fusion*, **7**: 223.

Molloy, J. F., Jr. 1968. The $12-billion financing problem of U.S. airlines. *Astronautics and Aeronautics*, October, p. 76.

Novick, S. 1969. *The Careless Atom.* Houghton Mifflin, Boston.

Oak Ridge National Laboratory. 1968. Nuclear energy centers, industrial and agro-industrial complexes, Summary Report. ORNL-4291, July.

Paddock, William. 1967. Phytopathology and a hungry world. *Ann. Rev. Phytopathol.*, **5**: 375.

Paddock, William, and Paul Paddock. 1964. *Hungry Nations.* Little, Brown & Co., Boston.

_____. 1967. *Famine 1975!* Little, Brown & Co., Boston.

Parikh, G., S. Saxena, and M. Maharaja. 1968. Agricultural extension and IADP, a study of Surat. *Econ. Polit. Weekly*, August 24, p. 1307.

Parker, F. L. 1968. Radioactive wastes from fusion reactors. *Science*, **159**: 83.

Parker, H. M. 1966. Environmental factors relating to large water plants. In: *Water Production Using Nuclear Energy*, R. G. Post and R. L. Seale (eds.). University of Arizona Press, Tucson, p. 209.

Population Reference Bureau. 1968. Population Reference Bureau Data Sheet. Pop. Ref. Bureau, Washington, D.C.

PSAC. 1967. *The World Food Problem.* Report of the President's Science Advisory Committee. Vols. 1-3. U.S. Govt. Printing Office, Washington, D.C.

Rose, D. J., and M. Clark, Jr. 1961. *Plasma and Controlled Fusion.* M.I.T. Press, Cambridge, Mass., p. 3.

Schmitt, W. R. 1965. The planetary food potential. *Ann. N.Y. Acad. Sci.,* **118**: 645.

Sporn, Philip. 1963. *Energy for Man.* Macmillan, New York.

————. 1966. *Fresh Water from Saline Waters.* Pergamon Press, New York.

Sukhatme, P. V. 1966. The world's food supplies. *Roy. Stat. Soc. J.,* **129A**: 222.

United Nations. 1968. *United Nations Statistical Yearbook for 1967.* Statistical Office of the U.N., New York.

U. S. Dept. of Commerce. 1966. *Statistical Abstract of the U. S.* U. S. Govt. Printing Office, Washington, D. C.

Wadleigh, C. H. 1968. Wastes in relation to agriculture and industry. USDA Miscellaneous Publication No. 1065. March.

Woodwell, George M. 1967. Toxic substances and ecological cycles. *Sci. Amer.,* March, p. 24.

Sex Control, Science, and Society

Amitai Etzioni

Using various techniques developed as a result of fertility research, scientists are experimenting with the possibility of sex control, the ability to determine whether a newborn infant will be a male or a female. So far, they have reported considerable success in their experiments with frogs and rabbits, whereas the success of experiments with human sperm appears to be quite limited, and the few optimistic reports seem to be unconfirmed. Before this new scientific potentiality becomes a reality, several important questions must be considered.

Amitai Etzioni, "Sex Control, Science, and Society," *Science,* 13 September, 1968, Vol. 161, No. 3846, pp. 1107-1112. Copyright 1968 by the American Association for the Advancement of Science. Reprinted by permission of the author and publisher. The author is professor of sociology at Columbia University, New York. An earlier version of this paper was presented to the International Symposium on Science and Politics at Lund, Sweden, June 1968.

What would be the societal consequences of sex control? If they are, on balance, undesirable, can sex control be prevented without curbing the freedoms essential for scientific work? The scientific ethics already impose some restraints on research to safeguard the welfare and privacy of the researched population. Sex control, however, might affect the whole society. Are there any circumstances under which the societal well-being justifies some limitation on the freedom of research? These questions apply, of course, to many other areas of scientific inquiry, such as work on the biological code and the experimental use of behavior and thought-modifying drugs. Sex control provides a useful opportunity for discussion of these issues because it presents a relatively "low-key" problem. Success seems fairly remote, and, as we shall see, the deleterious effects of widespread sex control would probably not be very great. Before dealing with the possible societal effects of sex control, and the ways they may be curbed, I describe briefly the work that has already been done in this area.

The State of the Art

Differential centrifugation provided one major approach to sex control. It was supposed that since X and Y chromosomes differ in size (Y is considerably smaller), the sperm carrying the two different types would also be of two different weights; the Y-carrying sperm would be smaller and lighter, and the X-carrying sperm would be larger and heavier. Thus, the two kinds could be separated by centrifugation and then be used in artificial insemination. Early experiments, however, did not bear out this theory. And, Witschi pointed out that, in all likelihood, the force to be used in centrifugation would have to be of such magnitude that the sperm may well be damaged (1).

In the 1950's a Swedish investigator, Lindahl (2), published accounts of his results with the use of counter-streaming techniques of centrifugation. He found that by using the more readily sedimenting portion of bull spermatozoa that had undergone centrifugation, fertility was decreased but the number of male calves among the offspring was relatively high. His conclusion was that the female-determining spermatozoa are more sensitive than the male and are damaged due to mechanical stress in the centrifuging process.

Electrophoresis of spermatozoa is reported to have been successfully carried out by a Soviet biochemist, V. N. Schröder, in 1932 (3). She placed the cells in a solution in which the pH could be controlled. As the pH of the solution changed, the sperm moved with different speeds and separated into three groups: some concentrated next to the anode, some next to the cathode, and some were bunched in the middle. In tests conducted by Schröder and N. K. Kolstov (3), sperm which collected next to the anode produced six offspring, all females; those next to the cathode—four males and one female; and those which bunched in the center—two males and two females. Experiments with rabbits over the subsequent 10 years were reported as successful in controlling the sex of the offspring in 80 percent of the cases. Similar success with other mammals is reported.

At the Animal Reproduction Laboratory of Michigan State University, Gordon replicated these findings, although with a lower rate of success (4). Of 167 births studied, in 31 litters, he predicted correctly the sex of 113 offspring, for an average of 67.7 percent. Success was higher for females (62 out of 87, or 71.3 percent) than for males (51 out of 80, or 63.7 percent).

From 1932 to 1942, emphasis in sex control was on the acid-alkali method. In Germany, Unterberger reported in 1932 that in treating women with highly acidic vaginal secretions for sterility by use of alkaline douches, he had observed a high correlation between alkalinity and male offspring. Specifically, over a 10-year period, 53 out of 54 treated females are reported to have had babies, and all of the babies were male. In the one exception, the woman did not follow the doctor's prescription, Unterberger reported (5). In 1942, after repeated tests and experiments had not borne out the earlier results, interest in the acid-alkali method faded (6).

It is difficult to determine the length of time it will take to establish routine control of the sex of animals (of great interest, for instance, to cattle breeders); it is even more difficult to make such an estimate with regard to the sex control of human beings. In interviewing scientists who work on this matter, we heard conflicting reports about how close such a breakthrough was. It appeared that both optimistic and pessimistic estimates were vague—"between 7 to 15 years"—and were not based on any hard evidence but were the researchers' way of saying, "don't know" and "probably not very soon." No specific road blocks which seemed unusually difficult were cited, nor did they indicate that we have to await other developments before current obstacles can be removed. Fertility is a study area in which large funds are invested these days, and we know there is a correlation between increased investment and findings (7). Although most of the money is allocated to birth-control rather than sex-control studies, information needed for sex-control research has been in the past a by-product of the originally sponsored work. Schröder's findings, for example, were an accidental result of a fertility study she was conducting (4, p. 90). Nothing we heard from scientists working in this area would lead one to conclude that there is any specific reason we could not have sex control 5 years from now or sooner.

In addition to our uncertainty about when sex control might be possible, the question of how it would be effected is significant and also one on which there are differences of opinion. The mechanism for practicing sex control is important because certain techniques have greater psychic costs than others. We can see today, for example, that some methods of contraception are preferred by some classes of people because they involve less psychic "discomfort" for them; for example, the intrauterine device is preferred over sterilization by most women. In the same way, although electrophoresis now seems to offer a promising approach to sex control, its use would entail artificial insemination. And, whereas the objections to artificial insemination are probably decreasing, the resistance to it is still considerable (8). (Possibly, the opposition to artificial insemination would not be as great in a sex-control situation because the husband's own sperm could be used.) If drugs taken orally or douches could be relied upon, sex control would probably be much less expensive (artificial insemination requires a doctor's help), much less objectionable emotionally, and significantly more widely used.

In any event both professional forecasters of the future and leading scientists see sex control as a mass practice in the foreseeable future. Kahn and Wiener, in their discussion of the year 2000, suggest that one of the "one hundred technical innovations likely in the next thirty-three years" is the "capability to choose the sex of unborn children" (9). Muller takes a similar position about gene control in general (10).

Societal Use of Sex Control

If a simple and safe method of sex control were available, there would probably be no difficulty in finding the investors to promote it because there is a mass-market potential. The demand for the new freedom to choose seems well established. Couples have preferences on whether they want boys or girls. In many cultures boys provide an economic advantage (as workhorses) or a form of old-age insurance (where the state has not established it). Girls in many cultures are a liability; a dowry which may be a sizable economic burden must be provided to marry them off. (A working-class American who has to provide for the weddings of three or four daughters may appreciate the problem.) In other cultures, girls are profitably sold. In our own culture, prestige differences are attached to the sex of one's children, which seem to vary among the ethnic groups and classes (11, pp. 6-7).

Our expectations as to what use sex control might be put in our society are not a matter of idle speculation. Findings on sex preferences are based on both direct "soft" and indirect "hard" evidence. For soft evidence, we have data on preferences parents expressed in terms of the number of boys and girls to be conceived in a hypothetical situation in which parents would have a choice in the matter. Winston studied 55 upperclassmen, recording anonymously their desire for marriage and children. Fifty-two expected to be married some day; all but one of these desired children; expectation of two or three children were common. In total, 86 boys were desired as compared to 52 girls, which amounts to a 65 percent greater demand for males than for females (12).

A second study of attitudes, this one conducted on an Indianapolis sample, in 1941, found similar preferences for boys. Here, while about half of the parents had no preferences (52.8 percent of the wives and 42.3 percent of the husbands), and whereas the wives with a preference tended to favor having about as many boys as girls (21.8 percent to 25.4 percent), many more husbands wished for boys (47.7 percent as compared to 9.9 percent) (13).

Such expressions of preference are not necessarily good indicators of actual behavior. Hence of particular interest is "hard" evidence, of what parents actually did—in the limited area of choice they already have: the sex composition of the family at the point they decided to stop having children. Many other and more powerful factors affect a couple's decision to curb further births, and the sex composition of their children is one of them. That is, if a couple has three girls and it strongly desires a boy, this is one reason it will try "once more." By comparing the number of families which had only or mainly girls and "tried once more" to those which had only or mainly boys, we gain some data as to which is considered a less desirable condition. A somewhat different line was followed in an early study. Winston studied 5466 completed families and found that there were 8329 males born alive as compared to 7434 females, which gives a sex ratio at birth of 112.0. The sex ratio of the last child, which is of course much more indicative, was 117.4 (2952 males to 2514 females). That is, significantly more families stopped having children after they had a boy than after they had a girl.

The actual preference for boys, once sex control is available, is likely to be larger than these studies suggest for the following reasons. Attitudes, especially where there is no actual choice, reflect what people believe they ought to believe in, which, in our culture, is equality of the sexes. To prefer to produce boys is lower class and discriminatory. Many middle-class parents might entertain such preferences but be either unaware of them or unwilling to express them to an interviewer, especially since at present there is no possibility of determining whether a child will be a boy or a girl.

Also, in the situations studied so far, attempts to change the sex composition of a family involved having more children than the couple wanted, and the chances of achieving the desired composition were 50 percent or lower. Thus, for instance, if parents wanted, let us say, three children including at least one boy, and they had tried three times and were blessed with girls, they would now desire a boy strongly enough to overcome whatever resistance they had to have additional children before they would try again. This is much less practical than taking a medication which is, let us say, 99.8 percent effective and having the number of children you actually want and are able to support. That is, sex control by a medication is to be expected to be significantly more widely practiced than conceiving more children and gambling on what their sex will be.

Finally, and most importantly, such decisions are not made in the abstract, but affected by the social milieu. For instance, in small *kibbutzim* many more children used to be born in October and November each year than any other months because the community used to consider it undesirable for the children to enter classes in the middle of the school year, which in Israel begins after the high holidays, in October. Similarly, sex control—even if it were taboo or unpopular at first—could become quite widely practiced once it became fashionable.

In the following discussion we bend over backward by assuming that actual behavior would reveal a smaller preference than the existing data and preceding analysis would lead one to expect. We shall assume only a 7 percent difference between the number of boys and girls to be born alive due to sex control, coming on top of the 51.25 to 48.75 existing biological pattern, thus making for 54.75 boys to 45.25 girls, or a surplus of 9.5 boys out of every hundred. This would amount to a surplus of 357,234 in the United States, if sex control were practiced in a 1965-like population (*14*).

The extent to which such a sex imbalance will cause societal dislocations is in part a matter of the degree to which the effect will be cumulative. It is one thing to have an unbalanced baby crop one year, and quite another to produce such a crop several years in a row. Accumulation would reduce the extent to which girl shortages can be overcome by one age group raiding older and younger ones.

Some demographers seem to believe in an invisible hand (as it once was popular to expect in economics), and suggest that overproduction of boys will increase the value of girls and hence increase their production, until a balance is attained under controlled conditions which will be similar to the natural one. We need not repeat here the reasons such invisible arrangements frequently do not work; the fact is they simply cannot be relied upon, as recurrent economic crises in pre-Keynesian days or overpopulation show.

Second, one ought to note the deep-seated roots of the boy-favoring factors. Although there is no complete agreement on what these factors are, and there is little research, we do know that they are difficult and slow to change. For instance, Winston argued that mothers prefer boys as a substitute for their own fathers, out of search for security or Freudian considerations. Fathers prefer boys because boys can more readily achieve success in our society (and in most others). Neither of these factors is likely to change rapidly if the percentage of boys born increases a few percentage points. We do not need to turn to alarmist conclusions, but we ought to consider what the societal effects of sex control might be under conditions of relatively small imbalance which, as we see it, will cause a significant (although not necessarily very high) male surplus, and a surplus which will be cumulative.

Societal Consequences

In exploring what the societal consequences may be, we again need not rely on the speculation of what such a society would be like; we have much experience and some data on societies whose sex ratio was thrown off balance by war or immigration. For example, in 1960 New York City had 343,470 more females than males, a surplus of 68,366 in the 20- to 34-age category alone (15).

We note, first, that most forms of social behavior are sex correlated, and hence that changes in sex composition are very likely to affect most aspects of social life. For instance, women read more books, see more plays, and in general consume more culture than men in the contemporary United States. Also, women attend church more often and are typically charged with the moral education of children. Males, by contrast, account for a much higher proportion of crime than females. A significant and cumulative male surplus will thus produce a society with some of the rougher features of a frontier town. And, it should be noted, the diminution of the number of agents of moral education and the increase in the number of criminals would accentuate already existing tendencies which point in these directions, thus magnifying social problems which are already overburdening our society.

Interracial and interclass tensions are likely to be intensified because some groups, lower classes and minorities specifically (16), seem to be more male oriented than the rest of the society. Hence while the sex imbalance in a society-wide average may be only a few percentage points, that of some groups is likely to be much higher. This may produce an especially high boy surplus in lower status groups. These extra boys would seek girls in higher status groups (or in some other religious group than their own) (*11*)—in which they also will be scarce.

On the lighter side, men vote systematically and significantly more Democratic than women; as the Republican party has been losing consistently in the number of supporters over the last generation anyhow, another 5-point loss could undermine the two-party system to a point where Democratic control would be uninterrupted. (It is already the norm, with Republicans having occupied the White House for 8 years over the last 36.) Other forms of imbalance which cannot be predicted are to be expected. "All social life is affected by the proportions of the sexes. Wherever there exists a considerable predominance of one sex over the other, in point of numbers, there is less prospect of a well-ordered social life." "Unbalanced numbers inexorably produce unbalanced behavior" (*17*).

Society would be very unlikely to collapse even if the sex ratio were to be much more seriously imbalanced than we expect. Societies are surprisingly flexible and adaptive entities. When asked what would be expected to happen if sex control were available on a mass basis, Davis, the well-known demographer, stated that some delay in the age of marriage of the male, some rise in prostitution and in homosexuality, and some increase in the number of males who will never marry are likely to result. Thus, all of the "costs" that would be generated by sex control will probably not be charged against one societal sector, that is, would not entail only, let us say, a sharp rise in prostitution, but would be distributed among several sectors and would therefore be more readily absorbed. An informal examination of the situation in the U.S.S.R. and Germany after World War II (sex ratio was 77.7 in the latter) as well as Israel in early immigration periods, supports Davis' nonalarmist position. We must ask, though, are the costs justified? The dangers are not apocalyptical; but are they worth the gains to be made?

A Balance of Values

We deliberately chose a low-key example of the effects of science on society. One can provide much more dramatic ones; for example, the invention of new "psychedelic" drugs whose damage to genes will become known only much later (LSD was reported to have such effects), drugs which cripple the fetus (which has already occurred with the marketing of thalidomide), and the attempts to control birth with devices which may produce cancer (early versions of the intrauterine device were held to have such an effect). But let us stay with a finding which generates only relatively small amounts of human misery, relatively well distributed among various sectors, so as not to severely undermine society but only add, maybe only marginally, to the considerable social problems we already face. Let us assume that we only add to the unhappiness of seven out of every 100 born (what we consider minimum imbalance to be generated), who will not find mates and will have to avail themselves of prostitution, homosexuality, or be condemned to enforced bachelorhood. (If you know someone who is desperate to be married but cannot find a mate, this discussion will be less abstract for you; now multiply this by 357,234 per annum.) Actually, to be fair, one must subtract from the unhappiness that sex control almost surely will produce, the joy it will bring to parents who will be able to order the sex of their children; but as of now, this is for most, not an intensely felt need, and it seems a much smaller joy compared to the sorrows of the unmatable mates.

We already recognize some rights of human guinea pigs. Their safety and privacy are not to be violated even if this means delaying the progress of science. The "rest" of the society, those who are not the subjects of research, and who are nowadays as much affected as those in the laboratory, have been accorded fewer rights. Theoretically, new knowledge, the basis of new devices and drugs, is not supposed to leave the inner circles of science before its safety has been tested on animals or volunteers, and in some instances approved by a government agency, mainly the Federal Drug Administration. But as the case of lysergic acid diethylamide (LSD) shows, the trip from reporting of a finding in a scientific journal to the bloodstream of thousands of citizens may be an extremely short one. The transition did take quite a number of years, from the days in 1943 when Hoffman, one of the two men who synthesized LSD-25 at Sandoz Research Laboratories first felt its hallucinogenic effect, until the early 1960's, when it "spilled" into illicit campus use. (The trip from legitimate research, its use at Harvard, to illicit unsupervised use was much shorter.) The point is that no additional technologies had to be developed; the distance from the chemical formula to illicit composition required in effect no additional steps.

More generally, Western civilization, ever since the invention of the steam engine, has proceeded on the assumption that society must adjust to new technologies. This is a central meaning of what we refer to when we speak about an industrial revolution; we think about a society being transformed and not just a new technology being introduced into a society which continues to sustain its prior values and institutions. Although the results are not an unmixed blessing (for instance, pollution and traffic casualties), on balance the benefits in terms of gains in standards of living and life expectancy much outweigh the costs. [Whether the same gains could be made with fewer costs if society would more effectively guide its transformation and technology inputs, is a question less often discussed (18).] Nevertheless we must ask, especially with the advent of nuclear arms, if we can expect such a favorable balance in the future. We are aware that single innovations may literally blow up societies or civilization; we must also realize that the rate of social changes required by the accelerating stream of technological innovations, each less dramatic by itself, may supersede the rate at which society can absorb. Could we not regulate to some extent the pace and impact of the technological inputs and select among them without, by every such act, killing the goose that lays the golden eggs?

Scientists often retort with two arguments. Science is in the business of searching for truths, not that of manufacturing technologies. The applications of scientific findings are not determined by the scientists, but by society, politicians, corporations, and the citizens. Two scientists discovered the formula which led to the composition of LSD, but chemists do not determine whether it is used to accelerate psychotherapy or to create psychoses, or, indeed, whether it is used at all, or whether, like thousands of other studies and formulas, it is ignored. Scientists split the atom, but they did not decide whether particles would be used to produce energy to water deserts or super-bombs.

Second, the course of science is unpredictable, and any new lead, if followed, may produce unexpected bounties; to curb some lines of inquiry—because they may have dangerous outcomes—may well force us to forego some major payoffs; for example, if one were to forbid the study of sex control one might retard the study of birth control. Moreover, leads which seem "safe" may have dangerous outcomes. Hence, ultimately, only if science were stopped altogether, might findings which are potentially dangerous be avoided.

These arguments are often presented as if they themselves were empirically verified or logically true statements. Actually they are a formula which enables the scientific community to protect itself from external intervention and control. An empirical study of the matter may well show that science does thrive in societies where scientists are given less freedom than the preceding model implies science must have, for example, in the Soviet Union. Even in the West in science some limitations on work are recognized and the freedom to study is not always seen as the ultimate value. Whereas some scientists are irritated when the health or privacy of their subject curbs the progress of their work, most scientists seem to recognize the priority of these other considerations. (Normative considerations also much affect the areas studied; compare, for instance, the high concern with a cancer cure to the almost complete unwillingness of sociologists, since 1954, to retest the finding that separate but equal education is not feasible.)

One may suggest that the society at large deserves the same protection as human subjects do from research. That is, the scientific community cannot be excused from the responsibility of asking what effects its endeavors have on the community. On the contrary, only an extension of the existing codes and mechanisms of self-control will ultimately protect science from a societal backlash and the heavy hands of external regulation. The intensification of the debate over the scientists' responsibilities with regard to the impacts of their findings is by itself one way of exercising it, because it alerts more scientists to the fact that the areas they choose to study, the ways they communicate their findings (to each other and to the community), the alliances they form or avoid with corporate and governmental interests—all these affect the use to which their work is put. It is simply not true that a scientist working on cancer research and one working on biological warfare are equally likely to come up with a new weapon and a new vaccine. Leads are not that random, and applications are not that readily transferable from one area of application to another.

Additional research on the societal impact of various kinds of research may help to clarify the issues. Such research even has some regulatory impact. For instance, frequently when a drug is shown to have been released prematurely, standards governing release of experimental drugs to mass production are tightened (19), which in effect means fewer, more carefully supervised technological inputs into society; at least society does not have to cope with dubious findings. Additional progress may be achieved by studying empirically the effects that various mechanisms of self-regulation actually have on the work of scientists. For example, urging the scientific community to limit its study of some topics and focus on others may not retard science; for instance, sociology is unlikely to suffer from being now much more reluctant to concern itself with how the U.S. Army may stabilize or undermine foreign governments than it was before the blowup of Project Camelot (20).

In this context, it may be noted that the systematic attempt to bridge the "two cultures" and to popularize science has undesirable side effects which aggravate the problem at hand. Mathematical formulas, Greek or Latin terminology, and jargon were major filters which allowed scientists in the past to discuss findings with each other without the nonprofessionals listening in. Now, often even preliminary findings are reported in the mass media and lead to policy adaptations, mass use, even legislation (21), long before scientists have had a chance to double-check the findings themselves and their implications. True, even in the days when science was much more esoteric, one could find someone who could translate its findings into lay language and abuse it; but the process is much accelerated by well-meaning men (and foundations) who feel that although science ought to be isolated from society, society should keep up with science as much as possible. Perhaps the public relations efforts on behalf of science ought to be reviewed and regulated so that science may remain free.

A system of regulation which builds on the difference between science and technology, with some kind of limitations on the technocrats serving to protect societies coupled with little curbing of scientists themselves, may turn out to be much more crucial. The societal application of most new scientific findings and principles advances through a sequence of steps, sometimes referred to as the R & D process. An abstract finding or insight frequently must be translated into a technique, procedure or hardware, which in turn must be developed, tested, and mass-produced, before it affects society. While in some instances, like that of LSD, the process is extremely short in that it requires few if any steps in terms of further development of the idea, tools, and procedures, in most instances the process is long and expensive. It took, for instance, about $2 billion and several thousand applied scientists and technicians to make the first atomic weapons after the basic principles of atomic fission were discovered. Moreover, technologies often have a life of their own; for example, the intrauterine device did not spring out of any application of a new finding in fertility research but grew out of the evolution of earlier technologies.

The significance of the distinction between the basic research ("real" science) and later stages of research is that, first, the damage caused (if any) seems usually to be caused by the technologies and not by the science applied in their development. Hence if there were ways to curb damaging technologies, scientific research could maintain its almost absolute, follow-any-lead autonomy and society would be protected.

Second, and most important, the norms to which applied researchers and technicians subscribe and the supervisory practices, which already prevail, are very different than those which guide basic research. Applied research and technological work are already intensively guided by societal, even political, preferences. Thus, while about $2 billion a year of R & D money are spent on basic research more or less in ways the scientists see fit, the other $13 billion or so are spent on projects specifically ordered, often in great detail, by government authorities, for example, the development of a later version of a missile or a "spiced-up" tear gas. Studies of R & D corporations—in which much of this work is carried out, using thousands of professionals organized in supervised teams which are given specific assignments—pointed out that wide freedom of research simply does not exist here. A team assigned to cover a nose cone with many different alloys and to test which is the most heat-resistant is currently unlikely to stumble upon, let us say, a new heart pump, and if it were to come upon almost any other lead, the boss would refuse to allow the team to pursue the lead, using the corporation's time and funds specifically contracted for other purposes.

Not only are applied research and technological developments guided by economic and political considerations but also there is no evidence that they suffer from such guidance. Of course, one can overdirect any human activity, even the carrying of logs, and thus undermine morale, satisfaction of the workers, and their productivity, but such tight direction is usually not exercised in R & D work nor is it required for our purposes. So far guidance has been largely to direct efforts toward specific goals, and it has been largely corporate, in the sense that the goals have been chiefly set by the industry (for example, building flatter TV sets) or mission-oriented government agencies (for instance, hit the moon before the Russians). Some "preventive" control, like the suppression of run-proof nylon stockings, is believed to have taken place and to have been quite effective.

I am not suggesting that the direction given to technology by society has been a wise one. Frankly, I would like to see much less concern with military hardware and outer space and much more investment in domestic matters; less in developing new consumer gadgets and more in advancing the technologies of the public sector (education, welfare, and health); less concern with nature and more with society. The point though is that, for good or bad, technology is largely already socially guided, and hence the argument that its undesirable effects cannot be curbed because it cannot take guidance and survive is a false one.

What may have to be considered now is a more preventive and more national effective guidance, one that would discourage the development of those technologies which, studies would suggest, are likely to cause significantly more damage than payoffs. Special bodies, preferably to be set up and controlled by the scientific community itself, could be charged with such regulation, although their decrees might have to be as enforceable as those of the Federal Drug Administration. (The Federal Drug Administration, which itself is overworked and understaffed, deals mainly with medical and not societal effects of new technologies.) Such bodies could rule, for instance, that whereas fertility research ought to go on uncurbed, sex-control procedures for human beings are not to be developed.

One cannot be sure that such bodies would come up with the right decisions. But they would have several features which make it likely that they would come up with better decisions than the present system for the following reasons: (i) they would be responsible for protecting society, a responsibility which so far is not institutionalized; (ii) if they act irresponsibly, the staff might be replaced, let us say by a vote of the appropriate scientific associations; and (iii) they would draw on data as to the societal effects of new (or anticipated) technologies, in part to be generated at their initiative, while at present—to the extent such supervisory decisions are made at all—they are frequently based on folk knowledge.

Most of us recoil at any such notion of regulating science, if only at the implementation (or technological) end of it, which actually is not science at all. We are inclined to see in such control an opening wedge which may lead to deeper and deeper penetration of society into the scientific activity. Actually, one may hold the opposite view—that unless societal costs are diminished by some acts of self-regulation at the stage in the R & D process where it hurts least, the society may "backlash" and with a much heavier hand slap on much more encompassing and throttling controls.

The efficacy of increased education of scientists to their responsibilities, of strengthening the barriers between intrascientific communications and the community at large, and of self-imposed, late-phase controls may not suffice. Full solution requires considerable international cooperation, at least among the top technology-producing countries. The various lines of approach to protecting society discussed here may be unacceptable to the reader. The problem though must be faced, and it requires greater attention as we are affected by an accelerating technological output with ever-increasing societal ramifications, which jointly may overload society's capacity to adapt and individually cause more unhappiness than any group of men has a right to inflict on others, however noble their intentions.

References and Notes

1. E. Witschi, personal communication.
2. P. E. Lindahl, *Nature* 181, 784 (1958).
3. V. N. Schröder and N. K. Koltsov, *ibid.* 131, 329 (1933).

4. M. J. Gordon, *Sci. Amer.* **199**, 87-94 (1958).

5. F. Unterberger, *Deutsche Med. Wochenschr.* **56**, 304 (1931).

6. R. C. Cook, *J. Hered.* **31**, 270 (1940).

7. J. Schmookler, *Invention and Economic Growth* (Harvard Univ. Press, Cambridge, Mass., 1966).

8. Many people prefer adoption to artificial insemination. See G. M. Vernon and J. A. Boadway, *Marriage Family Liv.* **21**, 43 (1959).

9. H. Kahn and A. J. Wiener, *The Year 2000: A Framework for Speculation on the Next Thirty-Three Years* (Macmillan, New York, 1967), p. 53.

10. H. J. Muller, *Science* **134**, 643 (1961).

11. C. F. Westoff, "The social-psychological structure of fertility," in *International Population Conference* (International Union for Scientific Study of Population, Vienna, 1959).

12. S. Winston, *Amer. J. Sociol.* **38**, 226 (1932). For a critical comment which does not affect the point made above, see H. Weiler, *ibid.* **65**, 298 (1959).

13. J. E. Clare and C. V. Kiser, *Milbank Mem. Fund Quart.* **29**, 441 (1951). See also D. S. Freedman, R. Freedman, P. K. Whelpton, *Amer. J. Sociol.* **66**, 141 (1960).

14. Based on the figure for 1965 registered births (adjusted for those unreported) of 3,760,358 from *Vital Statistics of the United States 1965* (U.S. Government Printing Office, Washington, D.C., 1965), vol. 1, pp. 1-4, section 1, table 1-2. If there is a "surplus" of 9.5 boys out of every hundred, there would have been $3,760,358/100 \times 9.5 = 357,234$ surplus in 1965.

15. Calculated from C. Winkler, Ed., *Statistical Guide 1965 for New York City* (Department of Commerce and Industrial Development, New York, 1965), p. 17.

16. Winston suggests the opposite but he refers to sex control produced through birth control which is more widely practiced in higher classes, especially in the period in which his study was conducted, more than a generation ago.

17. Quoted in J. H. Greenberg, *Numerical Sex Disproportion: A Study in Demographic Determinism* (Univ. of Colorado Press, Boulder, 1950), p. 1. The sources indicated are A. F. Weber, *The Growth of Cities in the Nineteenth Century,* Studies in History, Economics, and Public Law, vol. 11, p. 85, and H. von Hentig, *Crime: Causes and Conditions* (McGraw-Hill, New York, 1947), p. 121.

18. For one of the best discussions, see E. E. Morison, *Men, Machines, and Modern Times* (M.I.T. Press, Cambridge, Mass., 1966). See also A. Etzioni, *The Active Society: A Theory of Societal and Political Processes* (Free Press, New York, 1968), chaps. 1 and 21.

19. See reports in The New York *Times*: "Tranquilizer is put under U.S. curbs; side effects noted," 6 December 1967; "F.D.A. is studying reported

reactions to arthritis drug," 19 March 1967; "F.D.A. adds 2 drugs to birth defect list," 3 January 1967. On 24 May 1966, Dr. S. F. Yolles, director of the National Institute of Mental Health, predicted in testimony before a Senate subcommittee: "The next 5 to 10 years . . . will see a hundredfold increase in the number and types of drugs capable of affecting the mind."

20. I. L. Horowitz, *The Rise and Fall of Project Camelot* (M.I.T. Press, Cambridge, Mass., 1967).

21. For a detailed report, see testimony by J. D. Cooper, on 28 February 1967, before the subcommittee on government research of the committee on government operations, United States Senate, 90th Congress (First Session on Biomedical Development, Evaluation of Existing Federal Institutions), pp. 46-61.

Ethical Issues in Future Medicine

E. Fuller Torrey

The recent epidemic of heart transplants and synthesis of active viral DNA have drawn national attention. These exciting developments in medical technology have evoked unprecedented interest among the general population, and clearly showed how rapidly such technology is advancing. They also showed, by the comments of the doctors, how grossly unprepared medicine is to deal with the problems wrought by these developments. The surgeons, cardiologists, and geneticists all agreed that great advances were occurring, but cried out in bewilderment when asked to comment on the ethical and social issues that were raised by their work. Indeed, some even seemed surprised that their work had raised other issues at all.

Extracted from Chapter 3, "Ethical Issues in Future Medicine" by E. Fuller Torrey in *Toward Century 21* edited by C. S. Wallia, © 1970 by Basic Books, Inc., Publishers, New York. Torrey is a psychiatrist at Stanford University Medical School. For two years he was the Public Health Director for the Peace Corps in Ethiopia. He is the editor of *Ethical Issues in Medicine: The Role of the Physician in Today's Society.*

Following their bewilderment they rapidly convened numerous panels and committees of various medical groups, all committed to studying the ethical and social issues being raised. The general public asked embarrassing questions, and seemed disconcerted that some of the answers had not been thought through earlier, during the work rather than post facto. Perhaps sensing the leadership vacuum in medicine, legislators talked of creating public committees at the state and national level.

These developments represent the contemporary scene in medical technology quite nicely—mindless machines plowing relentlessly forward, oblivious to where they are going or what problems they may bring. There is no sense of direction except forward, to bigger and better machines!

Heart transplants and viral DNA are not the only developments taking place that have profound implications—only the most widely publicized. In order to obtain a true perspective on the magnitude of the problems both current and those on the immediate horizon, a brief summary of advancing technology is necessary.

First, in the area of contraception, one-shot contraceptives that are effective for up to 12 months are already being tested in humans. Other contraceptives, which can be implanted beneath the skin and probably last up to 20 years (unless you want it removed long enough to have a baby), will be tested within a year. Chemical contraceptives for males are also being tested on animals. Technically, it will soon be easy for a government to place a chemical in the water to cause statewide or national contraception, then issue a counteragent as a license to reproduce. Proposals for the control of population by abolishing the income tax deduction for children, or even putting a tax *on* children, have been seriously made.

Turning to artificial insemination, it is already claimed to be possible to separate male from female spermatozoa using chemical or electrical means, and thereby regulate the sex ratio if this were accompanied by artificial insemination. Even without artificial insemination, Nobel Laureate Joshua Lederberg has predicted a chemical method for biasing the sex ratio within 20 years.

Frozen sperm stored up to 2½ years has already been used successfully to inseminate 18 women. There is no known reason why this could not be extended indefinitely so that posthumous paternity could become as common in humans as it already is in bulls. The late H. J. Muller extended this idea to the creation of sperm banks stocked with sperm from outstanding men. Parents could then select the traits they wanted from a male and have the sperm artificially inseminated into the wife. It might be rather like selecting a new car or house, and would fit well into our consumer economy.

One step beyond freezing sperm is the possibility of removing a fertilized ovum from the mother and implanting it into a foster mother to grow to maturity and be born. It has already been accomplished not only in mice, but between species as well. Female sheep were fertilized by pedigreed rams, then the fertilized ovum was removed and implanted into female rabbits. The rabbits were flown to South Africa where the fertilized ova were removed and implanted into other female sheep. They grew and eventually were born. If eventually applied to humans, women who didn't want to carry their own child could hire a mercenary, a twentieth-century variety of a wet nurse, to do it for them.

The synthesis of active viral DNA raises the issue of the creation of life. Exactly where life begins at a chemical level is a matter of semantics; some consider that it has already been created, at a biological level. In 1961 an Italian researcher fertilized a human ovum with sperm and kept it alive for 29 days until it was the size of a pea. Noting that it was starting to grow into a monstrosity, he terminated the experiment—but only after he had given it conditional baptism and extreme unction. His work caused such a religious furor that subsequent experiments along these lines have not been publicized at all.

Other researchers have been trying to keep a 10-week-old human fetus expelled by a miscarriage artificially alive. If it begins to sound like the Central London Hatchery in Huxley's *Brave New World*, it is nevertheless what is technically possible. George Bernard Shaw had the children of the future emerging from eggs at the age of 18, an idea not without appeal at times.

A new medical technique for abortions, a vacuum extractor, is now widely in use in Eastern Europe. It is said to be 97 per cent successful, have minimal complications, and be able to do the job in 2 minutes—almost less time than it takes to get pregnant.

Progress is also being made in developing chemical methods of abortion. Recently "morning after" pills were tested that are effective up to 6 days after conception. And Sweden is now testing a chemical that causes abortions anytime in the early months. When it is perfected and becomes widely disseminated, it will revolutionize abortions and make the curette a museum piece.

Although direct changes of chromosomes by way of genetic surgery is still in the distant future, much work is taking place on embryos still in the uterus. Lambs, dogs, and monkeys have been removed from their mother's uterus as often as three times, had research procedures performed on them, and were then returned to the uterus to be born normally. Direct surgical intervention on the human fetus is imminent.

At the other end of the life spectrum, dramatic events are also occurring. Medical technology has made it possible to freeze humans at death, although not yet with much hope of being revived. Using machines, humans can be kept alive for longer and longer periods. In 1965, European doctors took a heart from a man who had died 1 hour earlier. They attached the apparently lifeless organ to a supply of oxygenated blood and it immediately began beating on its own until it was stopped by the researchers 6 hours later. In another experiment the brains of monkeys were removed and kept alive for 18 hours.

The heart transplants focused attention on the rapid advances in this field. They are only the latest in a continuum of successful transplants that have been performed since 1954 with kidneys, spleens, livers, pancreas, intestines, and ovaries. The Russians have claimed success in transplanting testicles and in grafting the heads of one dog to another. Certainly things will not stop here, and when immunology solves the antibody problem, a new era of unlimited transplants will begin. Even the sine qua non, sex, is being respectably changed at leading hospitals in the United States.

Artificial organs are also being rapidly developed. Artificial kidneys and cardiac pacemakers are widespread, with thousands of people being dependent on these machines for their life. Mechanical hearts and livers are being experimented with, as are synthetic bones and skin. It may be possible also to chemically change the color of skin, a development that would produce some of the most perplexing problems of all.

Machines are even making inroads into psychiatry and the human mind. Kenneth Colby, a psychiatrist at Stanford, is attempting to program a computer to do therapy; he calls it "the mad doctor." Conditioning by an electric shock was recently performed in England to cure an unfaithful husband of his illicit desires. Two psychiatrists in New York demonstrated that previously hypnotized subjects could be rehypnotized via television.

Finally, the possible uses of machines to control the mind are well illustrated by the work of Delgado at Yale. He has implanted electrodes in the brains of monkeys and caused them to reject their offspring when stimulated by a remote control radio signal. He also implanted electrodes into the brains of bulls and was able to stop their charge toward a matador in mid-flight by activating the signal.

The list of technological developments in medicine stretches on, but the point has been made. Heart transplants and the synthesis of active viral DNA are not the only developments bringing profound ethical and social problems, nor are they even the most awesome.

The Technological Revolution

Let it not be thought that it is only the medical machines that are running away from their creators. Disturbing effects of the technological revolution may be felt in all fields. Oil tankers with unlimited capacities are built without considering the consequences of a wreck. Detergents foam on our streams and lakes. Automobiles outrace safety standards, urban noises challenge our eardrums, and hidden eyes and ears invade our privacy.

Before answers can be found to these problems, it is necessary to understand two characteristics of the technological revolution—that it is mindless and that it is neutral. It is mindless because pure science is simply a desire to know, to uncover the facts, to unlock the secrets. A mind must be superimposed onto it if it is to have any limitations. The technological developments described above are inevitable unless man actively decides to stop their development. Scientists will continue learning how to unwind the intricacies of DNA, transplant organs, and implant electrodes in the brain as long as there are unknown areas and unless they are specifically told not to.

It is neutral because the changes wrought by the technological revolution in themselves are neither good nor bad. They acquire a value only by the way in which they are used. Science can tell us what we can do but not what we should do. It can tell us how to do something but not if we should do it. The potentials for good and evil of many of the developments described above stagger the imagination and recall the harnessing of atomic power.

Because the revolution challenging medicine and mankind is mindless and because it is neutral, then mind must be imposed on it to control it and determine its values. The present failure to do this has created a wide gap between man's technological and his humanistic imagination. Mindless technology threatens to become a Frankenstein, destroying its creator. The visions of the future would become specters. It is a warning being sounded increasingly often by thoughtful men, the warning asked editorially by *The New York Times,* on the morning after Hiroshima had been bombed: "Can mankind grow up quickly enough to win the race between civilization and disaster?"

So far the revolution has been, in the words of Michael Harrington, accidental. It has evolved episodically and randomly, following the whims of chance rather than the dictates of reason. The technological revolution has solved many problems, but left untended it has created many others. What remains to be done is to climb astride the machine and begin to truly direct its course. Only then will science and technology become a tool of man rather than enslave him.

Controlling the Technological Revolution

When one sets out to find avenues for exploring means to bring the machine under control, many impediments are encountered. One of the biggest of these is the deification of the scientist and his tools by the public at large. Certainly this is true in medicine. The medical scientist and his test tubes are accorded almost supernatural power by most people. As long as this deification continues it will be difficult to objectively evaluate and control the developments of technology—man is reluctant to do battle with a god.

Another impediment to solving problems wrought by technology is the decline of religious influence. Whether one considers this an actual impediment or the removal of an impediment depends upon his frame of reference; all I mean is that the quick, easy answers formerly supplied by a theological framework are no longer readily available. In the past, religion and medicine were wedded and philosophical problems encountered in medicine were answered theologically. Religion and medicine have now parted, though they remain friends. This has been accompanied by a decline in religious influence in general and by technology reaching out to capture even more of God's power, including the power over life and death. The net result of all this is to leave man free but free-floating, without the barriers that religion had erected beyond which technology could not pass but also without any limit to the horizon. One Catholic scholar sums it up accordingly: "The scientific humanist may be as much repelled by the prospect of the replacement of the family by the stud farms of artificial insemination as the Christian, but unlike the latter he has no final argument against it. If the power is there why should it not be used?"

A third impediment to clear thinking toward answers to these problems is the increasing dehumanization of our society. It is not possible to accurately identify and solve the problems discussed above unless man is identified as man. This is a well-worn theme and will not be replayed here except to note it. Erich Fromm has summarized it as an era "in which men build machines which act like men and develop men to act like machines, . . . an era of dehumanization and alienation in which men are transformed into things and become appendices to the process of production and consumption."

Physicians and Society

In spite of these impediments to bringing technology under control, ways must be found to do it. Who is to provide the answers? What role should the doctor play? Regarding the first, public policy should determine the ultimate answers. The social and philosophical problems of medicine do not belong to doctors alone, nor to theologians, lawyers, or any other single group. They are problems that belong to everybody. Abortion is not exclusively a problem of doctors because they wield the curette any more than chemical warfare is exclusively a problem of pilots because they push the release lever.

But in order for public opinion to be operative and effective, it must be informed. This is where the doctor's role begins. The medical profession should play a major role in outlining the facts, clarifying the alternatives, and establishing the limits within medical possibilities. Only with this perspective can intelligent discussion take place, and only thus will society know what it is choosing.

But doctors have an obligation to society beyond simply outlining the facts on these complex ethical and social questions. Their obligation extends to providing leadership. The issues should be raised by the medical profession itself; it should not be in the position of waiting until others raise them. If the profession fails to accept the leadership in promoting discussion of these problems, then its prerogative will be usurped by others such as the legal profession. But since law is a reflection of customs of the community, then it is less appropriate for law to assume leadership on these issues. Law enters to codify after the discussion has taken place.

Physicians generally fear playing god. What should be feared equally as much is a failure to play even man. Frequently in the past, medicine has been accused of adopting an ostrich-like posture on social issues, an accusation not without foundation. What medicine definitely does not need is the gunrunner mentality of simply supplying services to those who request it.

A doctor can no longer afford the luxury of sitting on the sidelines and watching. He now has power—real power, increasing power. Whereas 50 years ago he had to rely on digitalis leaves and a steady look in the eye, he now implants an electronic pacemaker for the former and shines a laser beam in the latter. Doctors now have power to do things, and this power is growing every day. It is a frightening power. Whether they want it or not, doctors are going to have to accept increasing responsibility for the way in which this power is used.

Forums for Discussion

If these problems are to be discussed, they will require forums. What forums are appropriate? What forums are already being used? What forums should be developed?

Popular periodicals are one forum that are already in use. They reflect the rapidly increasing public interest in and awareness of some of the issues. For instance, in the *Reader's Guide to Periodical Literature* between 1951 and 1953 there were only 18 articles on birth control, whereas between 1963 and 1965 there were 120. Headings such as euthanasia, vasectomy, and artificial insemination were not even listed in the early period but are included in the latter.

Doctors should not hesitate to contribute to this body of literature. The traditional hypersensitivity of the medical profession to publicity and advertising has led to a vacuum of reliable information for popular consumption. The vacuum becomes filled by flashy "science writers" whose facts are less accurate although their prose may be more palatable. The same may be said of books for popular consumption.

Certain nonmedical institutions lend themselves well to being forums for discussion of these questions. An example is the Center for the Study of Democratic Institutions, "a non-profit, independent educational institution devoted to clarifying basic issues confronting a democratic society." Thus far, the Center has not dealt with any of the problems outlined above in any detail, but a model such as this could be developed and would be ideal for developing the dialogue that is needed. An example of what can be done along these lines was the excellent symposium in 1963 sponsored by the CIBA Foundation in England entitled, "Man and His Future." Other nonmedical institutions that have attempted to project the development of medical technology into the future are the Rand Corporation, the Hudson Institute, and the Commission on the Year 2000 of the American Academy of the Arts and Sciences.

Private industry has also taken an interest in some of these questions. At a recent insurance convention, for instance, the companies were urged to cover people who wish to be frozen at death, and later, hopefully, revived. A rubber company is exploring artificial organs as a possible new market. The suitability of industry as a forum for discussion of these issues is sharply limited by their financial involvement, as can be readily seen.

Churches are another possible forum. In the past they have often taken the initiative in discussing these issues. With technology moving as fast as it is, however, organized religion must strive harder if it hopes to keep abreast of developments. Galileo proposed the Copernican Solar System in 1611, but it was not accepted by the Catholic Church until 1820. The challenge to religions to understand and respond is obvious; failure to do this may well result in a further reduction of their sphere of influence in medicine.

The federal government has recently shown interest in some of these problems. Its involvement in birth control, for instance, has rapidly enlarged. The distribution and costs of medical services have come under increasingly close federal scrutiny as the government has become involved in subsidizing it, and in 1967 the Public Health Service organized a National Center for Health Services Research and Development to study it. In 1966 Senator Fred Harris of Oklahoma, head of the Subcommittee on Government Research, held a four-day meeting on present trends in science. And later the same year Senator Edmund Muskie of Maine introduced a resolution calling for the creation of a committee on technology and the human environment. This resolution was echoed a year later by Senator Walter Mondale of Minnesota in response to the heart transplants. Such efforts are appropriate and potentially useful as long as the federal government is just one of several forums discussing these questions. To assign discussions of this nature predominantly to the government, however, would run the perpetual risk to a democracy of fiat replacing discussion and dialogue. At the international governmental level, the United Nations has dealt with these problems quite sparingly to date. Its potential could certainly be developed.

Universities can play a useful role in promoting discussion of the ethical and social problems facing medicine. Symposia have been held, such as at Dartmouth in 1961 entitled "The Great Issues of Conscience in Modern Medicine," at Ohio Wesleyan in 1963 called "The Control of Human Heredity and Evolution," and at Duke University in 1967 on "Medical Science and Moral Responsibility." On an ongoing level institutes can be organized, such as the Center for the Study of Culture and Technology at Harvard, the new Institute for the Study of Science in Human Affairs at Columbia, and the Program of Policy Studies in Science and Technology at George Washington University. The potential for such institutes as a forum for discussing these problems is unlimited; unfortunately there are but very few of them, and their work has only begun.

The Role of the American Medical Association

Turning to organized medicine, the American Medical Association would theoretically seem to be a logical place to organize dialogue on these difficult problems facing medicine and society. In actuality this has not been the case. With a few exceptions they have chosen to follow rather than lead on these issues, and there is no immediate prospect of their changing this position.

For example, contraception was first raised as an issue in the AMA in 1925 by their section on Obstetrics and Gynecology. It reached the House of Delegates in 1935 and in 1938, both times being accepted neutrally for study with neither endorsement nor opposition. It was not raised again until 1964, at which time it was finally endorsed. By this time, of course, most of the major battles on birth control had long since been waged.

Another example of the lack of AMA leadership in these problems is its attitude toward the question of abortion. In 1965 the Committee on Human Reproduction recommended that the House of Delegates support enactment of more liberal legislation on abortion by the states. The House of Delegates rejected the recommendation, saying the matter was one for each state medical society to decide by itself. Less than 2 years later abortion legislation began to be passed by several state legislatures, and as soon as it was, the AMA reversed its earlier decision and came out firmly endorsing the changes, post facto.

Probing Man's True Nature

F. H. Knelman

In the last few years science has been racked by vexing questions concerning the nature of man. The fallen angel has departed and the rising ape appeared. The Victorian debates on evolution, except in some remote and backward areas like Tennessee, have also departed. But new questions concerning the origin of man and the nature of his early ancestry have arisen. The age of technical violence has brought the question of aggression into new prominence.

Is man killer or kindly? Is he a naked ape whose African genesis makes him bent on aggression? Is human society built upon and dominated by the 'killer instinct?' Or has man survived because of the slow psycho-social evolution creating behavioural patterns of love and co-operation? Is man schizoid, with both heritages contending and if so which has greater survival value?

Two primary views contend. One is based on genetically inherited aggressive drives going back to the beginnings of our evolutionary history. It is the view that we are descended from carnivorous, predatory, killer apes. The other view is that man is a social and cultural product of history. What he was or is, whether gladiator or nuclear warrior, is a scar of culture, not a mark of birth. This is not to deny the evolution of species but to question the primacy of inheritance.

From *The Montreal Star*, June 16, 1969. The author is professor of humanities of science at Sir George Williams University.

Missing Link

In any case the link between a man-like ape and the first ape-like man is still missing. Even the concept recently popularized, of territorial imperative, is questionable when applied to humans since man's closest living relatives, the great apes, do not exhibit the smallest evidence of organization into group territories. Nor is there any evidence of organization into territorial groups among primitive hunting peoples like Bushmen, Pygmies or Eskimos. The great proponents of animal heritage from Dart to Lorenz have no satisfactory answers. Of course, historic and modern man exhibits group territorialism (nationalism) but this is much more attributable to culture than genetics.

These are the main points of the controversy which is now raging among scientists. Essentially, the questions they are asking reduce themselves to whether we behave badly because we can't help it (instinct, i.e., inherited), or because we have not yet found a way to control it (environment, i.e., culture).

Chief Disciples

The main proponents of the man-is-naturally-bad, "mark of Cain" theory are Konrad Lorenz (author of *On Aggression*), Dr. Raymond Dart, and Dart's disciple, the author of *African Genesis*, Robert Ardrey.

In 1924, Dr. Dart, and later in 1939, Dr. Leakey, discovered the fossil remains of the two-million-year-old prehuman ancestor, *Australopithecus.* "These," Dart says, "are the ogres of the fairy tales . . . people who would grind your bones to make their bread." And Dart goes on to testify to the "blood-spattered, slaughter-gutted archives of human history" as proof of the fact that man is (and was) a killer.

Dr. Dart refers specifically to the ferocity of prehumans rather than to the animal kingdom. Our earliest ancestors were *Australopithecus, Homo erectus,* and Neanderthal man in order of their historical appearance. There is evidence that *Australopithecus* ate the brains of baboons, and that Neanderthal man, although he was civilized enough to bury his dead, actually ate the brains of his fellow-creatures, a behavior not found among other animals. This may have been a symbolic attempt to incorporate the dead man's spirit. Warrior Indian tribes in North America did the same thing.

Essentially then, the "mark of Cain" argument suggests that man, dominated by his need for survival, has combined his naturally predatory instincts with the necessity of preserving and conquering territory, into the cultural patterns of the various societies he has created.

Thus, the tensions and aggressions of our twentieth century world, the racism, nationalism, wars and violence which we inflict upon each other can all be explained in terms of this inescapable pattern of survival acted out instinctually and there is no way of avoiding the sorry plight in which we now find ourselves. The awesome tragedy is that if this is the nature of man, modern technology makes the destruction of civilization inevitable.

Strong Dissent

However, anthropologist Ashley Montagu strongly disagrees with the Lorenz-Dart syndrome and has now written two books in refutation of their theories. According to Montagu "the myth of early man's aggressiveness belongs in the same class as the myth of the beast . . . and the myth of innate depravity and original sin." Furthermore, says Montagu, these "new" concepts are substantially old hat. They are little more than a re-hash of the Darwinian theory of the survival of the fittest, particularly Herbert Spencer's interpretation. Later Darwinists cite co-operation as a more powerful survival mechanism.

Montagu points out that it was during the nineteenth century that we abandoned "the eighteenth century conception of nature as harmony and design" and began to see it in terms of the Darwinian theory of evolution, and of the naked struggle for survival. This, in turn, led to the collapse of "the concept of harmony as an ideal of human relations." Since our ancestors were "wild animals" who followed the law of the jungle, then we, too, must behave like savages and beasts.

In actuality, Montagu says, the opposite is true. " 'Savages' live co-operatively with one another. . . . Men behave like 'beasts' in highly civilized societies, but the beasts of the field do not." The gorilla, for example, is not ferocious, but amiable and unquarrelsome. And even more essential to the point, animals do not fight with their own kind. It is man who is unusually quarrelsome and aggressive.

And herein lies the essence of Montagu's argument. He believes that the only way the world has survived is mainly through *co-operation*, not through killing. Primitive men could not afford to kill one another indiscriminately, and neither can contemporary man. The proponents of "the myth of the beast" are, he says, simply distorting the facts to suit their own arguments. Even the suggested cannibalism of primitive man arose because of a conscious symbolism, or a genuine necessity (e.g., starvation). And so it has occurred among so-called "civilized" men.

It should also be pointed out that there is no clear evidence of cannibalism until Neanderthal times. And in the period between the existence of *Australopithecus* and Neanderthal man, the human brain underwent a number of drastic changes, including the gaining of the large neocortex, which provided one of the main differentiations between the human and the animal species. *Homo erectus*, our earliest ancestors, hunted rather than killed, making Dart's views very questionable.

Think in Symbols

It is the neocortex which gives us our particularly human ability to think in symbols. Instead of experiencing our reactions at an unthinking, emotional level, as an instinctive response to the immediate, concrete world, as is done by the remainder of the animal kingdom, man can create abstractions. He is able, with the aid of the neocortex, to channel immediate experience into the symbolic terms created by whatever society he happens to be living in. In other words, a human act becomes "bad" or "good," "necessary" or "unnecessary," depending upon what is socially acceptable or necessary. It has been established that all human groups, even the most primitive, think in symbols.

Montagu points out how biased Dart and his followers are. They discover artifacts and call them weapons when they could equally have been tools.

They base their arguments on ambiguous biological evidence and ignore other evidence which contradicts their monolithic view.

Dr. Leslie White, the University of Michigan anthropologist, who supports Dr. Montagu's position, has this to say on the subject:

The essence of the cultural argument is that if human beings can talk themselves into eating each other for spiritual reasons, damming up their sexuality for moral reasons, killing their brothers for political reasons, and going to their own deaths for ideological reasons, where is the rationale for believing in an innate, aggressive drive unmodified by those same symbolic processes?

Culture's Impact

He also points out that the fundamental sex drive is, in man, mainly controlled by non-biological forces. "The same," says Dr. White, "is true of aggression." In effect, culture has cut man off from instinctive behavior.

Montagu and his supporters believe that man's greatest hope of survival lies in "the recognition and cultivation of individuality"; of the capacity of the human animal "to some extent control not only the world as he finds it, but also the world as he remakes it."

It would seem, therefore, that in our contemporary, fear-ridden world we are faced with a decisive and frightening choice. Either we accept the "myth of the beast" and fall into the immediately reassuring but ultimately dangerous trap of believing that aggression, cruelty and blood-lust are the natural condition of man. In which case, if we appear to be bent on self-destruction it is only because we are fulfilling our natural, biological heritage; our own inescapable drive marked as self-preservation at any cost, a kind of 'better dead than red' policy to all of living.

Or we can accept the much tougher challenge of admitting to full responsibility for the chaos which we have created for ourselves, recognizing it to be man-made, and, in so doing, having the courage to change and overcome it.

"To love and to think, these are the two great chords of might," says Ashley Montagu. For the sake of ourselves, and of posterity, we had better be courageous enough to prove him right.

The Future, If Any

G. Rattray Taylor

At a guess, there are about 200,000 biologists in the world, depending to some extent on how you define "biologist." The sensual man, reflecting on their hazardous activities, may well feel a sense of apprehension. The prospect of having to cope with a number of such innovations simultaneously takes on a nightmare quality, and prompts the question: is this all really a load of nonsense, mere science fiction divorced from present reality? And even if these procedures are technically possible, will they ever be more than laboratory curiosities?

If so, he has missed the point. We are not simply discussing a number of new procedures, but the fact that a revolution is occurring in biology. The things I have described are merely the salient points, the first-fruits of a breakthrough on a broad front. Naturally, biology still has numerous unsolved problems, just as physics has. But the degree of control now being achieved calls for a new relationship between biology and society. Just as physics and chemistry did in the past century, it will steadily bring about a totally new pattern of existence. Whether it will be a happier and more satisfying pattern is by no means obvious, and it is not even clear whether society can survive the strains which will be imposed.

Jacques Piccard, son of the inventor of the deep-diving bathyscaphe, told a symposium at the Stevens Institute at Hoboken, New Jersey, recently that he was 'seriously doubtful' whether mankind would last out the century. Aside from the atomic threat, he stressed the 'widespread, suicidal pollution affecting the air we breathe, the water we drink and the land we till.' Our whole technology was to blame, he said. Superimposed on these stresses, the social stresses created by biology may prove a sizeable final straw.

The question of how soon they will be upon us therefore deserves careful attention.

Reprinted by permission of The World Publishing Company from *The Biological Time Bomb* by G. Rattray Taylor. An NAL Book. Copyright © 1968 by Gordon Rattray Taylor. Taylor was a student of the natural sciences at Trinity College, Cambridge, but later he became a journalist. During World War II he worked for the BBC, and for the Psychological Warfare Division of SHAEF. Among his books are *Eye on Research* and a history of biology, the *Science of Life*. In addition, he edits a series of programs for the BBC.

Naturally, no one can predict the future with certitude and no doubt some of the advances about which we are now optimistic will prove impossible, or at any rate the solution will be found so far in the future as to be of little practical importance to us now. But it is equally certain that many of these advances will occur in the very near future. Indeed, many of the techniques described in Chapter 2, such as artificial inovulation, are available now. And as I write these lines comes news of a breakthrough on the transplantation front. Dr. G. J. V. Nossal, the new director of the Walter and Eliza Hall Institute of Medical Research in Melbourne, has reported a method of desensitizing the body to specific foreign materials by injecting ever smaller pieces of the antigen. It appears that the extent of the immune response is related to the size of the invading molecules. But once the body has met a fragment of the antigens so small that the immune response does not occur, it subsequently ceases to produce antibodies to the complete antigen molecule. On the strength of this, Nossal considers that organ transplantation can be perfected in the 1970's with control of cancer and other diseases following a decade or two later. He has called for a world-wide effort to purify antigens, to see if a molecule sufficiently small, and of the right structure to set up tolerance, can be developed. 'If it does,' he told the First International Congress of the Transplantation Society, 'the stage is set for experiments in human beings to see if injection of antigens can induce tolerance in a transplant patient.' There are also encouraging reports about tissue typing and anti-lymphocytic serum.

On the other hand, I would not personally place any sizeable bet on success in prolonging life, and, while I think it may well be possible to improve memory, I am somewhat sceptical of the possibility of transferring entire memories. Against this, the very recent discovery of a factor controlling nerve growth makes it look extremely probable that we could do something quite drastic about raising intelligence, provided treatment can be given in the foetal stage or the earliest weeks of life.

[Below], I have ranged the possibilities in three groups: discoveries which are going to affect us within the next five or ten years, if they have not already begun to do so; those which should become practicable within some fifty years; and those which are remoter.

The group which affects all of us, and on which no delay can be brooked, includes, in addition to transplantation techniques, parthenogenetic birth, prolonged storage of human eggs and spermatozoa, arrested death, choice of sex of offspring and the mind-modifying drugs. Surely enough to cope with.

In phase two, I forecast, we shall see all these problems become more acute, with hibernation and arrested death for prolonged periods; unlimited transplantation possibilities; and a very wide range of mind-modifying techniques, not only drugs but electrical effects, imperceptible odours and the like. If the artificial placenta has not been perfected in phase one, it now will be and naturally produced offspring will be brought to term on it. In addition, we shall see the start of life-copying. Living organisms will be produced by putting together units of life derived mainly from breaking down living systems; into these organisms a steadily increasing proportion of fully synthesized material will be incorporated. An impact will be made on the problem of prolonging youthful vigour. Hibernation and other storage methods will become practical. The first cloned animals will be produced.

Not till phase three should I expect to see the synthesis of life, control of ageing or a disembodied human brain. Above all, I think that it will take at least this long for genetic engineering to become practical. But all these things should reach fruition, unless war or politics or disaster drastically change the present curve of development, within the lifetime of those now young, and a few of those who are not so young.

Table of Developments

The dates are those of technical achievement, not of general availability, which depends on social and economic considerations.

Phase One: by 1975
   Extensive transplantation of limbs and organs
   Test-tube fertilization of human eggs
   Implantation of fertilized eggs in womb
   Indefinite storage of eggs and spermatozoa
   Choice of sex of offspring
   Extensive power to postpone clinical death
   Mind-modifying drugs: regulation of desire
   Memory erasure
   Imperfect artificial placenta
   Artificial viruses

Phase Two: by 2000
   Extensive mind modification and personality reconstruction
   Enhancement of intelligence in men and animals
   Memory injection and memory editing
   Perfected artificial placenta and true baby-factory
   Life-copying: reconstructed organisms
   Hibernation and prolonged coma
   Prolongation of youthful vigour
   First cloned animals
   Synthesis of unicellular organisms
   Organ regeneration
   Man-animal chimeras

Phase Three: after 2000
   Control of ageing: extension of life span
   Synthesis of complex living organisms
   Disembodied brains

Brain—computer links
Gene insertion and deletion
Cloned people
Brain—brain links
Man—machine chimeras
Indefinite postponement of death

A recent objective study of current trends arrived at not dissimilar conclusions. Eighty-two experts took part in the study, which was conducted by Olaf Helmer of the Rand Corporation and T. J. Gordon of Douglas Aircraft, who fed the forecasts back to the participants and refined the prediction. These specialists put drugs producing personality changes some sixteen years ahead but, more optimistic than me, expect to see primitive forms of life created in the laboratory by 1989 and the control of hereditary defects by gene engineering by 2000. More cautious than me, they don't expect long-term coma until 2050, nor do they see intelligence being raised by drugs until 2012, with brain—computer links soon after. But, like me, they don't expect extension of life until the same date, when they foresee 50 years being added to the expectancy. They put regeneration of limbs and organs down for 2007. Rather oddly, to my mind, they don't see the breeding of intelligent animals (to replace human labour) until 2050: I should expect this to come earlier than drugs for raising human intelligence, since these drugs will probably be tried out on animals before they are used in man; indeed, this is already occurring.

So it seems certain that many of these advances will occur in the life-time of those now middle-aged and nearly all in the lifetime of those now young. But how far are they in fact problems?

It is rather easy to sensationalize the issues, and some writers have already done so. Thus A. Rosenfeld in *Life* suggests that women may go into a kind of supermarket containing day-old frozen embryos and shop around for the one they want. Presumably there will be a glamorized 4-colour 3-D picture of the adult expected on the pack, as when one buys a package of seeds. For my part, I think this most unlikely. We already have frozen semen, but it is not sold at the dime-store or do-it-yourself shops. It is obtained only by doctors at their discretion, which they exercise with restraint. Anyone who wants an implanted embryo will no doubt have to take a similar course and persuade her doctor—although, as the process becomes familiar, little persuasion may be called for; it may be more like requesting a smallpox injection. But if all firms were to attempt marketing frozen semen, the state would intervene and a web of legal and conventional codes would be invoked to stop them. The firm's advertisements would be refused, and their other products might be boycotted. No firm of repute would risk tarnishing its image by unconsidered, headlong action in such a field.

However, the realities are alarming enough.

More realistically, we might distinguish between those advances which create problems which are probably within the scope of society to handle and those which, like the atom bomb in physics, create problems of a totally new order.

In the first category I would place such matters as specification of the sex of offspring, use of stored eggs and spermatozoa, and even the bringing of babies to term on artificial placentas. It is possible that the power to determine sex might lead to a gross disproportion of the two sexes, but not particularly likely, unless the technique becomes available to countries, like India and China, where sons are greatly preferred to daughters. Since this would in any case cause a limitation of population, the immediate effects would be desirable rather than otherwise. Professor Lederberg has expressed the view that the sex ratio might fluctuate violently, as a result of over-correction of a trend to one extreme, then the other. But with computers, adequate prediction should not prove difficult, and there is no evidence that more than a minority of the population would use such techniques.

Even the bringing of infants to term on artificial placentas does not pose insuperable problems. It is true that there is a real and important task in providing children thus born with the requisite parental love and care. And there is no moral justification for exposing even one child to an inadequate background in this respect. But the requirements are well understood, and the number of cases should be small. Most people will prefer to have children in the normal way, or, if that is not possible, by inovulation.

On the other hand, while discounting some of the wilder bogy-raising, there are developments which I have described which raise issues far more fundamental than these.

Four strike me as particularly fearsome. First, the development of techniques, probably quite near, for dramatically raising intelligence. Once a few highly intelligent children are born and have reached the age at which they win academic honours and get plum jobs, parents everywhere will begin to scream for the same treatment for their newborn or unborn babies. On grounds of national interest, the state may decide to foster such a trend. Once the level of intelligence rises widely, the educational system will have to be revised. Meanwhile, an elite group will have come into existence. However, perhaps the new race of super-minds will soon find the answers to the problems created by their own existence.

Secondly, a drastic extension of the life span or even of youthful vigour would cause tremendous social and economic repercussions. Medical services would have to be re-adjusted, retirement practices changed. Markets would alter. But in addition, the life of the young would suffer a severe impact from the existence of a preponderance of active older people. Already, the rub is felt by couples who do not inherit money from their parents until long after the phase at which it would be most useful. When parents survive to 80, their children may be over 50 before they inherit, and the costs of raising a family have been met. If survival to 150 occurs, the intermediate generations at 120, 90 and 60, most young couples will have not only grandparents but great-grandparents and great-great-grandparents to visit, look after, and put up with.

The remaining two I will indicate more shortly, since they have already been discussed at length: the prospect of the indefinite postponement of death and the power to modify heredity. Economics cannot cope with the first, nor politics with the second.

Section Four

The Chemical Revolution

The second half of the twentieth century is witnessing a profound revolution in man's ability to synthesize new materials, to manipulate molecules and atoms. This conquest of materials has brought a host of synthetics to replace partly the natural food, fiber, and shelter we formerly required. Of particular interest is our increased understanding of long-chain complex molecules, bringing us to the threshold of synthesizing complete proteins and, perhaps, living matter itself. Many of the great biological breakthroughs are chemical in nature.

Although the most pervasive of the technological revolutions, the chemical revolution remains largely covert. While we recognize revolutionary devices such as computers, jet aircraft, and space satellites, we fail to realize that these too incorporate the materials revolution in semiconductors, space-age fuels and alloys, and a host of others. Nor do we recognize how chemistry is involved in the elucidation of the mechanisms of our senses—seeing, tasting, smelling—as well as thinking, learning, and remembering.

The major backlash from the chemical revolution is pollution. The worldwide proliferation of chemicals, many of which are toxic, persistent, and unassessed, has added a global parameter to pollution while threatening regional air, land, and water. The biological and environmental hazards remain largely unassessed although disease correlations are mounting. The quantities and rates of production of some chemicals are threatening the natural balance of life. Among drugs, medicines, detergents, food additives, pesticides, and chemical warfare agents, we have produced chemicals so toxic that a few ounces could destroy everybody. We have stockpiled agents of death that are not safely stored or disposed of. DDT, like the fission products of nuclear explosions, is distributed globally and found in penguins and polar bears. We are endangering the integrity of the seas and degrading huge natural reservoirs like the Great Lakes and Lake Baikal in the U.S.S.R. In waging chemical warfare against our enemies, we have not distinguished between pests and humans. We commit the same biological errors in both cases, inducing resistance and resurgence and killing friend and foe indiscriminately.

Alcohol and barbiturates, "speed" and aspirin, like DDT, are household chemicals. Another backlash of the chemical revolution is the drug culture pervading our society at all levels from the underground to the medicine cabinets of millions of middle-class Americans. We cannot tolerate pain or pleasure with courage or grace unless chemically assisted. We consume billions of pills to ease pain, assist digestion, provide sleep or tranquility. Some of the great youth upheavals are associated with life styles based on drug assisted consciousness expansion or happiness induction. All of these problems attest to the cultural lag and the crisis in values.

The first two selections in this section, by Lessing, describe the general impact and nature of the new chemical technologies, the second dealing exclusively with our emerging conquest of the giant molecules that approximate many substances found in nature. The article by Walsh deals with a specific pollution problem, that of oil spills. Because most pollution problems arise directly or indirectly from our chemical technology, the choice was made here to illustrate the nature of technological backlash. The manner in which we all share the "drug culture" and the cultural lag in social institutions to control their misapplication makes up Johnson's selection. Krech's article on brain biochemistry illustrates the broad range of the chemical revolution and points to problems of social control in the future.

Where Is Chemistry Today?

Lawrence P. Lessing

Thus as we move out into the last half of the twentieth century we find chemistry underlying nearly all aspects of man's endeavors. Its enormous range runs from the revolutionizing of many industries to the broadening, understanding, and extension of life itself. Indeed, chemistry, reflecting this universality of application, is rapidly absorbing or being absorbed into nearly all industry, that basic index of human life and activity. There is nothing strange in this. As man has become more adept at changing and molding matter to his use, which is industry, he inevitably has moved deeper and deeper into chemistry, which is the controlled transformation of matter through science or knowledge.

The growth of the chemical industry itself in only the first half of this century, based on this revolution in knowledge, has been something phenomenal. In the United States it has been growing at a yearly rate about double the average of all manufacturing industry. From being only a minor part of all industry at the turn of the century, the chemical industry today has suddenly become the most dynamic, if not the premier, industry of the century. It is so big and expanding so fast in so many directions that its boundaries are difficult to place at any given moment. If the chemical industry is confined simply to the basic producers of chemicals and allied products—which is the core of the industry that orderly statisticians find most manageable—it ranks about fourth in size (total assets more than $20 billion), preceded only by petroleum, primary metals, and transportation equipment, in that order. This is one of the sharpest ascents of any new industry in history. If petroleum refining is included, a process merging more and more indistinguishably into chemistry year by year, then this total chemical industry is unquestionably the new colossus, with combined assets of over $50 billion.

But even this chemical-petroleum combination does not wholly cover all the permeations and penetrations of chemical industry into the broad reaches of the

Lawrence P. Lessing, "Where Is Chemistry Today?" in *Understanding Chemistry* (New York: Interscience Inc., 1959), pp. 174-184. Lessing started his career as a newspaper man in Pittsburgh. After serving there as the correspondent for *Time*, he joined the staff of *Fortune* and contributed articles on electronics, jet propulsion, automation, and metallurgy. From 1953 to 1955, he was an editor and contributor to *Scientific American*, and he is now consultant to *Architectural Forum*.

industrial scene. For instance, the steel, copper, zinc, and other ancient metal industries are on their way—through a new infusion of chemical research into the basic chemical elements, processes, and alloys with which they deal—to becoming strongly based metallurgical chemical industries. This transformation is likely to be seen completed well before the century is out. And the electrical-electronics industry is already deep in chemistry, developing and manufacturing many of the special materials, plastics, metal combinations, and ceramics upon which a steady stream of new, improved, or, in some instances, revolutionary products is based. Altogether, if all the products created by chemistry could be traced, they might be found to constitute well over 30 per cent, if not close to half, of the total output of goods in the country. Moreover, in ever-mounting volume, the basic chemical industry feeds materials and semi-finished products into all sixty-eight industrial categories into which the U. S. Department of Commerce and economists generally divide the total industry of the nation.

To be a chemist, therefore, is to be at the very center of a driving new force expanding the economy of life and of the country. Moreover, the chemist has a large hand in some of the vital developments for the future. It is characteristic of this science and this industry that it engages in or supports more research, stretching from all manner of industrial laboratories into the universities, than almost any other category of science or human endeavor. In sheer numbers, chemists today constitute the largest scientific professional group in the country, exceeded only by medical practitioners. This is reflected by the upwards of 80,000 members of the American Chemical Society, most of whom, paradoxically enough, are employed outside the chemical industry proper, again indicating the broad permeation of many activities by this new science. Yet the role of chemistry is expanding so rapidly that these numbers are judged to be not nearly enough. It is estimated that unless many more chemists and chemical engineers are created by 1965, there will be a deficit of 93,000 in meeting the needs of the chemical industry alone, not to mention the other growing areas in which chemists are needed.

The reasons for this large, urgent, and even fantastic-sounding need for more chemists and technologists, particularly of the creative variety, lie deep in the many revolutions that the chemical industry has under way in the most vital areas of human interest, and the many more revolutions that are on the verge of opening out into the future.

Consider first those basic areas of food, clothing, and shelter that underlie the life of man on earth. In the production of food, chemistry has had a big and still growing hand in an agricultural revolution that may well be a leading factor in the continuation of life on earth. One statistical observation may more graphically illustrate that revolution than many columns of figures: in 1958 the United States produced an all-time record crop of corn (3.8 billion bushels) on less than half the acreage required to produce its second largest (but nearly equal) bumper crop of corn just ten years before in 1948. A good part of this remarkable rise in yield per acre, true of nearly all United States crops, must be credited to farm mechanization and to the plant geneticists' creation of new, constantly improved plant varieties. But a large part of this jump in productivity also is to be credited to the endlessly mounting new fertilizers, insecticides, fungicides, weed killers, and growth agents which, cutting crop losses and labor, have brought a chemical revolution to the farm. As biochemistry unravels more of the inner secrets of plant and animal life, more and more subtle chemical products are in the offing that will build resistance to disease and attack right into crop structures and, beyond this, control growth itself to almost any desired limits.

Chemistry's success, along with other factors, in thus helping to raise United States farm productivity is already so great that it has brought on continuing large and embarrassing surpluses, despite all efforts at economic or political control. But this is only a local and passing situation in a world still largely underfed and expected to double in population before the end of the century. By then, if it is not already long overdue now, the greater dissemination and adoption of the knowledge, materials, and techniques accumulated and proved in this country will be imperative to human survival on the planet.

In clothing and textiles, of course, chemistry is in the midst of one of the most glamorous and far-reaching of its revolutions. Synthetic and semisynthetic fibers, taking in all types of man-made fabrics, today constitute one quarter of all United States textile production. In little more than another decade, at their present rate of growth, they will account for close to half of all production. Actually, for the first time in history, the man-made materials are beginning to make inroads on that king of natural fibers, cotton, which in turn is being modified by more and more chemical surface treatments, adding such desirable new characteristics as crease-resistance and the ability to be "drip-dried," in order to retain its markets. Meanwhile, still newer synthetic fibers are steadily being developed to add to the spectrum of textile properties, a spectrum which in its breadth, versatility, and blending qualities is something new on earth. This, too, has its relation to the world situation, for, as population pressures increase, the pressure for more food-growing acreage will inevitably squeeze the production of natural fibers, so that to clothe itself the world must turn more and more to the products of the test tube and chemical ingenuity.

In shelter, the chemical revolution has only begun, though about 15 per cent of United States chemical production already is going into the building industry in such important materials as paints and surface coatings, adhesives, plywood, insulation, floor tiling, interior finishing, furnishing, trim, and plastic paneling. Plastics alone in building now account for over $500 million a year, in such items as lighting fixtures, hardware, plastic pipe, roofing and glazing materials, but this is still only a drop in the immense construction bucket. As plastics gain in experience, development, and economy, they will be ready to move into major structural uses, still largely untouched. The all-plastic bathroom, for instance, molded in a single unit with all-plastic fixtures attached, appears to be just around the corner. And other integrally designed structural units, such as whole wall and roof sections, sandwich-panel members, and ingenious combinations of metals and molded plastics, promise new advances in prefabricated building construction.

The great moldability of plastics, and the almost endless range of different properties that can be built into them through molecular engineering—a range constantly being strengthened and added to by research into materials able to stand up to such extreme conditions as are encountered in high-speed aircraft and rocket flight—portend a structural revolution in human shelter that will take many forms. The Monsanto Chemical Company's experimental all-plastic House of the Future, viewed by fascinated millions at Disneyland in California, is only a single example and foretaste of things to come.

Still, all these things do not by any means exhaust the revolutions under way through chemistry. Perhaps the most portentous of developments for the future are those revolving around the tapping or transformation of new energy sources and the betterment of human health, the already visible extension of life on earth.

In the field of energy, where again the populous world is moving toward inevitable stringencies unless new sources can be unlocked economically and usefully, chemistry is pursuing many exciting lines of development. On chemistry's back shelf, as we have seen, are such processes as hydrogenation or partial oxidation of carbon compounds, which, by various routes, can turn coal, peat, lignite, or a large range of lighter organic waste materials, such as certain farm wastes, into gasoline and other liquid fuels to keep the wheels moving as soon as petroleum resources begin to falter.

There are also, as we have seen, a whole new group of strange metal combinations and intermetallic compounds in development that have the property of transforming heat or light from whatever sources directly into electricity, at generally low efficiencies as yet, but steadily rising. Some of these may hold a coming revolution in self-powered appliances, such as radios, television sets, and other small household equipment. Others will eventually be used to convert the enormous heat of atomic reactions directly and more efficiently into power, rather than go through the old roundabout route of steam turbines. The most notable of these new devices was discovered only recently when researchers at Los Alamos National Laboratory in New Mexico invented a so-called plasma thermocouple device which, through an ingenious combination of a metal (tantalum) and a gas (cesium vapor), converts heat to electricity at a theoretical efficiency of 30 per cent or better. This would be equal to some of the present steam turbines. Such efficiencies have not been achieved as yet, of course, but one of the new devices, inserted in an experimental power reactor, recently kept a single electric bulb burning for a day or so—an event that may be as historic as Faraday's first tapping of electricity through a dynamo.

Perhaps the most far-reaching of the energy revolutions ahead lies in the field of solar power, in which intensive work is going on in many directions, most of them employing chemistry or chemical materials as the unlocking key. The solar-heated house, already experimentally in existence with chemical heat collectors and heat-pump devices, is probably less than a decade away as a practical matter. Further off, but growing more feasible by the year, are methods for chaining the biochemical process of plant photosynthesis to the production of heat, light, or energy through such routes as the electrolysis of water to cheap hydrogen. The hydrogen would then be fed into chemical fuel cells, already in forward development, where, by oxidation or catalytic processes, the hydrogen would be converted to heat or directly to electrical energy. Thus, long before conventional fossil fuels run out, chemistry and nuclear physics will be ready to supply energy from a great variety of sources more limitless than any heretofore.

The deepest of all chemical revolutions is taking place, however, in the biochemical laboratories of the universities and the pharmaceutical industry, where the fight to control diseases and extend the human life span has marked up so many recent and well-known victories. Pharmaceuticals, indeed, constitute one of the most notable examples of an ancient industry almost completely revolutionized by chemistry within the last quarter of a century. From being an industry based largely on the extraction of drugs and nostrums from botanical and other natural sources, pharmaceuticals now compose an industry based strongly on creative chemistry, with research programs exceeding those of almost any industry of equal size. The success of this transformation of medical science through chemistry is written in the bluntest of vital statistics. In only the last fifty years, for the first time in recorded history, the average of human life expectancy has been raised, in countries cultivating the new science, from 42 years to about 70 years, a figure composed of an average life expectancy of 67 years for men and 73 for women.

Nearly all this heart-warming record has been achieved by a panoply of new chemical drugs, antibiotics, and vaccines for beating back the infectious diseases, the diseases caused by invading organisms, bacteria or viruses. Except for the more elusive viral diseases, on which a great deal of work still remains to be done, nearly all the once common diseases that took off so many men in their youth are now largely conquered or held closely in check. The remaining area to be vanquished, and a large one in which the broadest and most exciting research attacks are going forward, is the area of the so-called organic diseases, products of still largely obscure changes or maladjustments in the complex biological mechanisms of the human body itself. These are mainly the diseases of middle and old age, of which the major ones are heart diseases, cancer, mental diseases, and senility itself.

If these organic diseases can be brought under any large measure of control—and there is no indication that they cannot—the human life span may be usefully lengthened, according to all present theoretical calculations, to an average life expectancy of 110 years. And this may be accomplished by the year 2000, if the scientific research attack is deep and broad and well supported. Or at least that is now the exciting goal.

This quickening of prospects has come about through the finer and finer explorations into the body's cell structures and chemical mechanisms, and into the origins and generation of life itself, viewed in a previous chapter. Every advance into life's hidden recesses, in nearly every direction in which investigators have probed, illustrates ever more clearly that the secret of health or illness lies in the extremely delicate balance of complex, interlocking chemical systems that make up the life processes, processes which, with more knowledge, chemistry may come to control.

No more dramatic evidence of this is to be found than in the widely noted but still controversial discovery of 1956 by Dr. Robert Heath and a group at Tulane University that schizophrenia, the most prevalent and obdurate of human mental diseases, is marked by the presence in the blood stream of certain malformed protein particles not found in normal individuals. Heath and his group have shown that when these twisted proteins are injected into the blood stream of normal persons, they induce in them briefly all the derangements, withdrawal, and electrical brainwave patterns found in true schizophrenics. Thus, what was once superstitiously thought to be an evil spell cast upon the mind, or a purely "mental" aberration, is found to be traceable to some minute chemical malfunction, possibly traceable to some hereditary flaw, in the body's protein-building mechanisms.

Chemical factors more complex than a single protein may be found to be behind schizophrenia and other true brain diseases, but it is now generally accepted that research is on the right track. "No twisted thought without a twisted molecule," is the way a noted brain biologist, Ralph Gerard, has succinctly put it. And what is chemically caused may someday soon be chemically changed. It may take a long and arduous effort to trace the cause of these crooked molecules back to their source, for the chemistry of the blood, brain, and nervous system is exceedingly complicated, but that a solution will eventually be found to the age-old mystery of most mental illnesses and the human brain is now as nearly certain as that their causes are physical, and therefore graspable by the tools of science.

Some evidence of chemistry's ability to deal with such matters is already at hand in the pharmaceutical industry's recent development of the so-called tranquilizing drugs, based on the rediscovery by Western medicine of an old East Indian remedy made from the root of a native plant, *Rauwolfia serpentina*. From this starting point, the industry has gone on to synthesize, by chemistry's now well-known molecular juggling, a whole group of related, steadily improved, and more potent tranquilizers, which have had some marked success in quieting violently psychotic patients, alleviating mental disturbances, and treating many other ills in which emotional tensions are a factor. Conversely, the industry also has developed a group of so-called energizing drugs—derived oddly but not inappropriately from the rocket fuel, hydrazine—which have had some remarkable results in bringing deeply depressed, withdrawn schizophrenics to life and making them more amenable to treatment.

These psychiatric drugs open a whole new area of research, extending up into the very functioning of the human brain, and demonstrate forcefully that chemistry can be employed to good effect in dealing even with mental processes.

Psychiatrists now foresee the day when such chemical agents, greatly improved and extended, will be used not only to cure the mentally deranged, but also to raise healthy brains to powers still dormant within them. And this, too, may be a necessary measure not unrelated to the continued survival of the human race.

In much the same way as seen in mental illness, another abnormal molecule in the blood stream has been found to be a major concomitant of the most prevalent of all so-called heart diseases, called atherosclerosis. This is the constriction of arteries by irregular fatty deposits on the interior walls of blood vessels, accompanied by high blood pressure or hypertension, the danger of blood-clot formations or thromboses, and other organic ills. In 1950, Alfred Gofman and a group at the University of California discovered that the fatty deposits were formed mainly by abnormal-sized molecules of cholesterol, the form in which fat is carried to the tissues by the blood stream. Again, the exploration for the causes of such abnormal molecules has been long and difficult, with no final conclusion as yet. For it is not simply a matter of diet—though a high intake of saturated animal fats, i.e., hard fats whose molecular structure is closed, seems to be strongly involved in abnormal cholesterol production—but of the body's own chemical system which synthesizes cholesterol from other foods even when little or no fats are present. Some evidence is accumulating, however, that a diet leaning toward unsaturated vegetable oils or fats alleviates the situation.

Meanwhile, though atherosclerosis cannot yet be attacked directly, pharmaceutical research has raised a whole army of new drugs to control or turn aside some of its deadly effects: a group of highly useful anticoagulant drugs to prevent formation of possibly dangerous blood clots, a steadily growing range of drugs to lower blood pressure, and new drugs that show promise of reducing the level of cholesterol in the blood. Without a doubt, the day is drawing ever closer when the root causes of so-called heart attacks, today's No. 1 killer of men in their prime, will be exposed and brought under control.

Cancer is even more complex than the heart diseases, but no less hopeful of eventual solution in the current strides of research. What makes it particularly difficult is that there are so many different complex forms of cancerous growth, many hard to diagnose, some not even readily identifiable as yet. The leading indication now is that many cancers are triggered by still unknown viruses, acting in ways different from known viruses, and probably in concert with certain malfunctions in the body cells' genetic and growth-controlling material, setting off that wild, uncontrolled reproduction of misshapen cells that is cancer. A few rare types of cancer recently have proved to be eradicable by specific antibiotics, indicating that the virus theory is not unfounded. But a great deal more needs to be learned about the intricate chemistry of the body's cells, their control and reproductive mechanisms, and the interplay of viruses with these materials, before enough is known to design the specific agents needed to control the range of cancers effectively.

As this research moves deeper into what essentially is the mystery of life itself—the living cell—the probability is that these studies will also have a profound effect on the understanding of old age and senility, and the aging process, which is the reverse of cancer—for old age without other complications is simply the running down of the cell's reproductive, growth, and repair facilities.

Nothing is simple in this area of life's chemistry, and achievements will not come easily. But in this direction lies the greatest of all challenges to the adventurous and inquiring mind, the bold explorer of the future. In this chemical research area arises the proposition that not only the gross material surroundings of man can be improved but that human life itself can be greatly improved in its inner being, both mental and physical.

All this opens new philosophic vistas of understanding. "The chemical descent of man," says Robert R. Williams, isolator and synthesizer of vitamin B_1, "extends his perception of kinship and his sense of the trends of evolution through far greater ranges than the anatomical evidence with which Darwin had largely to be content. It tells us where we have come from and, if we read it wisely and well, I believe it may tell us much about where we are going."

The Giant Molecule

Lawrence P. Lessing

One of the most fruitful ideas to arise in modern chemistry in the last half century is the concept of the giant molecule. From this essentially structural idea, comparable to an architect's blueprint, have come not only the many synthetic fibers and plastics that now immediately leap to mind as major products of the chemical industry, but also synthetic rubber, many new synthetic drugs, and many substances vital to an understanding of the life processes themselves. The slowness with which the rather simple idea arose that molecules could exist in giant forms is a good example of the immense difficulties encountered in trying to see beneath the riotous diversity of natural

Lawrence P. Lessing, "The Giant Molecule" in *Understanding Chemistry* (New York: Interscience Inc., 1959), pp. 84-91.

materials into the basic structure of things. It also is a good example of how an apparently simple concept, once arrived at, can effect enormous changes upon which whole new industries are built. And it holds forth the prospect that other concepts are yet to be discovered that will unfold still greater matters.

Up to the 1920s there was little or no attention paid to the hints, which had begun to come out of a few pure research laboratories around the turn of the century, that very much larger molecules existed in nature than classical chemistry supposed, and that similar substances might be built up in the laboratory if the secret of their complex structure could be unraveled. For over a century chemists had been preoccupied with the necessary task of tearing down and analyzing natural substances to find out, first, what elements they were composed of, and second, how these elements were joined in simple basic molecules to form characteristic compounds. For a century the major drive of chemistry was to isolate pure substances or simple molecules for which simple, concise formulas could be written. This effort had settled beyond doubt the constitution of a vast number of compounds, including not only such simple ones as benzene, urea, acetic acid, alcohol, acetone, and the like, but also more complicated ones such as those of various pigments, dyes, and drugs. None of these molecules, however, contained more than a few dozen atoms at most. Up through the 1920s, therefore, chemistry was dealing almost wholly with relatively small molecules which could be reacted with one another to form a great range of products, many of them closely resembling or exactly imitating simple natural products.

But there was a large range of important natural substances, such as plant and animal fibers, cellulose, rubber, starch, and many other constituents of living organisms, which did not yield to this kind of simple destructive analysis. The usual methods of separation decomposed or changed these substances to something else. At considerable labor, the basic molecular components of these substances were worked out.

Rubber, it was established at a relatively early date, was based on a hydrocarbon, called isoprene, composed of five carbon and eight hydrogen atoms. Cellulose, the main structural material in all plant life, was primarily made up of glucose, a sugar compound composed of six carbon, ten hydrogen, and five oxygen atoms. And the proteins—an enormous class of materials that forms the tissue of all living things, fish, flesh, fowl, and good red hair and herring—were found to be most complex concatenations of components called amino acids, and, contrary to the general experience of chemistry, neither isoprene nor glucose nor the amino acids, once they were broken down from their original natural form, could be put back together again into anything resembling natural rubber, cellulose, or a protein. The way in which the molecules of isoprene, glucose, or the amino acids formed these natural products remained a great mystery.

The lack of knowledge did not prevent such materials as cellulose from gaining wide chemical use, as we have seen, in nitrocellulose products, the first man-made textile fibers, and the first man-made plastic, celluloid. But in all these products nothing much was done to the cellulose except to modify and slightly rearrange its molecular structure into different forms. The cellulose remained much as it came from the cotton boll or the tree, its inner structure still a mystery. With the fortuitous discovery of phenolic plastics in 1906, the first all-synthetic plastic, a clue was given to a new way of building up molecules to high molecular weights. But chemists continued to search for the simple molecular unit that could be expressed in a short, closed formula and that could be termed the "molecule" of cellulose, or of rubber, reversibly capable of being built into the characteristic natural material.

The first clue that there was a different and higher structural pattern to be discovered in these most complex natural substances came about 1900. The great German organic chemist Emil Fischer, in the closing years of the century and of a notable career, had taken to studying the composition of proteins, and encouraging associates to study these and other complex materials. Fischer and his colleagues succeeded with much labor in stringing together a few amino acids into an identifiable fragment of a total protein molecule. Since the total structure was unknown, however, this fragment was only a tantalizing clue to what must be a truly gigantic structure as molecules go, much too complex for the instruments and techniques of the time. Fischer and the early pioneers worked largely by intuition, as other great chemists before them, inferring from the way that the protein fragment had been strung together that it had a chainlike structure—an intuition as prophetic as Kekule's dream of the benzene ring.

Meanwhile, the growth of the first plastics, stumbled on empirically—the cellulosics and later the phenolics, on which many variations and substitutions were being rung—made it increasingly necessary for the purposes of efficient manufacturing and more controllable results to find out exactly what basic principles governed the structure and behavior of these materials, obviously close to complex natural materials in the size and weight of their molecules. After the turn of the century, therefore, there was rising research interest in so-called "big-molecule chemistry." And new instruments and techniques were rising to make the study more feasible, chief among them the appearance of x-ray diffraction apparatus that made it possible to peer into the structure of molecules, inferring the arrangement of their atoms by reflected patterns on x-ray plates. In the early 1920s, following the interregnum of World War I, a concerted research attack was launched from a number of directions to determine the precise structural principles behind complex natural substances and the new plastics.

One leading research group in Germany, led by Kurt Meyer and Herman Mark, a brilliant young Viennese chemist, set out to measure by x-ray diffraction the precise dimensions and atomic arrangements of the natural molecules themselves, choosing cellulose to begin with as being less complex than the much larger protein molecules. Mark and Meyer established beyond doubt that cellulose was made up of long chains of glucose units strung together in a regular, repetitious way, 50 to 150 units long or longer, and that this long chainlike structure was, in fact, the characteristic structure of supermolecules of cotton, wool, and all natural fibrous materials. The long narrow shape of the natural fibers was simply a reflection of the long narrow shape of their constituent but invisible molecules. Rubber and other materials yielded to the same techniques. There were, in fact, but two broad types of these chainlike giant molecules (still excluding the more complex proteins): a linear chain, lined up in straight, more or less rigid bundles like wires in a cable, which formed fibers and plastics; and a coiled-up chain structure, like a mass of tiny springs or a fine chain mail, which formed rubber and other elastic materials. All this represented only a subtle but highly important shift from the traditional way of looking at molecules.

With this general pattern of natural big molecules to go by—the important first step in understanding and later duplicating all very complex materials—rival groups sought to find out how to put chemical materials together in a similar way and to study precisely their formations and characteristics. One of the most intense rivals in this line of synthesis was another German group of chemists led by Hermann Staudinger, who later received the Nobel Prize for his fundamental studies of big-molecule synthesis, and who enunciated the formula for all chain-type molecule building, which consisted simply of the basic molecular unit repeated n times.

Acceptance of such an unorthodox formula and the structural view behind it was still generally slow through much of the twenties. Chemists were reluctant to give up the quest for finite cellulose or rubber molecules that could be expressed in the precise closed formulas they were accustomed to, and to put in their stead vague chain formulas of an almost indeterminate length. They also found it difficult to understand, as laymen still do, that it was not so much the specific chemical formula of these molecules as it was the long chainlike structures in which they were arranged that determined the really characteristic properties of fibers, elastics, and similar complex materials. All such materials were some combination of ubiquitous carbon compounds, hence, these new findings indicated, it was largely structure that made the difference in all the different forms of living or organic matter.

Perhaps the most decisively successful exponent of this new view was the late Wallace Hume Carothers, a brilliant young American investigator in this field at Harvard University in the twenties. In 1929 he joined E. I. du Pont de Nemours & Co. to head a basic research study for which he chose as subject the structure of giant molecules and how they might be polymerized—a term for the hooking up of small molecules into big ones. Du Pont had no specific product in view, but was ready to gamble that any widening of basic knowledge would have some future value. Carothers therefore plunged into the basic problem of hooking up long-chain molecules, fixing on condensation reactions as the likeliest way to do it. He reasoned that if he took simple substances whose molecules had reactive groups of atoms at both ends and reacted them, two such molecules would join to give a molecule whose length was the sum of the two, still with reactive groups at each end to go on in a chain reaction, hooking on similar molecules, until very long-chain structures were created. Aided by a large and able staff, he reacted dozens of possible substances, developing a broad systematic knowledge of the chemistry of polymerization in dozens of papers.

This massive campaign for new knowledge was to pay off sooner than anyone expected, and from a quite unrelated and unexpected direction. In 1925 a du Pont research group had been given the task of making another stab at the century-old problem of finding a synthetic rubber, picking up where the Germans unsuccessfully had left off in the late war with a sticky, fast-deteriorating product called methyl rubber. By chance a du Pont chemist heard a paper by the Rev. Julius A. Nieuwland of the University of Notre Dame, a devoted researcher in acetylene chemistry, who reported production of a new compound formed of three molecules of acetylene, which seemed a promising starting material for synthetic rubber. It proved unsuitable but still somehow promising. After long, hard work, and eventual modification of Nieuwland's process to produce a two-molecule acetylene, the du Pont group found after numerous experiments that they had a material which, when reacted with hydrochloric acid, produced an entirely new and more than promising substance which they called chloroprene—because it differed from isoprene, the long-known key constituent of natural rubber, only by having chlorine substituted for hydrogen on its carbon backbone. At this point the broad background work of the Carothers' group came into play to show how chloroprene could be polymerized into a truly rubberlike material. And in 1931 du Pont announced production of neoprene, the first successful all-purpose synthetic rubber, which went on to find hundreds of uses in preference over natural rubber because its chlorine content made it much more impervious to oils, acids, oxidization, and sunlight, the great banes of natural rubber.

In 1931 the Carothers group studying big molecules and polymerization in general had a more direct, unlooked-for, and history-making episode of its own. One of Carothers' assistants, poking a glass rod into a molten mess resulting from one of the experiments, observed that when he withdrew the rod a long threadlike filament came out that rapidly solidified in the air. What was more amazing, this filament could be stretched like rubber to about four times its length, and, though it did not retract like rubber, it retained some of its elasticity in the stretched state. Stretching changed the filament from a rather weak, dull-looking material to a much stronger, lustrous substance, indicating that its long molecules had been pulled into parallel bundles like true fibers. Thus it was proved that if sufficiently long molecules were built up, they showed fiber-forming qualities. But the material of which this first synthetic fiber was built had a low melting point and other drawbacks, and a long, arduous search was made for more suitable fiber-forming compounds.

The materials finally settled on were of a class called polyamides—supermolecules made by the condensation reaction of a diamine, a relatively short-chain molecule having reactive nitrogen groups at each end, and a dibasic acid, another short-chain molecule with double reactive groups. Du Pont gave this new class of materials the inspired generic name of nylon. Dozens of different nylons were put together, each somewhat deficient in one or another textile quality. Finally, the one with the best all-round properties, which was to appear commercially in 1939, was designated nylon 66, because it was made up of two compounds, adipic acid and hexamethylene diamine, each containing six carbon atoms. Both compounds were originally derived from benzene through phenol, which, oxidized with nitric acid, gave adipic acid, and which in turn was converted in a series of steps to hexamethylene diamine. Later the company moved to other starting materials, including furfural, derived from oat hulls, and butadiene from petroleum, either of which may be used to make hexamethylene diamine. It also moved to cyclohexane, from either petroleum or coal, to derive adipic acid. This illustrates the enormous flexibility of synthetic organic chemistry, showing how various source materials may be made to yield by different routes the same carbon chains required to build up giant linear molecules. . . .

Pollution: The Wake of the "Torrey Canyon"

John L. Walsh

London. When the tanker *Torrey Canyon* ran aground near the southwest tip of England last year, it gave its name to a new kind of maritime disaster, the cost of which is counted not in human life but in widespread economic and ecological damage. This in part accounts for the special efforts subsequently made to assess the implications of the accident. And while the last word has certainly not been said, two recently published British government reports contain much of what is likely to be learned about the effects of the wreck.

John L. Walsh, "Pollution: The Wake of the 'Torrey Canyon,'" *Science*, 12 April 1968, Vol. 160, No. 3824, pp. 167-169. Copyright 1968 by the American Association for the Advancement of Science. Reprinted by permission of the author and publisher. The author is a staff writer for *Science*.

A review of events and a set of recommendations for future action are contained in a report[1] published late last year by the committee of scientists organized at the time of the crisis by Sir Solly Zuckerman, chief scientific adviser to the British government. Then, on the anniversary of the stranding itself, a report[2] based on a survey and analysis of the biological consequences of the wreck was published by the government-financed Plymouth Laboratory of the Marine Biological Association of the United Kingdom.

Taken together, the two reports offer a good account of the lessons learned. What is insufficiently suggested is the effect of the crisis atmosphere which prevailed in the days when oil was escaping from the stranded ship. As the Zuckerman committee notes, "most of the decisions taken during the crisis had a scientific and technical aspect." But a lack of relevant scientific information, the necessity of improvising a coordinated response to the emergency, and perhaps most of all the legal, political, and economic specters raised by the incident made it difficult to put countermeasures on a "scientific" footing.

The government was criticized, for example, for waiting a full 10 days before ordering an attempt by aerial bombing to burn oil still left in the tanker. First the government hoped the ship might be refloated or the oil might be transferred. Then there were doubts that the oil could be effectively released by bombing, ignited, and kept alight. And Britain, as a major maritime nation, was reluctant to take a step such as bombing while the salvagers held out hopes and so many questions about responsibility were unanswered.

Pollution of the English coast by oil is a perennial problem. What was unprecedented was the scale of pollution threatened by the *Torrey Canyon*, loaded with 117,000 tons of Kuwait crude oil. Exposed to the threat were the beaches of the southern coasts of England, Britain's principal holiday area. Very heavy pressure was immediately exerted to "save the beaches."

With first priority given to safeguarding coastal amenities, the reflex action was to employ measures developed by the Navy in dealing with oil spills in harbors. This meant using detergents to emulsify and disperse the oil. Some 10,000 tons (2 million gallons) of detergents were used to treat 13,000 tons of oil on Cornish beaches, and another half million gallons were sprayed at sea.

In its effects on marine life this detergent "cure" proved much more damaging than the oil itself. The chief conclusion of the Plymouth Laboratory study is that, except for serious effects on some species of sea birds, the oil was not lethal to flora and fauna. Detergents used to disperse the oil, on the other hand, were highly toxic to marine life, most conspicuously to intertidal life such as limpets and barnacles. In the open sea, detergents in quantities as small as one part of detergent per million parts of seawater proved lethal to planktonic growth.

---

[1] *The Torrey Canyon* (Her Majesty's Stationery Office, London, 1967).

[2] J. E. Smith, Ed., *"Torrey Canyon" Pollution and Marine Life* (Cambridge Univ. Press, London, 1967).

Toxic Effects

Detergents used in spraying operations are mixtures of several compounds—a surfactant (or surface-active agent), an organic solvent, and a stabilizer. A stable emulsion of oil and water was necessary if the oil was to be dispersed. Solvents which enable the surfactants to mix with oil to form an emulsion contain a high proportion of aromatic hydrocarbons. Research indicated that the detergents with the highest proportion of aromatics are the best emulsifiers, and also the most toxic to flora and fauna.

Spraying of a half-million gallons of such detergent could be expected to have a devastating effect on plankton living near the surface of the water. Biologists reported surprisingly little damage to planktonic organisms in the spraying area. The explanation, they suggest, is that toxic aromatics evaporate very rapidly from the surface of seawater. Otherwise, as the report puts it, "the biological consequences in the English Channel would have been vastly worse than they were."

The worst sufferers from the oil were sea birds; the heaviest casualties were suffered by diving birds—guillemots, razorbills, cormorants, and shags. Gulls seem to have learned to avoid oil, and very few were affected. Ornithologists have reported a decline in the number of auks and other diving birds breeding on southern British coasts in the last 30 years and have attributed it to oil pollution. Total casualties of the *Torrey Canyon* oil were estimated at 20,000 guillemots and 5000 razorbills. A sad aspect of the oil fouling of sea birds was the failure of rescue operations. The British are unrivaled bird lovers, and a big effort at cleaning birds was made by the government and by voluntary agencies and individuals. But of nearly 8000 birds recorded as treated, only 450 were alive by mid-April and only about 1 percent of the birds treated were expected to be returned to the sea.

Little Effect on Seals

Contrary to some predictions, effects on offshore fisheries seem to have been negligible. The seal population does not appear to be seriously affected, although some breeding caves were badly polluted by oil and scientists suggest that ill effects may become apparent later. No commercial shellfish ground was affected by oil, as such grounds were in France, and care was taken not to spray detergent near such beds.

France's battle with *Torrey Canyon* oil was different from Britain's, in part because the French had more time and perhaps because they profited from the British experience. The main difference was that the French shunned detergents. Oil came ashore on the coast of Brittany in higher concentrations than in most parts of Cornwall, but the French relied on mechanical means of removal and such natural effects as waves, tides, and bacterial degradation. Oil did do considerable damage to Breton shellfish beds, but these are expected to recover. At sea, a big patch of oil in the Bay of Biscay was successfully treated with powdered chalk. The chalk binds the oil into particles which sink to the bottom. The French estimate that 3000 tons of chalk will sink 20,000 tons of oil.

The two British reports give the impression that, after the accident, luck was with the defenders. A northerly wind blew for nearly 2 months afterward, at a time of year when the wind normally blows from the southwest. Under normal conditions much more oil would have come ashore, instead of being blown out to sea. It even appears that if the bombing and the burning of oil aboard the *Torrey Canyon* had been done earlier, a lot of unburned residue would have ended up on the beaches. The immediate costs of the wreck to Britain (estimated at £3 million), the setback to the tourist industry, and the damage to coastal ecology all could have been devastatingly increased if even half the oil in the *Torrey Canyon's* tanks had come ashore.

Research Needed

The recommendations of both reports follow logically from the *Torrey Canyon* ordeal. The Zuckerman committee asks that better means be developed for transferring cargo from disabled tankers and for destroying or dispersing oil at sea. Detergents should be used judiciously, and less toxic detergents should be developed, both reports agree. And more research needs to be done on the neglected questions of the effects of pollution on marine life and ways of minimizing these effects.

Chances for a more effective government response in future crises have probably been enhanced by the decision, late last year, of the House of Commons Select committee on Science and Technology to form a subcommittee on coastal pollution. This subcommittee, the first formed by the parent committee, is looking into all aspects of the problems raised by the *Torrey Canyon* episode and should eventually make recommendations for across-the-board action in future disasters.

And the odds are that there will be other Torrey Canyons. Some 10 percent of the world's shipping accidents occur in Britain's heavily trafficked coastal waters. And tankers are getting bigger. The 210,000-ton Japanese supertanker *Idemitsu Maru,* for example, dwarfs the *Torrey Canyon.* And within a few years tankers of a half-million tons deadweight may be plying the seas.

The Plymouth Laboratories scientists say in summing up, "We are progressively making a slum of nature and may eventually find that we are enjoying the benefit of science and industry under conditions which no civilized society should tolerate."

The Use and Misuse of Pills

George Johnson

You may be one of the five million Americans alive today—thanks largely to drugs unknown twenty-five years ago.

No estimate is available of the number of Americans dead today—thanks largely to drugs unknown twenty-five years ago. We do know that one in ten general hospital beds is occupied by someone suffering from efforts to treat him, often involving misuse of modern drugs.

The average American's life expectancy has increased more than seven years since 1940—thanks largely to drugs unknown then. The death rates from such killers as influenza, pneumonia, tuberculosis, and syphilis is down 70 to 90 percent—thanks to modern drugs.

More than half of all recorded suicides in 1962 were caused at least partly by barbiturates unknown in 1940. (There is no record of the number of accidental barbiturate suicides, including such noted victims as Alan Ladd, Dorothy Kilgallen, and possibly Marilyn Monroe.)

The new drugs affecting the mind have revolutionized mental health care. Twenty-five years ago, a person entering a mental hospital could expect to be confined most if not all of the rest of his life. Today, two-thirds of all mental patients are discharged within a year. The "mind" drugs have freed fifty-four thousand Americans from mental hospitals since 1955, and have averted the commitment of eighty-two thousand others.

Some one and one-half million Americans now depend on the "minor" tranquilizers and other habit-forming sedatives. One out of six of us reaches for the pill bottle at the first sign of stress.

The recent torrent of new and powerful drugs has worked miracles in curing and preventing certain diseases—and has made us a nation of Pill Poppers, who have been led to believe, and who eagerly embrace the suggestion, that there is *nothing* wrong with us that some pill won't cure.

George Johnson, "The Use and Misuse of Pills," in the *Pill Conspiracy* (Los Angeles, Sherbourne Press Inc., 1967). After a year at Indiana University Johnson began a varied career as journalist and freelance writer. In addition to many TV and radio scripts, he is the author of the following books: *Richard Nixon, Eleanor Roosevelt*, and *Eisenhower* (all in 1962); *The Washington Waste Makers* (1963); and *The Abominable Airlines* (1964).

We firmly believe that:

Pills can pick us up—or slow us down. Pills can produce babies—or prevent them. Pills can whet our appetite—or dull it. Pills can shield us from the world—or sharpen our perception of it. Pills can cure any illness, physical, mental, or imaginary. Pills always help, never harm.

Pills can produce health and happiness.

Speaking of the "mood modifiers"—the tranquilizers and stimulants— Dr. Morton Schillinger, director of the Lincoln Institute for Psychotherapy in New York City, has said:

An unbelievable fraud has been perpetrated on the public about medication which influences emotions . . . (these drugs) cannot provide magic contentment. They cannot provide miraculous cures.

(Yet) we have arrived at a point where 'herd psychology' is taking over . . . swallowing pills . . . has become the thing to do . . .

People must learn and some are learning—through violent sickness and even death—that drugs are no solution to life's problems.

People also are learning—through sickness and death—that some drugs are no more of a solution to physical or mental ills than they are to life's problems. Too often, drugs are hastily created, insufficiently tested, falsely promoted, thoughtlessly demanded, carelessly prescribed, and indiscriminately taken. Very often they produce damage as bad as or even worse than the ailment being treated.

Take thalidomide, the drug whose misuse had more to do with the long-overdue strengthening of our national drug laws in 1962 than any other influence, including the late Senator Estes Kefauver's exhausting investigation of the situation.

Thalidomide was introduced in West Germany in 1957, hailed as a sleeping pill free of hangover effects. Countless thousands of pregnant women in Europe and America took thalidomide during the four years before 1961, when it was hastily jerked off the market—and at least five thousand of these women bore children without arms and legs.

This from a drug whose sole "benefit" was prevention of sleeping pill hangover!

Take the antibiotic chloramphenicol, sold here under the trade name of Chloromycetin, which ran up a formidable record as a drug that killed patients by inducing blood disorders. This drug was advertised in medical journals for general use against infections—these ads running side by side with editorial warnings that it should never be prescribed except for typhoid, because of its great danger.

This from a drug being handed out for such minor discomforts as the common cold!

Take the antidepressant tranylcypromine, sold under the more felicitous name of Parnate. It was removed from the market by its maker *under protest* only after fifty reported cases of patients who took it suffering strokes or other cerebral vascular "accidents," fifteen of them fatal. Announcing Parnate's "voluntary" withdrawal, the Food and Drug Administration (which was responsible in the first place for its approval) conceded that there were other antidepressants without Parnate's lethal side effects. Nevertheless, the FDA allowed Parnate back on the market six months later, with "revised" labeling which consisted of a virtual blanket admission of the drug's enormous potential for harm.

Responsible study has indicated that Parnate is no better than, and in numerous instances inferior to, other antidepressants—and, unlike them, its effects are unpredictable and can be fatal. (At the same time, we must realize that the fact that a person dies while taking medication does not necessarily mean that the drug was the cause.)

When first ordering Parnate off the market, the FDA virtuously stated:

"The FDA bends over backward in the interest of safety."

As we shall see, the FDA—the people's agency for regulating the sale and use of drugs—far too often has bent too little and too late.

Which drugs now in common use will turn out to be the thalidomides, the Chloromycetins, and the Parnates of tomorrow? And are such risks necessary?

It is well known in the pharmaceutical and medical trades that all drugs produce side effects, effects other than those they are intended to produce. Even aspirin causes stomach irritation, or bleeding, or asthma, in some people.

Such effects may be caused by a particular individual's sensitivity to the chemicals in a particular drug, or by excessive or prolonged use of the drug. Long usage among many humans is necessary before it can be certain that the drug is as safe as may have been indicated by experimental testing of it in animals, or even controlled clinical testing on humans under close observation.

Today's powerful drugs are much more likely to cure disease than the comparatively weak drugs of the past—and they are just as likely to produce massive side effects, because of their strength.

Drug makers know the vastly increased danger of harmful side effects; doctors know this, pharmacists know it—but the general public does not.

We take pills on faith, faith that they have been thoughtfully made and properly tested, that they will do what our doctor says they will do, and that they are "safe."

This faith often is no more justified than our subprimitive belief that pills will cure us of anything.

Then we multiply our risk by drug misuse, sometimes our doctor's fault but more often our own, and invariably with serious consequences.

In California, a respected school teacher is arrested for shoplifting. She is released after doctors testify that she stole while suffering a temporary mental disturbance brought on by birth control pills. The doctors add that the same psychiatric problem can be induced by such common drugs as cold tablets!

In Minnesota, a woman comes to her doctor complaining of suicidal depression, a "vile" taste in her mouth which makes it impossible to eat, and itching around her shins.

Baffled by these bizarre symptoms, her doctor resorts to the habit he has learned in this Age of the Pill of asking how many medicines she is taking.

She says she is taking seven, including one to "wake up" and two to "give me sleep"!

A woman is admitted to a hospital for the fourth time in four years, and within thirty-six hours develops all the indications of delirium tremens, seemingly from acute alcoholism.

Her husband objects angrily to that diagnosis, insisting that she doesn't drink. Questioned further, he reveals that for some time he has been finding half-empty packages of carbromal hidden in her room, and it turns out that she has been taking twenty or more tablets a day for years.

What she is suffering from is drug withdrawal. Shocked by the sudden cutting off of her habitual carbromal overdose, her mind and body have become unhinged.

But more than temporary insanity results from drug abuse.

A fourteen-year-old suburban boy kills his father and murderously slashes his mother for no reason at all—after taking barbiturates and whiskey.

A seventeen-year-old girl stabs a classmate to death—under the influence of barbiturates.

A tractor truck careens across a West Virginia turnpike into an oncoming mobile post office, killing both drivers and three sorters in the mobile post office. Autopsy discloses amphetamines—"pep pills"—in the truck driver's stomach, and more are found in his luggage.

A respected legislator, given pills for a slight infection, blacks out while driving on a busy metropolitan street in midday, and causes an accident.

An elderly man quietly walking his dog is seriously knifed by a boy who has been taking "pep pills."

A young radio announcer comes home after having a couple of drinks to celebrate a promotion, takes sleeping pills, and lies down and quietly dies from the combination of alcohol and drugs.

A patient appears at a hospital with familiar symptoms. Treated for the ailment doctors have become accustomed to associate with those symptoms, he dies—because he was addicted to some "nice" drug, did not or could not admit it, and was given another drug which was fatal in combination with the one he was guzzling by the bottleful.

Beyond the hospitals and the police and court records go the submerged millions of Pill Poppers, the "walking wounded" being mistreated by doctors or mistreating themselves, wandering along life's precipice under the delusion that a pill is the answer to what ails them.

Such is life in this Age of the Instant Cure, and how many voices are raised against it?

Oh, there are a few, but they are faintly heard and unheeded amid the clang of coin into the coffers of the drug trade, from the manufacturer to the pharmacist; the scratching of the doctor's pen as he turns out prescriptions like Detroit turns out cars; the snoring in Congress and the regulatory agency, the FDA, and above all the piteous wails of the individual unable to weather the faintest distress without chemical help.

The biggest vested interest of all is you and me. We have so lost our tolerance for even transitory discomfort, and our belief in man's mastery of his fate, that we need to believe in the miracle of the pills. We want to believe. We believe.

In 1939, pharmaceutical sales in this country, for prescription and nonprescription drugs, totaled $300 million at manufacturers' prices. (The retail value of these drugs was about $800 million—which may suggest to you where your friendly neighborhood druggist's interest lies.)

In 1963, pharmaceutical sales amounted to an estimated $3.3 billion at manufacturers' prices ($8 billion at retail). Thus, in twenty-four years, drug sales increased *1100 percent.*

We now spend forty-two dollars per year per capita on drugs—forty-two dollars for every man, woman, and child in this nation. This is about half what those stoics, the British, spend even with their government footing the bill, and beats the world except for Belgium and Italy.

And the pharmaceutical manufacturers have not just been plowing these billions back into research, as their publicity intimates, or using them to pay higher production costs. *Fortune* magazine's 1964 survey of the five hundred biggest American companies showed the pharmaceutical giants with a 10.6 per cent profit on sales, highest profit ratio of any American industry.

And what of the future?

We can sum up the future in three words:

Buy pharmaceutical stock.

One current analysis predicts that the pharmaceutical industry's sales will increase at least another 50 per cent by 1975, which means that this $3.3 billion business will grow to $5 billion—or more than $12 billion at retail.

Certainly, the industry's discovery of the value of clever promotion had a great deal to do with booming business. But could it have run up this dramatic record unless it was following that classic admonition for success: find a need and fill it?

What of the physician? Does he make any genuine effort to reduce our national dependence on drugs, to prescribe fewer of them, to control or reduce the cost of the drugs he does prescribe?

Not so you can notice it, for several reasons.

There are about 260 thousand doctors among our population of 190 million. Eliminate those who practice part time or not at all, and you have one practicing doctor per one thousand people. The doctor simply doesn't have time to effectively treat all those who come to him, and so in many instances he settles for giving a pill to all but the obviously serious cases.

Now, using pills as standard treatment how can he admit candidly that many of them are dangerous, and how can he talk freely about their excessive use? To do so would diminish his patients' confidence in him. So he discourages any talk about the peril in pills.

Furthermore, the doctor has become market oriented. As anxious to prosper as the next businessman, he succumbs to the business ethic that he has to give his "customers" what they want if he wants to keep their business. The trouble is, he isn't dealing with something as innocuous as shampoos or packaged pizza, but human life. Yet when his patients demand pills, especially the latest sensation they've heard about on the hypochondriac circuit, the businessman-doctor rationalizes that if he doesn't acquiesce, another colleague will, and he bows, not to Hippocrates, but to Mammon.

En masse, the physican is even less responsible.

When the tetracycline war began in 1964, over whether to prescribe this drug by its more expensive brand names of Tetracyn and Achromycin, or by its inexpensive generic name, tetracycline, many individual doctors, sensitive to their patients' interests, began writing prescriptions using the generic name. (By law, no substitution can be made in filling a prescription using a brand name; when a generic name is used, any drug of that kind may be dispensed by the pharmacist.)

But the doctors' union, the American Medical Association, thrust itself into the battle with an editorial in its *Journal* (where drug company advertising provides a rich source of income for the AMA) urging prescription by brand name, on the basis that this is the only way to assure the patient of getting drugs of the necessary quality and potency. The *Journal* restrained itself from commenting about the price differential between brand name and generic drugs.

The last place you will hear any opposition to pill popping is down at the corner drugstore.

Total sales in our fifty-three thousand drugstores in 1963 amounted to about $8.8 billion. Of this amount $2.5 billion came in prescription sales, and another $1.2 billion from selling packaged medications—commonly known as over-the-counter or proprietary drugs, available without prescription. Almost 43 per cent of the druggist's business—and a much higher percentage of his profit—comes from drugs. Twenty-five years ago, drugs accounted for less than half as much of his income.

Is he going to knock the pill business? Would you?

Another deterrent to any call for drug sanity from the drugstore is that, more and more often, the druggist is your physician in disguise. Many doctors have discovered recently what a profitable business a drugstore can be, especially one that limits itself almost entirely to filling high-profit prescriptions, and the number of medical men owning drugstores has doubled since 1960.

Some malcontents may wonder about the ethics of a doctor owning the drugstore to which he sends you to buy drugs which he has prescribed, but the doctor's self-appointed voice, the American Medical Association, sees absolutely no conflict of interest here. The AMA assures us that the dedicated man with the stethoscope would never, no never, write a prescription for drugs you don't need, just to make 142 per cent or so profit on you at his captive drugstore.

The druggist's future, whether he is what he seems, or actually your doctor in disguise, is going to be fabulous, the way we're going now. One industry projection suggests that prescription sales alone will reach $5 billion a year by 1975.

Is this necessary to your and my good health?

The Kefauver-Harris drug law amendments of 1962—passed only in the wake of the thalidomide disaster—strengthened the power of the responsible federal regulatory agency, the Food and Drug Administration, for only the second time since the FDA came into being in 1906—after a series of exposes of food adulteration and fake medical preparations. (The first strengthening took place in 1938, after more than one hundred Americans, many children, died after using a sulfanilamide which contained a poisonous solvent.)

In the past, partly because of a "dangerously meager" budget and staff, the FDA was little more than a sieve through which new drugs flooded onto the market at a rate which once reached one every four days, and once on the market they were almost impossible to get removed. Until 1962, the law said that the FDA's only job was to certify the new drug as safe, with no concern for its need or effectiveness.

Under this restraint, and often confusing the public interest with the private interest of the industry it is supposed to regulate, the FDA has been a singularly somnolent watchdog.

Vice-President Hubert H. Humphrey, himself a licensed pharmacist, said in 1962:

> *The more we have examined the handling of new drugs by the Food and Drug Administration, the more we have been surprised, shocked and disappointed . . . . Often, testing has been going on in a manner which should have sent shivers down the spine of the medical profession . . . .*
>
> *Drugs intended for use by victims of chronic disease—day after day, year after year—were released by FDA even before—I repeat, before—chronic toxicity (poison) tests had been completed on animals . . . shocking reports of injuries to test patients, as received by drug companies, have often gone unreported to the FDA, or have been downgraded by skillfully contrived half-truths, or have been reported accurately to FDA, but virtually ignored . . .*
>
> *Drugs have been approved which FDA now admits should never have been approved. Drugs have been kept on the market long after FDA admits they should have been eliminated . . . .*

The Kefauver-Harris amendments certainly have dammed the flood of new drugs, by requiring proof of effectiveness as well as safety, but the proof still comes from the drug maker, who remains responsible for all testing, and whether the reports are truthful or not is for him to know and the FDA to find out, if it can.

Even honest clinical testing on human subjects under close observation of experienced physicians is no sure proof of a drug's worth. Only years of general use—on you and me—can reveal its true balance of benefit and risk.

And, as *Consumers Reports* has noted, "With the potent drugs now coming on the market, the penalties for inadequate testing are nearly always threatening to the patient's health or his life."

Does this knowledge sober the pharmaceutical industry to the point where it will accept, if not encourage, closer FDA supervision?

Well, the Pharmaceutical Manufacturers Association's executive vice-president contributed an article titled "New Drug Regulations—A Year's Perspective," to the trade journal, *The New Physician,* one year after the Kefauver-Harris amendments went into effect, and this furnishes some clues.

He contended that the new regulations are impeding "still further" (!) the availability of new drugs to "the persons most interested in having them—physicians, pharmacists and, of course, patients."

He finished with " . . . one might say that the patient may be slightly better protected in 1964 than he was in 1963 or 1962 against the dangers of potent drugs, but there is reason to question whether he is better protected against disease."

Lack of space, or something, prevented him from documenting this latter claim.

Sir William Osler, the renowned physician, teacher, and medical historian, once wrote, "The desire to take medicine is perhaps the greatest feature which distinguishes men from animals." And the feature which distinguishes modern man from primitive man is that, whereas primitive man took medicine to heal sores, relieve pain, and cure disease, modern man has added the fourth goal of modifying healthy life as well as sickness.

The late author Aldous Huxley, an enthusiastic seeker after heightened sensations through drugs, wrote, "In the course of human history, many more people have died for their dink and their dope than have died for their religion or their country." If so, perhaps we aren't so different after all.

Today, "We are becoming a pill-swallowing civilization," says Dr. Herbert Ratner, of the Loyola (Chicago) University School of Medicine. "None of these pills is innocuous, and the damage they do frequently far outweighs the good they intend."

Brain Biochemistry

David Krech

Many and varied have been the tricks tried and expertises exploited as the newer breed of psychoneurobiochemists have sought to understand the workings of the mind, but they have one most curious thing in common. They neglect almost completely the knowledge accumulated from over 100 years of work, which indicates so clearly and so convincingly that the brain consists of differentiated systems and subsystems, of specialized areas, organs, centers—all intricately bound up with each other and organized in functional and interdependent hierarchies. Many of our biochemical researchers, in seeming ignorance of all this, attack the cranial cavity as though it were a huge test tube, and the brain within it but an unorganized suspension of free-floating proteins and enzymes and RNA's and diverse macromolecules—a chemical brain-soup, as it were—which can be made to reveal its secrets of operation by chemical analysis alone.

However, most researchers who behave in this way are not doing so through ignorance, doubt, or disrespect of the gains made by the ablation and electrophysiological methods. These researchers know, they believe, and they regard as extremely important the findings that relate behavior to brain structure, but they deem it expedient to set these findings aside for the time being while they go about their own business with their own working assumptions. For it often happens in the development of a scientific problem that the posing of different questions requires different and even seemingly incompatible working assumptions. Everyone is perfectly aware, of course, that the time will come when all these questions and assumptions and answers will have to be made harmonious. But time enough for that later on—seems to be the strategy.

What are the differences in the questions being asked? Where formerly, in the era of the ablationist and electrophysiologist, we emphasized the anatomy or

Extracted from Chapter 2, "Brain Research: Some Recent Developments and Some Speculations for the Future" by David Krech in *Toward Century 21* edited by C. S. Wallia, ©1970 by Basic Books, Inc., Publishers, New York. The author is professor of psychology at the University of California at Berkeley. He is author of two widely used textbooks, *Individual in Society* and *Elements of Psychology*. During the past several years his research has centered on the problems of brain biochemistry in learning processes.

statics of brain events and asked where the important events took place, in the era of the psychoneurobiochemists, we shift our emphasis to physiology or dynamics, and ask what takes place.

In essence, we now ask the following questions: How do we retain the remembrance of things past? In what corporal forms do memories exist that enable us to carry within us, through action and repose, over minutes and over years, the images of things smelled, heard, tasted, seen—images that guide our conduct, color our dreams, and in later years, if they remain with us, turn us into reminiscing old bores, and if they forsake us, convert us into senile burdens? And some biochemical brain researchers believe that we already know, in the rough, the form the answers will take to these questions. And it is this: The physiological substrate of memory, whatever else it may be, is, most importantly, chemical in nature. And when we are pressed to be more specific about the chemistry, different ones of us will implicate the production of new proteins, or the release of differentiated RNA's as essential, or the induction of higher activity levels in this or that enzyme, or more cautiously, an increase in the synthesis of differentiated but as yet unidentified macromolecules. If I weren't afraid of the tut-tutting of my sober-sided scientific colleagues (and some of my best friends are sober-sided scientific colleagues) I would be quite content to summarize it all by saying that we are really talking about "chemical memory pellets."

And now let us look at this research. Of the many research approaches currently being exploited, I shall pick out five to discuss, beginning and ending with work from our Berkeley laboratory.

Enriched Environment Studies

The first research is not only one of the earliest in this area, but also involves the most simple hypothesis. Some time ago we set ourselves the following problem: If the laying down of memories involves the synthesis of chemical products in the brain, then one should find that an animal that has lived a life replete with opportunities for learning and memorizing would end with a brain chemically and morphologically different from an animal that has lived out an intellectually impoverished life. For almost 2 decades, now, E. L. Bennett, biochemist; Marion Diamond, neuroanatomist; M. R. Rosenzweig, psychologist; and I, together with technical assistants, graduate students, and thousands of rats have labored—and some of us have even sacrificed our lives—to find such evidence.[1]

At weaning time we divide our rats into two groups—half of the rats being placed in an intellectually enriched environment, the other half—their brothers, in the deprived environment. While both groups receive identical sanitary care,

---

[1] D. Krech, M. R. Rosenzweig, and E. L. Bennett, "Relation between Brain Chemistry and Problem-Solving among Rats Raised in Enriched and Impoverished Environments," *Journal of Comparative and Physiological Psychology* (1962), LV.

food, and water, their psychological environments differ greatly. The animals in the first group live together in one large cage, are provided with many rat toys (tunnels to explore, ladders to climb, levers to press), have comrades with whom to "relate," are assigned to graduate students who are admonished to give them loving care and kindness and teach them to run mazes, and in general, we provide them with the best and most expensive supervised education available to any young rat at the (Pre-Reagan) University of California. While these rats are thus being encouraged to store up many and varied memories, their brother rats, in the deprived group, live in isolated, barren cages, devoid of stimulation by either their environmental appurtenances, fellow rats, or graduate students. After about 80 days of this differential treatment, all the animals are sacrificed, their brains dissected out and various chemical and histological analyses performed. The results are convincing. The brain from a rat from the enriched environment—and presumably, therefore, with many stored memories—has a heavier cortex, a better blood supply, larger brain cells, more glia cells (cells whose functions are not quite known but are found in huge numbers in the brain), and increased activity of the two brain enzymes acetylcholinesterase and cholinesterase than does the brain from an animal whose life has been less memorable.

We can draw two morals from these experiments. First, even the rat brain does not live by bread alone. The growing animal's psychological environment is of crucial importance for the development of its brain. By manipulating the environment of the young, one can truly create a more robust, healthier, more metabolically active brain. I shall speculate later on what this can mean socially and politically if it should turn out that what is true for the rat brain is also true for the human brain, and that by careful manipulation of this or that group's early environment we can develop among them bigger and better brains—or smaller and meaner ones. Speculations, here, will be no more insightful than the ones that must have already suggested themselves to you. The wondrous promises of a glorious twenty-first century or the monstrous horrors of a Huxlian Brave New World or an Orwellian 1984 are fairly self-evident from the data presented.

"Chemical Memory Pills"

James L. McGaugh at the University of California at Irvine has argued that injections of chemical compounds such as strychnine or metrazol, which are central nervous system stimulants, might serve to enhance the effectiveness of the reverberatory process in establishing long-term memories.[2] Apparently his idea is a sound one. In one of his experiments, which is most pregnant with social implications, promises, and foreboding for the future, McGaugh tested the maze-learning ability of two quite different strains of mice. One of the strains

---

[2]J. L. McGaugh and M. C. Madsen, "Amnesic and Punishment Effects of Electroconvulsive Shock," *Science* (1964), CXLIV.

was, by heredity, particularly adept at maze learning; the other, particularly stupid at that task. Some animals from each strain were injected with different doses of metrazol after each daily learning trial (to see whether there would be an improvement in their ability to retain what they had learned that day) and some were not. The findings can be stated quite simply: With the optimal dosage of metrazol, the chemically treated mice were 40 per cent better in remembering their daily lessons than were their untreated brothers. Indeed, under metrazol treatment the hereditarily stupid mice were able to turn in better intellectual performances than their hereditarily superior but untreated colleagues. Here we have a "chemical memory pill," which not only improves memory and learning but can serve to make all mice equal whom God—or genetics—hath created unequal. One might begin to speculate on what it can mean—socially, educationally, politically—if and when in Century 21 we can find drugs that will be similarly effective with human beings.

Short-Term vs. Long-Term Memory

Bernard Agranoff's (University of Michigan) experiments carry McGaugh's story to the next logical step.[3] Agranoff argued that if we could somehow prevent the brain from synthesizing the chemicals involved in the long-term memory process, then even if we were to set up robust reverberatory processes in the brain, the long-term process could not be established. We would thus create an animal with normal short-term memory but with no long-term memory. Using goldfish as his experimental animals, Agranoff trained his fish to swim from one side of an aquarium to another whenever a signal light was turned on. Failure to swim to the other side earned the goldfish an electric shock. Goldfish, given a large number of trials within a 40-minute period, learn this shock-avoidance task quite easily—and they remember it over many days. Now Agranoff varied his experiments. Immediately before, and in some experiments immediately after training, Agranoff injected the antibiotics puromycin or actinomycin-D (which inhibit the formation of new proteins or nuclear RNA) into the goldfish's brain. His findings were most encouraging. The injected goldfish were not impaired in their learning of the shock-avoidance task since, presumably, the short-term reverberatory process that enables the fish to remember its lesson from one trial to another—a matter of a few seconds—does not involve the synthesis of new proteins or of nuclear RNA. But when tested a day or two later, the fish showed almost no retention for the task it had known so well the day before—indicating that the long-term process, which makes memory possible from one day to the next—is dependent upon the synthesis of these compounds in the brain. Here, then, we find not only support for our general theory and increased understanding of how the brain works, but we have a suggestion that there exist in anti-metabolites entire families of chemical

---

[3]B. W. Agranoff, R. E. David, and J. J. Brink, "Memory Fixation in the Goldfish," *Proceedings of National Academy of Sciences* (Washington, 1965), LIV.

memory preventatives. Conjure up, if you are of that mind, what evils such weapons can wreak in the hands of the Orwellian authorities of 1984.

The first three researches—our Berkeley experiments, McGaugh's, and Agranoff's—involved experimental designs that are perfectly acceptable to the Scientific Establishment and discombobulate no one. But there are many ways to make progress in science. There is, for example, the slow stately walk, wherein the scientist progresses from one relatively small—albeit important—increment of knowledge to the logically next step. On the other extreme there is the hurried, unseemly, running broad jump, which seeks to hurdle intervening steps to land on some more distant point. Now sometimes, in attempting such a jump, the scientist falls flat on his face—to the glee of the academy about him; but sometimes he lands clean, and running forward—way ahead of the walker. And in the fourth set of experiments, we will see an example of just such an attempt.

McConnell's Planaria Experiments

A number of years ago, James McConnell[4] at the University of Michigan threw all the brain researchers into a tizzy by reporting that he could teach planaria—a fairly primitive type of flatworm—to learn to make simple response to a light signal, then grind up his educated flatworm, feed the pieces to untrained fellow worms—and lo and behold, the uneducated flatworms wound up with the memories of the worms that they had just eaten, and without any training, could perform the responses of the late-lamented and digested "donor"worms!

McConnell's report really upset those of us who had been weaned on the importance of the integrity of the organization of the nervous system for the control of memory and learning. For although much of the biochemical brain research neglects the structural problems of neural control, they nonetheless use animals with intact brains. McConnell, on the other hand, by grinding up his worms, had deliberately and wantonly destroyed all neural organization and was claiming that shredded and eventually digested tissue from one brain carried with it intact memories that could be transferred to another. McConnell's work was greeted with suspicion—and, in most quarters, with disbelief.

But then all hell did break loose when first A. L. Jacobson, at UCLA, and then other workers in other laboratories and in other countries reported that they could train a rat, make an extract from its brain, inject this extract into an untrained rat, and that by so doing the recipient rat would acquire the memories of the now-dead donor rat. Now it is one thing to claim this for the primitive planaria, which, after all, do not have very much in the way of structurally differentiated and organized brains—but it is a very different thing to claim this for the rat, which is a serious mammal, with a highly developed brain—as a

---

[4]J. V. McConnell, "Memory Transfer Via Cannibalism in Planaria," *Journal of Neuropsychiatry* (1962).

matter of fact, with a brain that is not too different in complexity, in differentiation, and in organization from our own.[5]

The dust raised by these reports has not yet settled. Indeed, most scientists are definitely on the side of the nonbelievers—but the work goes merrily on, and at this writing it is hazardous to predict the final outcome of these inter-animal-information-transfer experiments. However, many brain researchers have been moved, over the last 2 or 3 years, from the position of stiff-necked disbelief to the position of "Well, maybe—I don't believe it, but well, maybe." And this is where I stand at the moment, fearless and foursquare proclaiming, "Well, maybe . . . ." Now, if it should come to pass that McConnell and Jacobson and Byrne and Ungar (just to name a few of the experimenters who have reported positive results and are to be numbered among the believers)—if it should come to pass that they are right—then we will indeed have made a huge jump forward. For we would then have a most effective behavioral assay method that should enable us, with our available biochemical techniques, to "zero in" on this marvelous brain-goulash, which can transfer information from one brain to another and isolate and identify in detail all the proteins, enzymes, RNA's or other macromolecules that comprise the "chemical memory pellets." After that—the world of the mind is ours! But that day is not yet here. Let me leave these broad jumpers (who have yet to land safely) and end my survey where I began it—in our Berkeley laboratories.

A New Study

E. L. Bennett and I are engaged in research—research so recent that none of it has been published and subjected to outside scrutiny.

To continue with the metaphor, Bennett and I are not trying a broad jump, nor are we exactly proceeding in stately decorum. One might say that we are attempting a quick, furtive hop. Or, more simply stated, we are seeking to test a weak version of the animal information transfer hypothesis. I will now describe the reasoning behind our "weak jump" or "hop."

Among the most compelling of the a priori arguments against the inter-animal-information-transfer notion is the one already outlined: memory, whatever chemistry it may involve, depends upon a spatial-temporal patterning of the activity of anatomically differentiated units and pathways in the nervous system. As long as one believes this, it is difficult to see how a chemical extract from a trained donor's brain could possibly create and activate, in a naïve recipient's brain, the complex organization of neural "hookups" and activity that must characterize a specific memory.

But now let us suppose that we had some way of preparing the recipient's brain so that it would have a suitable structural organization, but be chemically—or functionally—inert and inactive. If now there be anything to the

[5]A. L. Jacobson, F. R. Babich, S. Bubash, and A. Jacobson, "Differential Approach Tendencies Produced by Injections of RNA from Trained Rats," *Science* (1965), CL.

notion that chemical brain extracts can carry information, then we would have here a set of the most favorable conditions for such extracts to activate and control the recipient's memory and behavior. Perhaps as I describe our experiments and results, this will become clearer.

Our apparatus consisted of two chambers separated by a solid wall. One chamber was painted black, and darkened, and had an electrified grid floor; the other was painted white, was lighted, and had a smooth, harmless floor. Weanling rats were placed for 10 minutes in the black chamber where they received 30 painful electric shocks; they were then removed to the white chamber where they were allowed to rest quietly for 10 minutes.

Four weeks later the animals were tested for their memory of this infantile traumatic experience. For testing, the wall separating the two chambers had an opening cut into it that permitted the rat to go from one chamber to the other at will, and neither chamber was now electrified. The animal was placed in the white chamber, and the time elapsing before it dared enter the black chamber was recorded. Presumably the longer it delayed in entering the black box, the more vivid was its memory of its long-ago, brief but painful experience there. This test is particularly appropriate, it should be noted, because rats of our strain that have not been shocked in the black box normally spend no more than about 25 seconds in the lighted white box before scooting to the safety of the darkened black box.

Three groups of animals were used: a group that received the original traumatic training, after 4 uneventful weeks was given its memory test; a group with the same traumatic training but which, during the 4-week waiting period received injections of ground-up or homogenized brain taken from donor rats that had had the same traumatic training—only more recently; and finally, a group, which after its traumatic training, received brain injections from donors that had never had any traumatic experience with this apparatus.

Bennett and I have, to date, completed seven such experiments involving well over 1,000 rats. In six (or five—depending on our statistical juggling) out of the seven experiments, the rats injected with brain homogenate taken from animals that had recently undergone the traumatic experience showed a greater fear of the black box than did either the rats that had received no injections at all, or the rats that had received injections from untrained donors. We suggest the following interpretation of the results already in (the experiments are continuing, of course): Any intense experience that results in a long-term memory process lays down structural and chemical changes in the brain. With the passage of time, the effective chemical compounds of these long-term memory processes "decay" or become attenuated, and thus while many of the structural changes or "hook-ups" of the neuronal network may remain, the attenuated "chemical memory pellets" that do remain are inadequate to activate this network, and the individual is said to have "forgotten" the experience. However, a fresh supply of the effective chemicals (obtained from a donor animal that has recently had the same or similar experience) when injected into the recipient rat will reactivate the previously established network, and thus act as a chemical "memory booster" to revive afresh its old and almost forgotten experience.

As soon as we are convinced that we can reliably replicate these findings, we will then seek to isolate and identify the specific biochemicals that act as memory boosters. Success in this project may tell us as much as the more audacious experiments of Jacobson et al. It should tell us a great deal about the chemistry of memory. If all goes well, we hope to have our studies completed sometime before the twenty-first century. But we are fully aware that one can fall flat on his face even in attempting a "hop."

And thus I finish my sampling of current biochemical brain research. I do not pretend that I have presented a representative sample—but neither do I think that I have seriously misrepresented the state of the art. In any event, it seems obvious to me that we can confidently expect most wondrous achievements in this most wondrous research field in Century 21.

Speculations

One of the next steps forward will come when the biochemical researchers join forces with the ablationists and electrophysiologists, when the modern descendents of Gall and Flourens and Fritsch and Hitzig work together with our contemporary biochemical brain researchers. Instead of working on the biochemistry of the brain—as though it were an undifferentiated, sovereign, unitary organ—we will work with the biochemistry of different organs, centers, pathways, and hierarchically related and functionally differentiated areas of the brain. It is perfectly reasonable to suppose that each functionally differentiated area of the brain has its own chemical signature. It is perfectly reasonable to suppose, therefore, that we will be able to find specific biochemical boosters and biochemical inhibitors for different kinds of memories and imagery—visual, auditory, tactual, olfactory; for different kinds of abilities—verbal, musical, spatial, visual; for different kinds of personality or temperament traits; aggressiveness, submissiveness, hyperactivity, hypoactivity.

With such chemical agents in hand, we will apply them—for good or for evil. We may use them as supplemental therapy for those failing in any ability or trait—and we will have it within our power to heal many of the mentally retarded, and many of the senile. We may use these chemical agents as supplemental reinforcers where we wish to develop special strengths above the normal. We may use them to perform localized chemical surgery to reduce a specific potentiality to reduce specific motivational urges; or to create docile, intellectually limited but efficient human beasts of burden; or we may do so to remove from man's brain life's inevitable painful memories, and release man's present and future from crippling memories of his past.

In addition to these special uses, I also foresee great changes in the first and most general business of society—the education of its young. The development of the mind of the child, the shaping of its strengths and weaknesses, and the potentiation of its inherent possibilities will not rest in the knowledge and in the skills of the biochemist alone. Certainly our early work at Berkeley—and the work of others—indicates clearly enough that not only is behavior affected by brain chemistry, but brain chemistry is affected by early educational stimulation and training. (Remember our psychologically enriched and our psychologically deprived rats?) Brain research and procedures will have to be combined with educational research and procedures to potentiate the effectiveness of each. The education of the young of Century 21 will be in the hands of a new kind of expert—the psychoneurobiochemeducator! And this multihybrid Century 21 expert will have recourse—as I have suggested elsewhere—to protein memory consolidators, antimetabolite memory inhibitors, enzymatic learning stimulants, and many other portions and elixirs of the mind from our new psychoneurobiochemopharmacopoeia. But even all this will not suffice.

One overriding, overwhelming, and most foreboding set of questions remains. Experts—whatever else they may be—are notorious order-takers. Who will direct our psychoneurobiochemeducator where to work his expertise, and what shall we tell him to do? Here we are talking about goals and values and aims. Here we, all of society, must provide our expert with political, moral, and ethical guidance. Shall our expert raise or lower docility, aggressiveness, musical ability, engineering ability, artistic sensitivity, effective intellectual functioning, mental retardation, mediocrity, and/or senility? Shall different ethnic or racial or national or social groups receive different treatments? In past centuries—and even today in Century 20—this is precisely what we have ordered (either through default or through conscious social policy)—our relatively primitive but quite effective medical and educational and psychological experts to do. And lo, they have done so! And they have created enclaves of the sick, the weak, the ignorant, the unskilled and the brutalized—and on the other side of the walls of the city, they have created the healthy, the strong, the knowledgeable, the skilled, and even the somewhat civilized. Will we continue to do this in Century 21 with our much more sophisticated and effective psychoneurobiochemeducators? Who, in other words, will control the brain controllers—and to what ends?

To me, in any event, it is clear that some of the possible outcomes of our present brain research can raise problems surpassingly strange in their novelty, bafflingly complex, and of serious social import. If we fail to prepare ourselves, we might find it too late to institute effective, carefully thought through, and humane controls.

Section Five

The Nuclear Threat

No scientific innovation rivals in social impact the unleashing of the enormous power locked into the nucleus of atoms. The atomic age changed the world abruptly and permanently and rendered obsolete traditional international relations. Nuclear technology represents the supreme symbol of the ambivalence of technical knowledge, which can be used constructively or destructively. Even peaceful uses of the atom involve the hazards of radiation and waste disposal. Atomic weapons and their delivery systems have contributed to converting the world to a "global village" as much as the new communication devices. While this collective threat has created the basis for global unity, the politics of the real world is fraught with tension and filled with violence.

A great controversy rages over the peaceful applications of atomic energy whether for primary power sources or for special engineering projects like "Gasbuggy," in which underground nuclear explosions are used to release huge pockets of natural gas. The supporters of these projects defend their safety, social necessity, and nonpolluting nature while opponents deny all of these. Economic and political imperatives are woven into the fabric because the military and economic power of states depends to a large degree on nuclear energy. The eventual depletion of fossil fuels demands the development of alternative energy sources—of which nuclear energy is the most promising. The editor is convinced, however, that these economic and political imperatives are not always consistent with maximum safety and health. Technological determinism seems to be operating.

For many scientists, the bombs dropped on Hiroshima and Nagasaki have left a permanent psychological mark, a trauma of conscience. Undoubtedly, the nuclear threat has taken its toll of the collective psyche. The fear of impending nuclear destruction of civilization has created in many, especially the young, the need to live in relevant 'now.'

The major threat to human survival remains the direct military nuclear arsenal. The building of huge stockpiles of nuclear weapons has consolidated our commitment to nuclear energy. (For every pound of U_{235} produced, 143 pounds of U_{238} are also produced.) Among the world military powers, five are known to possess nuclear weapons—U.S.A., U.S.S.R., China, United Kingdom, and France. All possess both atomic (fission) and hydrogen (fusion) bombs, but only two have 'second strike' capacity (ability to absorb a first attack and strike back). These two—U.S.A. and U.S.S.R.—can strike any target on the face of the earth at short notice through their operational delivery systems (ICBM and FOBS). Winston Churchill's phrase, "sturdy child of terror," an apt but euphemistic description of the nuclear deterrent, shows the dominant basis of contemporary big-power military policy. The total world stockpile of nuclear weapons has been conservatively estimated as the equivalent of 20 tons of TNT for every individual in the world, or a total of 60 billion tons. This is super overkill capacity, because the power of a few pounds of TNT can kill an individual.

Besides the military nuclear powers, a larger group of nations have civil nuclear reactors. Some 50 countries, those of Western and Eastern Europe, Scandinavia, Canada, Japan, Pakistan, Israel, U.A.R., India, and others have these civil reactors, and by 1980 the U.S.A. and Western Europe will be well on the way to the almost complete transformation of their energy sources to nuclear power. By the year 2000, over half of the world's electric power will be generated from civil reactors, a great proliferation of reactors both in numbers and countries. Now the danger, what Ralph Lapp, in his book *The Weapons Culture* calls the "honey-venom" aspect of nuclear power, is that, without strict international control and inspection systems, these civil reactors can be used to siphon off weapons-grade Uranium 235 and to produce Plutonium 239, a weapons-grade waste product. At the present time, the U.N.'s International Atomic Energy Commission is supervising safeguard systems in some 25 countries, but the control and inspection lag is critical and cannot guard against clandestine acquisition of weapons-grade fissionable material by terrorist criminal groups. There may soon be a black market in bombs or bomb components. The crime syndicates must realize the ransom value of an atomic weapon. As more small and less responsible countries enter this new civil nuclear club, what the late President John Kennedy called a disaster by "accident, miscalculation, or madness" seems inevitable unless provision for adequate international controls is made. Thus, we see the innate ambivalence of nuclear power. Of course, radioactive waste disposal is another environmental hazard of great concern and a major example of technological backlash.

The editor has not attempted to provide a balanced picture of the debits and credits of nuclear power. The established trends of nuclear proliferation do not require moral or intellectual support, but the basic questions of control and misuse should be raised, in accord with the dominant theme of the reader.

Among the nations who have the potential to make atomic weapons, including the requisite technology and the necessary fissionable material, are Sweden, India, Japan, Canada, and Israel. As a background to the grave Mid-East situation we must assume that Israel, at least, has two or three atomic bombs or the necessary parts to assemble them.

In the light of the above situation and with the involvement of the two major nuclear powers, the U.S.A. and U.S.S.R. in the Mid-East conflict, the dangers cannot be overemphasized. When the activities of terrorist organizations are also considered, we have a frightening scenario. The buildup of an Arab-Soviet military system sufficient to threaten Israel's existence balanced against Israel's potential nuclear delivery system raises the real question of whether an atomic weapon would be used on Egypt. This situation reaffirms the precariousness of existence under a nuclear deterrent that in the end might not deter. The only way to ease this problem is a strong, viable international treaty and control system supported by an equally operational United Nations Organization.

The selections in this section all express concern about the nuclear threat, whether civil or military. Lapp's essay provides an overview of the social, political, and cultural aspects of military nuclear capacity. Inglis also deals with the nuclear arms race, but more from the aspect of environmental problems, while Novick writes of the hazards involved in the civil application of nuclear energy. The section ends with the famous Vienna Declaration of the Pugwash Conferences, a prophetic statement of great concern about the nuclear threat by some of the leading scientists in the world.

Weapons and Society

Ralph E. Lapp

"Priorities are reflected in the things we spend money on. Far from being a dry accounting of bookkeepers, a nation's budget is full of moral implications; it tells what a society cares about and what it does not care about; it tells what its values are."

—*Senator J. W. Fulbright*
August 8, 1967

Any accountant going over the postwar books of the United States would find some rather discouraging facts. Over seven tenths of federal expenditures have been for national security. In the vital area of federally funded research and development, almost nine tenths of this work was directed to defense-atomic-space activities. Less than one tenth of one percent of these funds went to support research in problems of urban development. Naturally, a nation must look to its security, but the material developed in previous chapters suggests that the United States overreacted to foreign threats. Furthermore, in view of the recent decision to build up ballistic defenses, it appears that this country is stepping up the tempo of the arms race.

Robert L. Heilbroner, in his *Limits of American Capitalism*, states: "No attempt to speak of the long-run prospects for American capitalism can overlook the central fact that it is now a semimilitarized economy and that it will probably become even more so during the next decade." Gradually the U.S. involvement with defense industry has proceeded to the point where weapons-making begins to dominate our society. This protracted dedication of American effort to devising and manufacturing new arms has created a techno-military

Reprinted from *The Weapons Culture* by Ralph E. Lapp. By permission of W.W. Norton & Company, Inc. Copyright © 1968 by W.W. Norton & Company, Inc. The author, a physicist and author of numerous books, received his Ph.D. from the University of Chicago in 1945, and soon after became active in the wartime Manhattan Project. Since 1950 he has been a consultant physicist with the Nuclear Science Service in Washington. Among his books are *The New Force* (1953), *Atoms and People* (1956), and *Roads to Discovery* (1960).

establishment that threatens to make greater inroads upon our economy. A central problem for democracy is the control of this military-industrial complex that has grown in influence as its political connections have ramified.

No nation can devote so much of its ingenuity, manpower, and resources to the works of war without at the same time being deeply changed in the process. Many of the changes are subtle, slow to surface, and hard to trace as to origin. There is a certain aseptic and detached quality to our techno-militarization which insulates people from its impact. The Long Island housewife who assembles tiny electronic components for a bomb mechanism does not associate herself with the weapons that may bring death to some victim. She lives in her own microcosm and, if queried about her occupation, may shrug off the questioner with the reply, "A job is a job." The scholarly professor who probes the chemical secrets of certain compounds may fail to associate his research with destructive defoliants. The senator who champions a $40 billion Nike-X defense will reject the charge that he is his own lobbyist, asserting that his only concern is with national security. The industrialist who mass-produces napalm may brush aside any qualms he may have with the contention that he simply fulfills orders given to him by his Government.

This is a deteriorating situation that contributes to allowing the arms race to run out of control, for if all are compliant and feel no responsibility, then our democracy is in jeopardy. A new order of discourse is called for—linking the American people to major national decisions in which their security is intimately involved. It needs to be a spirited dialogue, marked by the sharpest questioning of techno-military issues. Those who criticize or seek to examine the wisdom of national decisions need not have the answers; it is sufficient if they phrase the questions properly and publicly. Any operations analyst knows that half the problem is finding the right questions to ask.

Here are some of the key questions that need expression:

1. *How does the nation arrive at rational determination of the strategic forces adequate for a policy of nuclear deterrence?*
2. *Given the decision on a "thin" ballistic-missile defense, how does a democracy prevent automatic escalation to a "thick" defense system?*
3. *What constitutes an effective mechanism for objectively evaluating whether or not a "megaton gap" poses a real threat to U.S. security?*
4. *What should be done about future defense contracting with firms fully committed to having the U.S. Government as a single customer?*
5. *How should the nation's scientific and technical resources, so preponderantly oriented to atomic-space-defense, be converted to a larger share of peaceful missions?*
6. *What can the United States do to arrest the momentum of the runaway arms race and start on the road to arms controls?*
7. *How does a democracy go about applying restraints to the military-industrial-political complex, which fuels the arms race?*

This list of questions does not end here; it is merely a beginning, but it may serve to suggest the dimensions of the debate needed if democracy is not to be tyrannized by defense technology. . . .

If the U.S. aerospace industry—by all odds, the most rambunctious component of the military-industrial complex—is to fit into the national economy without depending primarily on defense contracts, then the means must be found to convert it to new objectives. This is an especially acute problem for companies like Lockheed, which are so top-heavy in arms sales. The state of California, anticipating conversion problems in the event of defense or space cutbacks, let four study contracts to aerospace companies for analysis of certain problems, such as transportation. The results were widely advertised but added little to California's knowledge of how to solve its transportation problem. The fact is that aerospace industries are quite specialized in their know-how and lack experience in diversifying to invade the civilian market for consumer products on a competitive basis. Much of the aerospace technical talent lies in the field of engineering which is not easily adapted to new endeavors. Furthermore, lack of dollar consciousness in the artificial aerospace business hamstrings companies when they try to penetrate fields already served by experienced corporations. Here the Federal Government, long the exclusive patron of many of the aerospace firms, has a responsibility to help in converting the defense contractors to enter the free play of the marketplace.

The author is no dreamer who thinks that the United States can abandon its commitment to arms overnight. He does not recommend giving up a policy of nuclear deterrence that has been the mainstay of our national security for so many years. It would be foolish in the extreme to believe that peace will break out on this planet in a great wave of international understanding. Therefore, we must be reconciled to large defense budgets for some years to come, but we must also avoid too great extremes in defense, which provoke equal reactions from hostile powers. Since it is the U.S. Congress that controls defense purse strings, it is imperative that this legislative body be equipped with some better and more objective means of analyzing the nation's security needs. . . .

The public may be confused when experts disagree on a national issue, but it is essential that opposing viewpoints be aired; otherwise policy will be determined by a technological elite. It is not proper that Americans should bow their heads before the altar of technology, averting their eyes as did ancient multitudes when high priests sought auguries in animal entrails. As Robert Oppenheimer has remarked: "We do not operate well when the important facts, the essential conditions, which limit and determine our choices are unknown. We do not operate well when they are known, in secrecy and in fear, only to a few men."

The fundamental issue of nuclear superiority as opposed to nuclear parity has never been fully exposed to the public view. In general the news is leaked from the Pentagon or via Capitol Hill that the Soviets have developed or are about to produce a new weapons system. Then there is a clamor for the United States to "catch up" and surpass the Soviets. Most recently this sequence of events was illustrated for ballistic-missile defense. Now an attempt is being made to have the United States "match" the orbital-eject bomb delivery system of the Soviet Union, even though its military value for the Soviets is highly dubious and is even more so for the United States. There is the automatic assumption that any Soviet military development represents a margin of superiority and that it must be offset by a corresponding counterdevelopment. In this manner the arms race escalates and provokes corresponding reactions by the Soviets, which in turn set off new cycles of armament.

If there is ever to be any stability in arming, people must recognize that there is a point in armament beyond which no additional security is purchased. By the same token, an enemy may achieve the same degree of security—that is, nuclear parity by fashioning his strategic deterrent forces to the lethal point. But when either side attempts to multiply its killing power, it invites duplication. In effect, a nation signs its own death certificate in multiple copies.

The concept of nuclear sufficiency—of the military ever having enough of anything—is still so novel that it has not yet gained acceptance in some military and political quarters. Defense Secretary McNamara understood and adopted the principle of nuclear parity as applied to the U.S. missile force, only to be overruled by President Kennedy. The latter, having campaigned on a missile-gap platform, apparently found it politically necessary to commit the nation to more missiles than Mr. McNamara believed to be enough for strategic deterrence. The full consequences of this missile escalation will have to be assessed by historians, but one thing seems clear: If the politics of defense dominates national security, then the world may never disengage from a spiraling arms race. When defense decisions are taken for political reasons—and domestic ones at that—a democracy may become an escalator in the arms race.

On November 6, 1967, the Joint Committee on Atomic Energy began investigating the nation's nuclear defenses in hearings headed up by Sen. Henry M. Jackson. Ostensibly the hearings were designed to explore the nature of the anti-ballistic missile defense problem, but in the course of the investigation it became clear that the committee was concerned with nuclear parity. Senators expressed their alarm over the increasing number of Soviet ICBM's, while the United States did not attempt to add more ICBM's to its own strike force. As I listened to the committee members question witnesses, I could not help but reflect that many of the committee members had served for many years on the Joint Committee; they had heard much testimony in previous years about the catastrophic nature of nuclear war. These men were granted access to data denied the great majority of the Congress. Yet it seemed as though the most elemental arithmetic of the nuclear age had not been absorbed. If these men with access and with so much exposure to the facts about nuclear weapons could not accept the principle of nuclear sufficiency, then how could the other members of Congress be expected to do so?

If a U.S. President authorizes a $5 billion Sentinel system to protect himself from Republican charges of failing to insure the nation's security, then one might just as well junk all the elaborate systems of defense analysis that we possess. If our representative form of government gives disproportionate influence to the military-industrial constituency, we had better seek out checks and balances to offset this menace. If our legislators act as promotional lobbyists for the military-industrial complex, then reforms must be enacted. Needless to say, corrective measures will not be easy because the disease of our weapons culture has metastasized itself into the lymphatic system of our society.

On December 13, 1967, Senator J. W. Fulbright surveyed the impact of the "military-industrial complex" in a Senate speech. "More and more our economy, our Government and our universities are adapting themselves to the requirements of the continuing war—total war, limited war, and cold war." Warning that this adaptation was "making ourselves into a militarized society," Senator Fulbright described the "military-industrial complex" as forming "a giant concentration of socialism in our otherwise free enterprise economy."

Moreover, we have exported our weapons culture. Our Military Establishment has deployed its forces on a global basis. U.S. military forces bulked in groups of more than 3,000 uniformed personnel are to be found in each of 17 foreign countries. We have 132 major installations in foreign countries, some of which have been negotiated at a loss of our prestige. For example, to secure air-base rights in Spain we had to make a deal with Generalissimo Franco. While these foreign military bases are meant to increase our national security, some become liabilities—as in the case of Jupiter missile bases in Turkey.

Not only has the United States stationed its own troops abroad; it has engaged in advising, supervising and training armed forces in 35 foreign nations. This activity includes bringing officers from other countries to the United States for training at our military schools. In 1967 some 12,000 Americans were engaged in military-training operations overseas, not counting the U.S. commitment to Vietnam.

The major U.S. military and foreign-assistance programs covering most of the postwar years have involved over $102 billion. In some cases, as for India, Austria, and a few others, the extent of military aid is kept secret. Sen. J. W. Fulbright, chairman of the Senate Foreign Relations Committee, has maintained that much of this foreign aid is dangerous in that it may backfire and encourage conditions that lead to war. Again, there is the action-reaction principle about which Defense Secretary McNamara has warned—the U.S. initiative may be followed by enemy-supported countermoves, and the United States then has to pour in more aid to offset these. This could well have been the case in Vietnam and, if so, the tragedy of our position there was that we boxed ourselves into a situation which our own action magnified into a commitment out of proportion to its strategic significance. Then face-saving, traditionally an Oriental monomania, became critical to the United States.

The U.S. military-industrial complex has profited from contracts for arms that foreign assistance made possible. There is little doubt that the political support for these foreign programs was linked to this domestic tie-in. At one time (1963) the United States was engaged in the sale of armaments to no fewer than 63 foreign governments. As *Business Week* magazine commented: " 'Buy American' is becoming an increasingly prevalent slogan in the world arms market." Considering the diffusion of modern arms across national borders, it is inevitable that American arms become weapons used against us or nations whose cause we support.

The redemption of our weapons-oriented society is a monumental undertaking; armaments have acquired such momentum that they dictate their own policy. As Konrad Lorenz wrote in *On Aggression:*

An unprejudiced observer from another planet, looking upon man as he is today, in his hand the atom bomb, the product of his intelligence, in his heart the aggression drive inherited from his anthropoid ancestors, which this same intelligence cannot control, would not prophesy long life for the species.

The separate worlds of Darwin and Einstein are nearing collision. Man, the twig-tip of the fabulous evolutionary tree, is in danger of nuclear blight—a disease of his own making. All too quickly Einstein's ideas have become arsenal items; all too sluggishly do men forget the ways of war.

America is now a land of incredible violence—in many forms and in many places—

A thousand sleek missiles, deadly warheads pretargeted at Soviet cities, stud our western prairies, once solely a source of life-giving grain.

Sunny California slopes, once orange-blossomed and fruitful, now sprout cavernous plants where engineers design orbital weapons.

Boston's Route 128 is festooned with mushrooming research laboratories, a Cold War-financed necklace of industrial innovation.

In Maryland's richest farmland, a few miles west of Frederick biologists at the highly secret Fort Detrick perfect virulent weapons of biological warfare.

Not far away, at the Pennsylvania border, lies the subterranean command post to which the President will be spirited in time of national emergency.

—America, the beautiful; now America, arms-maker and arms merchant to the world.

Nuclear Pollution and the Arms Race

David R. Inglis

Both the arms race between the nuclear giants and the rapid growth of industry are making appalling inroads on our environment. The manufacture and testing of nuclear weapons add to the world's burden of radioactive contamination, while industrial activity, stimulated by the arms race and civilian demand, belches noxious contaminants into the atmosphere and watercourses.

Yet in our ardor for preserving the environment we must not forget that there is a far more compelling reason for putting a lid on the arms race, namely, reducing the risk of nuclear war.

The direct way to modify the arms race is by negotiation and wise example. It is our country that has principally fired the nuclear arms race by insisting on being way ahead in most categories. Our overkill is such that we could afford to set an example of moderation and watch for reciprocal restraint on the other side. The U.S. negotiation stance should be one of initiative to attain substantial mutual limitations and reductions, rather than one of stalling until we get ABMs and MIRVs before talking seriously.

The recent sudden shift of liberal concern from the ABM to the environment seems to be leaving a vacuum where pressure is urgently needed to stop the arms race by diplomacy and restraint.

The way President Nixon has hopped on the environment bandwagon with enthusiastic words, if little substance, suggests he may have sensed its importance in weakening the opposition that was nearly successful last time, as he seeks to step up the ABM program. With the perpetual expansion of the military establishment, nuclear weapons production is likely to grow, increasing radioactive pollution at home and around the world, strengthening the military-industrial complex, and moving mankind closer to the full horror of nuclear war.

Concern for the environment, and even legislation protecting it, can mildly shackle some of the details of weapons production, but only a change of foreign

Reprinted with permission from *The Progressive* magazine. Copyrighted © 1970 by The Progressive, Inc., Madison, Wisconsin. David R. Inglis is professor of physics at the University of Massachusetts. Previously he was engaged in research on the theory of nuclear structure at Argonne National Laboratory. He is on the editorial board of the *Bulletin of Atomic Scientists* and is a frequent contributor to scholarly journals.

policy can stop it. The basic shortcoming of the President's budget message was that it called for no really substantial transfer of funds from Vietnam and the arms race to the anti-pollution effort, and gave no indication of an intention to taper off the arms race and make this transfer possible in the future.

The production of nuclear materials—plutonium, tritium, and separated uranium—involves the production of enormous amounts of radioactive materials that must be disposed of as waste, and in the production of power which ends up by heating rivers and lakes enough to affect aquatic life. Furthermore, the uranium separation consumes a lot of power generated by burning coal. It is the disposal of radioactive wastes that is the most serious problem nuclear power presents to the environment. Nuclear materials are produced to fuel both the arms race and the electric utilities industry. The needs of both threaten the environment in a cumulative way.

The most dramatic effect of the arms race on the environment came from the testing of nuclear weapons in the atmosphere in the era before the partial test ban of 1963. Radioactive fission products in unprecedented quantities were carried high in the atmosphere by the mushroom clouds of the big H-bomb explosions, and gradually settled over much of the earth. Yet, people went about their daily lives without noticing any tangible or identifiable effects on the environment. We normally live with a weak exposure of radiation from cosmic rays and from ordinary rocks. In terms of this natural background, the increase of overall radiation was not large and some authorities scoffed at misgivings. The normal background causes some cancer and genetic change, and a slight increase could not be easily isolated and recognized.

Yet this oft-quoted comparison with natural background is unfair because the fission process, that which takes place in bomb explosions and in electric power generating reactors, does not merely increase the background radiation. It produces kinds of radioactive substances that are different and which settle in and attack the human body in specific ways, unlike the natural background radiation. Rocks and cosmic rays provide a natural background of gamma rays (deeply penetrating X-rays) and less penetrating beta-rays (electrons) that pass through the whole body indiscriminately, causing weak ionization on the way; cosmic rays passing through the atmosphere also make a special radioactive substance, carbon 14, that becomes rather generally distributed through body tissues. But the fission process creates new types of radioactive atoms that do not exist in nature, and that are dissipated through the air (and water and food supplies) until they settle in the body. Depending on their chemical nature, some of them locate preferentially in certain sensitive parts to do their radioactive damage in a concentrated fashion. Thus, while the overall radiation dosage may be raised only a few per cent by bomb test fallout, the biological damage is disproportionately serious.

During the course of nuclear bomb testing, the danger of one particular element of fallout, strontium 90, was initially denied by Federal Government spokesmen. Its threat was first established by university scientists in independent research. Strontium 90 has a long-lived radioactivity. It is chemically similar to calcium and settles in bone. It concentrates particularly rapidly in the fast-growing bone of fetuses and young children. It gets there by settling on grass eaten by cows and is concentrated in milk. Starting in St. Louis, and then more widely, records have been kept of strontium 90 in the teeth normally lost by children, as well as in fetal skeletons. As a radioactive part of the bone, within which blood is made, strontium 90 can cause leukemia and other forms of cancer. It also attacks the genes, and causes birth defects and infant death. Yet these maladies arise also from other causes and one cannot pinpoint which cases are caused by the arms race. Invisible though the fallout was, we are well rid of the insidious atmospheric testing which might have been much heavier by now if we had had no test ban.

We should be eager to preserve and extend the test ban. Instead, after all our early worries about the Russians, it is we who are callously breaking it. Of more than two hundred U.S. underground tests, seventeen have vented seriously and the radioactivity from two has been officially reported as observed in Canada. Further pressure to abandon the test ban is apt to come with the growth of the ABM system.

Yet even without nuclear war and without nuclear testing, the arms race still has its effect on the environment through the preparation of nuclear materials. The mine and uranium mill tailings—the waste products—are themselves a serious local danger. They expose ores that were once locked underground to leaching by rain and consequent radioactive pollution of our rivers. But this is still only an accelerated recirculation of nature's radioactivity, mainly that of radium with its slow and therefore relatively weak decay.

More serious are the new man-made radioactive elements, by-products of the reactors that make plutonium and tritium for bombs. Some of these have lifetimes that are short enough to make the immediate radiation intense and yet long enough that they create a hazard for tens or hundreds of years, such as strontium 90 and cesium 137, which have half-value decay times of about thirty years. This means that after a hundred years, they would still be about one-tenth as radioactive as now and still a grave hazard in view of the huge amounts being put in perpetual-care storage.

Some of the nuclear reactors are operated for the Federal Government exclusively for the production of bomb materials. Such plants are at Hanford, Washington (the site of the original wartime plant), Paducah, Kentucky, and Savannah River, South Carolina.

Still other nuclear reactors are owned and operated by the electric utilities industry under Government subsidy for the dual purpose of producing plutonium (much of it for bombs) and electric power.

The subsidies provided by the Atomic Energy Commission at the taxpayers' expense take several forms. One is risk insurance. The Federal Government pays for most of what limited insurance coverage there is, and beyond that lets the public take the risk of the possible consequences of a serious reactor-runaway accident.

As another form of subsidy, the Government runs the huge, expensive, energy-consuming, thermal-diffusion plants. These supply the enriched uranium used as fuel in the industrial reactors at a favorable price to industry. A third form of subsidy is the guaranteed price at which the Government will buy all the plutonium industry produces. It is hoped that plutonium as well as enriched uranium will be used to fuel future reactors, but we do not yet know how.

The only current use for plutonium is for bombs. Both because this subsidy was necessary to make the rather marginal hoped-for profits sufficiently attractive to get the industrial program started and because the plutonium is used for bombs, the nuclear electric power program may be considered a handmaiden of the armaments program and its contribution to environmental pollution may be blamed partly on the arms race.

Most of the radioactivity produced by a reactor stays inside the metal fuel elements in the reactor core. After a period of a year or two the reactor is shut down while the fuel is removed and replaced. The partially spent fuel is sent to a reprocessing plant where the radioactive wastes are extracted in acid solution that is kept so hot by the radioactive decay that it boils if it is not continually cooled. This extremely lethal brew must be prevented from entering the environment, but the containment is not perfect despite all the care taken.

At present, such high-level wastes in this country are stored in about 200 large underground steel-and-concrete tanks, holding as much as a million gallons each. Most of these wastes came from weapons production not associated with electric power production. The radioactive intensity of the liquid (measured in a unit known as a "curie") may run as high as a thousand curies per gallon or more. This is so lethal that if only three gallons were distributed equally among the entire world's population this would suffice to reach in everyone on earth what is considered the danger point in radiation for the human body. Yet we already have in those buried tanks a hundred million gallons of the stuff, and apparently plan to go on producing it at an ever-increasing rate. These storage tanks require most elaborate perpetual care. They not only need power to cool them, but new high-quality tanks must be installed about every twenty years, on through the centuries, to replace old tanks damaged by radiation. Already failure of one tank has spilled 60,000 gallons of that lethal brew to find its uncertain way through the soil.

During the routine operation of reactors and fuel-processing plants there are also both planned and inadvertent releases of low-level wastes that contaminate air and water. The hot fuel elements in a reactor are sealed in a thin metal bonding intended to prevent the cooling fluid from coming into direct contact with the uranium and absorbing the radioactive fission products. However, in the power-generating plants, technology is pushed to its limit of high temperature and the metal seal frequently fails. It would be too expensive to interrupt operation for each failure, so leaks are tolerated in something like one per cent of the fuel elements before shutdown. This is one route by which strontium and other radioactive fission products get into rivers.

Krypton 85 is a radioactive gas which, like neon and argon, does not easily react with other atoms to form solids, and remains a gas that escapes into the atmosphere. Some of it goes up the stack at the reactor, because of leaks, and the rest of it escapes at the fuel-processing plant. When breathed in air, a little of it dissolves in body fats. Radioactive tritium, the stuff of the H-bomb, is also produced in reactors and finds its way both into the atmosphere and into water supplies. It enters into bodily processes as part of water molecules.

The annual amount of the release of hazardous elements from any nuclear plant is limited by standards set up by the Atomic Energy Commission. Since it is impossible to pinpoint all radioactive damage at low levels, the standards necessarily depend on somewhat arbitrary judgments. At high levels, it is known how much radiation will probably kill a man, and how much will probably give him serious radiation sickness. Permissible doses for workers in atomic plants are set well below that level, about one per cent of the lethal standard per year. But for the general populace, the permissible level is set about ten times lower, partly because of the possible seriousness of genetic damage.

Thus the "maximum permissible dose" for the public is far below the level of identifiably radioactive damage to the individual and may seem to be a conservative standard. The guideline figure for the permitted level of radiation exposure for the general public as a result of reactor operation is set at such a level that if the whole population of the United States were to receive this additional exposure continuously, data now available on cancer incidence show that it would result in more than ten thousand deaths annually. While this number is small compared with the population, it is a large number of people to kill with a deliberate change in the environment. The radiation specialists who arrived at this conclusion, J. W. Gofman and A. R. Tamplin of Berkeley and Livermore, California, advocate that the permitted limit be reduced tenfold. Such a reduction, if enforced, would drastically modify the operation of commercial reactors.

The release from the stack of a single atomic plant is limited, so that it may not exceed the permitted level for people in the neighborhood, on a yearly average. If it does exceed the permitted level for a short time in an accidental release, as sometimes happens, the power level must be reduced the rest of the year to compensate. But a combination of a temperature inversion to keep the gases close to the ground, wind direction, and an accidental release can give some people a dose far above the "maximum permissible." As nuclear power plants become more numerous, the release from many plants may compound the exposure to radiation for persons in a wider area.

The commercial fuel processing plant at West Valley, New York, is responsible for keeping its low-level waste within permissible limits after discharge into a creek. It remained for University of Rochester scientists, acting on their own initiative as environment buffs, to discover that the radioactivity of the creek was far above the maximum permissible limit. Such considerations have led to clamor for an effective independent agency to set and enforce the safety standards, since AEC is now both promoter of nuclear power and its own policeman.

Radiation does its damage to individual cells within the body, and there is good reason to believe that genes and the rapidly multiplying cells in unborn and young children are more sensitive to such damage than are the cells in adults. Study of survivors of Hiroshima showed little genetic damage, but there the bomb burst high in the air and its debris was carried away in the mushroom cloud. More recent studies on mice have shown that strontium 90, which is spread from bomb debris and reactors, has a special affinity for causing genetic damage leading to fetal and infant mortality, in addition to its tendency to settle in bone and cause cancer and leukemia more in the young than in adults. It thus appears that radiation-induced fetal and infant mortality may pose a more serious problem than cancer in adults.

As the arms race goes on piling overkill on overkill, an all-out nuclear war could cause fallout extremely more intense than that caused by testing in the late 1950s and early 1960s. If testing caused fetal and infant deaths at the rate of something like one per 100 births, as Dr. E. J. Sternglass of the University of Pittsburgh claims, then a nuclear war causing 100 times as much fallout could presumably kill approximately all children born, and thus end the human race. From the way heavier doses affect adults, it could be surmised that considerably less than 100 times the test-era fallout might eliminate the next generation.

Even though we take the view that the Sternglass thesis has not been proved, the very possibility that all-out nuclear war could end the human race is a more cogent reason than any other that such large-scale nuclear war should be avoided, and that the arms race should be terminated.

The marvelous natural resources that eons of geologic history have provided for us are limited indeed. We have used as much fossil fuel in the last quarter century as in all previous history, and we are beginning to feel the pinch. Rather than planning still more rapid consumption, madly doubling power consumption every ten years, we should be acting as careful stewards of the planet's resources for the maximum long-term benefit of mankind. Every gallon of valuable fuel, every pound of copper and uranium that goes into the arms race is robbed from the present and future quality of human life. If we could stop this arms-race robbery from human needs and if we could evolve an economic system dependent on stability rather than continual growth, then we could both spread the bounty of our environment more equitably over the centuries and get rid of the awful pollution with which our Twentieth Century gluttony is poisoning us.

The Menace of the Peaceful Atom

Sheldon Novick

In the late 1940's, when atomic power plants were first being discussed in public, highly respected individuals predicted that the atom would make electricity too cheap to meter. Although this has not turned out to be quite the case, atomic power plants are becoming cheaper, and are appearing on the outskirts of our largest cities—New York, Boston, Chicago, Los Angeles, Detroit, and San Francisco. By the early 1970's there will be more than a hundred of these plants operating, most of them enormous, each capable of producing a million kilowatts of power, more than enough power for a city of a million inhabitants. By the end of the century, half of America's electricity is expected to come from the atom.

Despite its possible benefits, this development poses certain serious problems involving the public health and safety—problems which have scarcely attracted any notice, let alone the careful consideration they demand. A warning of the hazards we may be facing here can be found in the history of the Pacific Gas and Electric Company's nuclear power plant at Humboldt Bay on the Northern California Coast.

Soon after the nuclear reactor for this plant went into operation in August 1963, General Electric, the manufacturer, discovered that it had made a mistake in designing the fuel system. Uranium fuel for a reactor is compressed into pellets and loaded into long thin tubes which are then bundled together into "fuel assemblies" for ease of handling. These fuel tubes, or "cladding," must be made of a material with certain special properties, and the search for such a material by the reactor industry led to the development of a new alloy called zircaloy. But General Electric, trying to bring the price of its reactors down, settled instead on stainless steel for its fuel cladding, and equipped the Humboldt reactor accordingly. By late 1963, after the initial fuel loading for Humboldt had already been made, the stainless-steel tubes at GE's testing facilities in Vallecitos, California, were showing signs of cracking and flaking during reactor operation. Pacific Gas and Electric, learning that it would eventually run into trouble, made arrangements to replace the stainless steel in the Humboldt reactor with zircaloy-clad fuel, which at that time seemed more reliable. But the replacement was not to be made until the first loading of stainless-steel fuel, worth about four million dollars, had been used.

By June 1965, the expected trouble began to materialize. In the core of the Humboldt reactor, cracks were appearing in the long slender fuel rods. Radioactive wastes from the fission process going on in the uranium within the rods were leaking out through the stainless-steel containers and into the cooling water flowing between the rods. Some of these radioactive wastes were gases and, mingling with the steam produced in the reactor, were piped out to the turbines which drove the power generators. Both gases and steam were then passed into a condenser cooled with sea water; here the steam was transformed back into water and returned to the reactor, but the radioactive gases were separated and discharged through the plant's tall stack and into the surrounding air. Little by little radioactivity in the vicinity of the plant increased.

In order to slow down the disintegration of the stainless-steel fuel, PG&E was operating the reactor at only 40 per cent of its full power. Nevertheless, radioactive discharges continued to increase. By September 1965 the release rate had climbed to a point which might have been interpreted as exceeding the limits set by the Atomic Energy Commission. Although PG&E denied this, it did shut down the plant until early December for refueling and modifications; during this time about one quarter of the stainless-steel rods were replaced with zircaloy-clad fuel. Most or all of the badly leaking fuel rods, the company announced, had been removed.

Soon after the plant was started up again, however, radioactivity in the gases flowing out of the stack began inching up once more, and by August 1966 it was reported to be approaching the permitted maximum. By this point PG&E had applied to the AEC for a fourfold increase in allowed releases or emissions of radioactive gases. The application was denied, and in the fall another two quarters of the steel-clad fuel were replaced by zircaloy-clad elements.

Meanwhile, at Parr, South Carolina—where the Carolinas-Virginia Tube Reactor (CVTR), owned by four Southern utilities, is located—trouble was also developing with zircaloy-clad fuel. In hearings before the Joint Committee on Atomic Energy in early 1967, Milton Shaw, director of the AEC Division of Reactor Development and Technology, testified:

The CVTR has . . . experienced failures in two of the normal fuel assemblies clad with zircaloy 4—the same material being planned for other commercial plants. . . . Although there is serious concern, I don't believe we can make a judgment at this time in the absence of determinations as to what caused the failures, sir. The failure could have been caused by defective manufacturing techniques or by something not understood about the design of the fuel.

At the very moment Mr. Shaw was speaking, 16 large new power reactors were under construction, and within a few months orders had been placed for 36 more; utilities across the country had indicated plans for about two dozen additional plants which had not yet been ordered. Some 70 to 80 large reactors, then, were being planned or were already under construction, representing a capital investment of several billion dollars. Roughly one fifth of the initial investment in a reactor is its first batch of fuel; over the plant's life the cost of fuel and fuel services is about equal to the initial cost of the plant itself. In the face of this enormous investment, it is almost certain that presently available fuel tube materials—particularly zircaloy—will be used; the story of Humboldt Bay may soon be repeated on a massive scale.

Nor are reactors themselves the only—or even the worst—source of radioactive pollution in the atomic power industry.

The fuel for reactors undergoes a complex series of extractions and transformations over a course of years. Uranium ore is mined, the uranium is extracted and shipped to a chemical plant, where the extracted ore, called "yellow-cake" from its appearance, is converted into uranium hexafluoride, which is then shipped to one of the government's huge gaseous diffusion plants at Oak Ridge (Tennessee), Portsmouth (Ohio), or Paducah (Kentucky). Here the content of fissionable uranium 235 is increased, or "enriched." The product is now shipped to a series of other plants, where it is converted to uranium oxide, compacted into small pellets, and packed into the long tubes which are assembled into finished fuel shipments for use in a reactor. But this is by no means the end of its travels. After wastes, or fission products, have accumulated in the fuel to the point where it is no longer usable, it is stored for a while and then sent to a reprocessing plant. Here the radioactive wastes are extracted, and the depleted uranium is usually shipped to a chemical plant to begin the fuel cycle all over again. As for the extracted wastes, they are either discharged into the air and water or packaged and transported to a storage or burial site. At every step in this long path there is some release of radiation into the environment.

Radiation problems in the reactor industry, then, begin in the shafts of uranium mines. Uranium ore also contains radium and other radioactive substances. Radium, in the process of slow decomposition, releases a gas called radon. When the ore is mined, radon gas and its own decomposition products accumulate in the mine shaft and pose a hazard to miners. The first disastrous effects of this gas were observed in the 1930's in mining communities in the Erzgebirge Mountains (between Germany and Czechoslovakia). A study performed between 1935 and 1939 revealed that approximately half the deaths among miners were due to lung cancer, and that 80 per cent of the remaining deaths were due to other lung diseases.

Shortly after World War II, great efforts were made by the Atomic Energy Commission to encourage uranium mining in the United States; by the early 1950's vast deposits in the West and Southwest had been uncovered, and by 1960, there were 1,000 active underground mines. Although the AEC published its first price schedule for uranium in 1948, it was not until July 1967 that a safety standard of any sort for uranium miners was enforced, despite the experience in European uranium mines.

A very similar pattern can be seen in the history of radioactive water pollution from uranium mines. Twelve million tons of radioactive sand, the refuse of uranium mining in the Colorado River Basin, is heaped in largely untended piles—called "tailings"—in an area affecting at least seven states in the Southwest. For nearly twenty years these sands have been accumulating, being blown by the wind into neighboring communities and being washed by the rain into the tributaries of the Colorado River and eventually into Lake Mead: a water system which provides water for drinking and irrigation to parts of California, Nevada, Utah, Wyoming, Colorado, New Mexico, and Arizona.

In the late 1950's the magnitude of the pollution hazard from uranium mining was discovered by the Public Health Service, which began pressing for control of wastes from the uranium mills in the area. Yet, as in the case of the miners, the measures eventually taken were partial and were in any event only proposed twenty years after the problem had been created. By now, about 30 million tons of such tailings have accumulated in various parts of the country and the total, of course, is growing.

Potentially the most serious hazard, however, is in the reprocessing plant where the radioactive "ashes" are extracted from the fuel and the depleted uranium is recovered. It must be borne in mind that it is precisely these "ashes" which constitute the radiation hazard in the civilian atomic energy program. Uranium fuel elements, before they have been placed in a reactor, are nearly harmless, and may be held in a bare hand. But after undergoing a slow controlled chain reaction in the reactor for several months, the same fuel element becomes the most dangerous object, short of an atomic bomb, known to man. It can only be transported in enormous lead and steel casks weighing many tons, and contains within it enough radioactivity, if distributed, to poison whole cities.

Much of this waste is so radioactive that it must be stored in underground tanks or buried in salt caverns. Even so, some of the radioactive gases which are released in the process of breaking up the fuel get into the air, while other radioactive matter gets into the plant's waste water and is discharged into nearby streams, thereby adding to the contamination of the environment.

Later on, we shall look at the criteria by which the AEC determines standards to regulate the discharge of radioactive wastes. Before doing so, however, it will be necessary to say something about what happens to these wastes once they are released into the environment. White Oak Lake—which served, before it was finally drained, as a radioactive waste-disposal pond at the AEC installation in Oak Ridge, Tennessee—provides a useful starting point.

Radioactive wastes routinely discharged into this man-made lake followed a complex career. When, for example, a small quantity of radioactive cesium 137 was dumped into the lake, it did not simply disappear. It remained dissolved in the water until its absorption by one of the microscopic plants, which existed there in the billions. These algae, mistaking the cesium 137 for the potassium they need (and which it resembles chemically), incorporated it into their tissues. Then, the cesium 137 was passed on through a "food chain"—zooplankton eating the algae and in turn being eaten by crustaceans; crustaceans being eaten by small fish who in their turn were eaten by larger fish. At each stage of this chain, the originally dilute cesium 137 became further and further concentrated.

This ability of living things to extract and concentrate extremely dilute substances is quite remarkable. The phenomenon was studied in Par Pond, a small lake very much like White Oak Lake and used for the same purposes at another atomic energy installation. During several months in 1962, the concentration of radioactive cesium in the water was 0.033 picocuries per gram (a very tiny quantity). But the flesh of bass caught in the pond contained, on the average, 35 picocuries—a thousandfold increase. For other radioactive substances, the concentration factor was even higher. Thus the *average* concentration of radioactive zinc in the bones of bluegill fish was 8,720 times that of the water in which they swam, while the concentration of radioactive strontium had increased more than 2,000 times in the bones of these same fish.

A great deal has been learned about the way in which radioactive materials are concentrated by different organisms, much of it through investigation of the problem of fallout from weapons testing. The testing of nuclear weapons, in fact, was probably the most massive (and unintentional) experiment in biology ever undertaken, and the results are just now beginning to come in. It will be many years before we fully understand the effects of fallout; certainly they were not even guessed at when testing began. In *Living with the Atom*, Ritchie Calder quotes a statement attributed to Clement Attlee, Prime Minister of Britain when the first atom bomb was dropped in Japan:

Of course, at the time we knew nothing, I certainly knew absolutely nothing, about the consequences of dropping the bomb except that it was larger than an ordinary bomb. . . . We knew nothing whatever at that time about the genetic effects of an atomic explosion. I knew nothing about fallout and all the rest of what emerged after Hiroshima. As far as I know, President Truman and Winston Churchill knew nothing of these things either, nor did Sir John Anderson, who coordinated research for our side. Whether the scientists directly concerned knew, or guessed, I do not know. But if they did, then as far as I am aware, they said nothing of it to those who had to make the decision.

"It is debatable," Calder goes on to comment, "whether those scientists who were party to the decision did, in fact, know about the biological risks."

In *Science and Survival*, the eminent biologist Barry Commoner points out that this ignorance persisted through the early years of bomb testing, and that our knowledge of the biological effects of fallout has still not caught up with our skill in nuclear physics. According to Commoner, in 1953, "the AEC stated that the only possible hazard to humans from strontium 90 [from fallout] would arise from 'the ingestion of bone splinters which might be intermingled with muscle tissue during butchering and cutting of the meat [from cattle exposed to fallout].' No mention was made of the simple biological fact that the milk from such an animal would also contain strontium 90. By 1956 the AEC had acknowledged that milk represented the most important source of strontium 90 in human food."

Little by little, more was learned about the ways in which plants and animals concentrate chemicals in their tissues. Strontium, which resembles calcium, was concentrated in bones and milk; radioactive iodine would be concentrated by cows grazing over large areas in which fallout had settled. The iodine 131 in their milk would be further and drastically concentrated in the thyroid gland of anyone drinking the milk. Children, with their large milk consumption, were particularly vulnerable; a group of children in a heavy fallout area of Utah is presently being studied by the Public Health Service, and a number of thyroid abnormalities which may be due to fallout have been discovered.

Some years ago it was found that Eskimos were absorbing far more fallout radioactivity than people living in temperate zones, even though the distribution of fallout was believed to be just the reverse, with a larger proportion settling in the temperate zones than at either the poles or the equator. The answer to this puzzle lay in the enormous concentrating ability of the Arctic food chain. The first link in this chain is the tough, scrubby lichen, which has the unusual characteristic of deriving its mineral nourishment from the air instead of from the soil. Ordinarily, dust and soil particles settling on the lichen provide it with needed minerals; when radioactive fallout joins the dust and soil, the lichen absorbs it too. These plants were and are extremely efficient collectors of fallout. They are also one of the principal foods of the caribou, which graze over large areas, thus effectively collecting and concentrating all the fallout which has descended in those areas. But the caribou in turn are an important—and in some areas and seasons almost the exclusive—food of Eskimos. Thus it was that the residents of Anaktavuk Pass and elsewhere received and go on receiving, as fallout continues to drift down from the stratosphere, radiation exposures which are close to, and in some cases may exceed, what are considered maximum permissible exposures.

Radioactive wastes from reactors contain the same substances that are found in fallout, which is not surprising, since both derive from the same source— atomic fission. (The fallout from hydrogen [fusion] bombs also comes principally from their uranium or plutonium "trigger.") When released into the environment, they follow paths as complex and unpredictable as those of fallout components.

Thus, at White Oak Lake, the food chain did not end with fish. Birds fed on the fish, and on one occasion it was found that enormously dilute radioactive phosphorus had followed the long trail from water to algae to fish to bird; radiophosphorus was appearing in high concentration (as compared with the level in the lake water) in the flight muscles of waterfowl.

The degree to which radioactive matter gets concentrated as it passes through the food chain is astonishing. Studies made of the Columbia River—into which the reactors for plutonium production at Hanford, near the town of Richland, Washington, empty their cooling water—tell the story with dramatic force. For example, radioactivity of the river plankton—microscopic plants and animals—

averages 2,000 times the radioactivity of the water. Caddis-fly larvae achieve concentrations 350,000 times that of the water. One survey of bird life on the river showed that the birds which feed on river insects also have a high concentration of radioactivity, which is mainly radiophosphorus; first the insects and then the birds selectively concentrate this isotope, even though it is only a tiny fraction of the total radioactivity of the river water. Adult swallows have a concentration factor of 75,000.

At White Oak Lake, many of the birds were migratory. We do not know when it was first suggested that these birds might be carrying some radioactivity off with them when they continued their migrations. Probably this had not yet occurred to anyone when the Tennessee Valley Authority was asked to do an ecological survey of the area. (That eight years elapsed between the establishment of Oak Ridge and the making of this survey gives some idea of the nearly total ignorance of biological effects under which the atomic energy program operated in its early years.) The TVA scientists, discovering that the thousands of waterfowl which migrated through White Oak Lake each year were picking up small quantities of radioactivity, initiated a program of banding the ducks in the hope of getting back reports from hunters who shot them. The reports, once they began coming in, showed that the radioactive ducks were being killed anywhere from the provinces of Canada to the counties of Texas. Shortly after the results of the banding were in, White Oak Lake was drained.

What had been going on in White Oak Lake was that the highly dilute wastes dumped into the water were being reconcentrated and then neatly packaged and dispatched all over the continent. When we remember that some migratory birds which stop in the United States are on their way from the Arctic to the Antarctic, the potential scope of this distribution is truly impressive.

There is no way of knowing what has happened to all of the radioactive chemicals which were dumped into White Oak Lake before it was drained. A given atom of radioactive cesium 137 may have passed from water to plankton to fish to bird and then been transported thousands of miles, at which point the bird may have been shot and eaten. Nor would this be the end of the cesium 137's career. After being retained in the muscle tissue of the person who had eaten the duck, perhaps for days or weeks, the cesium 137 atom would be excreted, picked up once more by plankton in a river, and would perhaps pass yet again through fish, bird, and man. Endless other paths might be followed. From White Oak Lake, the radioactive substance might have been carried by an insect for a mile, and then when the insect died, became part of the soil, thereupon starting on a cycle through plants and back to the soil for years or decades; perhaps eventually it might be ingested by another insect as part of a plant leaf and carried elsewhere, picked up by a bird, and finally appear in the human food supply a generation after its creation.

In short, every time radioactive waste is dumped into a stream, buried, dropped into the ocean, discharged into the air, or otherwise released from human control, it passes into the complex world of living things. It will move from living thing to living thing, sometimes becoming concentrated, at other times being dispersed, with an efficiency and ingenuity which man has not yet come to understand. At unpredictable times and places this radioactive waste will reappear in man's food, air, or water. It will not go away for decades or centuries or even millennia. Although the quantity of radioactive material will be slowly decreasing during that time, it is precisely this process of decay which releases radiation and which is therefore the source of damage.

There is nothing peculiar to radioactive materials in this phenomenon. Nearly every living animal on the surface of the globe, from deep-sea fish to arctic birds, carries some DDT in its fatty tissues; the number of pesticides which are achieving such universality grows every year. Lead from gasoline additives can be found in the snows of Antarctica. As to radioactivity itself, nearly every child born on earth in the last ten years has carried some radioactive strontium in his bones. The amount of radioactive carbon in the atmosphere has been doubled, and all of us bear some of this burden in our tissues.

We are slowly coming to realize that the thin film of life which covers the earth is a single complex web; a chord plucked at any one point vibrates throughout the world. And man is a part of this web; he depends on it totally for his food, air, and water.

What are the effects of radiation on man? Our ignorance of this matter is even greater than our ignorance of the means by which radiation returns to man after being released into the environment.

The effects of radiation are divided into two classes by most scientists—somatic and genetic. Somatic refers to the effect of radiation on an exposed person's body (soma); genetic refers to the effects on his progeny. Both kinds of effects are believed to be due to the same causes—the disruption by radiation of a cell's basic self-regulatory machinery. Whether this disruption eventually results in disease or in inherited malformation seems to depend simply on which of the body's cells are affected. Radiation lodged in a child's thyroid gland may produce cancer; radiation directed at the adult's gonads may, through a similar effect on germ-tissue, produce mutation and malformation in later generations.

Radioactive substances are chemically identical to the familiar elements, except that they have been rendered unstable. In the process of changing, or decaying, from one form to another, they emit radiation. This radiation can take the form of tiny particles, actually fragments of the atom, or of penetrating rays similar to X-rays, which can pass through seemingly solid substances.

Radioactive substances in food are incorporated into tissue just as their stable twins would be; embedded deep within a cell, the radioactive atom may emit a particle which then streaks away, or a ray which penetrates into other cells. In either case, a sudden and violent chemical reaction ensues. In the delicately balanced economy of the cell, this sudden disruption can be disastrous. The individual cell may die; it may recover. But if it does recover, its self-regulatory powers may be affected in some way we do not yet understand. After the passage of weeks, months, or years, it may begin to proliferate wildly in the uncontrolled growth we call cancer. If the damaged cell is in the gonads, the damage may be reflected in inherited malformation, even though there is no apparent disease in the affected person.

In other words, on a microscopic scale the release of radiation within the cell is very much like the release of radiation into the macroscopic human environment. Once the complex living system is disturbed, we are at a loss to predict the ultimate consequences. Under what circumstances the disturbance of a cell may result years later in the formation of a cancerous growth we simply do not know; we are equally ignorant of the circumstances under which a cell may recover from radiation damage.

Still more mysterious is another effect of radiation on most living things—the shortening of life. A wide range of animals and insects show no visible damage when exposed to low doses of radiation over long periods of time, except that their lives become shorter. Radiation has somehow accelerated the aging process. This effect is believed to occur also in man.

Dr. Herman Blumenthal offers one likely explanation of the life-shortening effect. As a person grows older, more and more of the cells of his body show definite alterations, or mutations. These may be caused by natural radiation, or other factors. If the disturbance to a given cell is not lethal, it may cause significant alterations in the cell's proteins:

The consequences of these alterations involve the concept of biological individuality which holds that, except in the case of identical twins, each individual's proteins differ in some subtle way from those of every other individual. The rejection of organs transplanted from one person to another, which has received so much attention in recent years, is based on this principle. The transplanted organ, which has a different "individuality" from that of the recipient, gives rise to an immune reaction from its host, and the result is its rejection. The analogy in respect to aging would be that mutations occurring in a particular organ would render the mutated cells of the organ "foreign" and thus lead to an auto-immune reaction.

The process of aging is therefore seen as the body's attack on its own tissues, as these are subtly altered over the years. Since radiation is known to produce mutations in all cells, it is reasonable to suppose that constant low levels of radiation exposure simply hasten the process of change which leads to aging.

Dr. Blumenthal points out that there is gathering evidence that this attack of the body on its own tissues may be involved in a number of the diseases of the old, as well as in aging itself. He includes vascular disease, cancer, diabetes, "and several of the less frequent diseases of old people." There is a suggestion, therefore, that all of the effects of radiation—cancer, inherited malformation, and life shortening—may be due to the same cause, a subtle reorganization of the body's cells following damage from radiation.

All this gives some picture of the difficulties of estimating the damage to people from a given amount of radiation in the environment. We can only say that with *any* release of radioactivity there is *some* risk of damage. This risk grows steadily with every release of radioactive waste anywhere in the world, and it is shared by all of us.

As the nuclear reactor program expands, its wastes will also increase, and the burden of radioactivity in our surroundings will rise, and go on rising. At some point the deleterious effects of this radiation will become unacceptable even to a nation which is able to tolerate 50,000 deaths on its roads every year. Because the effects of radiation go on making themselves felt decades after the first damage is done, it would be well to anticipate the eventual saturation of our surroundings. For the environment which supports us has only a limited capacity for radiation, and that capacity can only be used once.

This is not the point of view which has been taken in the establishment of federal radiation standards. The regulations of the Atomic Energy Commission are not designed to limit the total amount of radioactivity released into air or water by any given power plant. Instead, they seek to insure that radioactivity, in whatever amount, is released in such a way as not to do visible harm to plant employees or the nearby public. In releasing gases, therefore, the reactor operators first dilute them with large volumes of air and then discharge them through a tall stack so that by the time they reach the outside public, no one person can acquire an exposure beyond the limits set.

Because any exposure to radiation, no matter how slight, may produce some damage, the setting of limits is a difficult business. A complex philosophy and elaborate techniques have been developed since the end of World War II to deal with this problem. One long-standing principle, which might be called the "no noticeable damage" principle, has been that large numbers of people should never be exposed to more than the equivalent of the "natural" or "background" radiation to which they are always exposed. It should be remembered, however, that the reassuring adjective "natural" does not imply that radiation from minerals and cosmic rays is harmless. On the contrary, it does the same sorts of damage as artificial radiation. Radioactive potassium in sea water is just as harmful as radioactive potassium made artificially. Radium and thorium, which are naturally present in small quantities in coal, are released into the air when coal is burned and pose a radiation hazard of their own.

In other words, man-made radioactivity once released is simply an *increase* of a hazard already present. Those setting radiation standards generally seem to feel that a new risk of about the same size as the risk which has always been around is acceptable.

The second widely-accepted principle is that of balancing benefits against risks. This is the approach which has been taken by the Federal Radiation Council, a cabinet-level committee which advises the President on radiation standards. Despite the fact that its recommendations are binding on no one, the Federal Radiation Council some years ago issued a number of standards or guides. These were at first called Radiation Protection Guides, or RPG's. Since at the time of their issuance the principal source of radioactivity was fallout from nuclear weapons testing, the RPG's were treated by the press as safe limits below which fallout was harmless. But treating the guides as safety standards was simply misleading, as they were nothing of the sort. We have already seen that there is no "safe" level of radiation exposure. What the Federal Radiation Council has done was to estimate the damage which would result from fallout in terms of increased numbers of thyroid cancers, cases of leukemia, mutations, etc., and to balance these in some fashion against the presumed benefits of weapons testing. The Radiation Protection Guides expressed the highest levels of radiation to which the whole population might be exposed and still receive benefits that would outweigh the damage done.

This is a far cry from a safety standard. Nor is it easy to see how any group, even a committee of cabinet officers, could carry out the procedure just described. For neither the benefits nor the risks of bomb testing could easily be translated into numbers, and even if they could, the result would not necessarily be very useful. How many dollars saved in the weapons program, or how many new bombs, justify how many cases of leukemia? Actually, the FRC was following precisely the philosophy of the AEC in assuming that an acceptable damage was one that roughly duplicated the amount of damage from natural causes already being done.

There is a growing proliferation of agencies which in some way are responsible for regulating activities having to do with exposure of the general public to radiation. On the other hand, there is no agency with overall responsibility for finding out what *total* exposures to the population are and setting standards or limits on these. The result has been the almost universal adoption of the AEC's approach.

Clearly a great deal is wrong with the current state of affairs. First, there is a world of difference between "no damage" and "no noticeable damage." Reactors, X-ray machines, and even coal-burning plants are doing *some* damage; because so many people throughout the world ordinarily die from cancer, many thousands of additional cases could occur without notice. The fact that our biological knowledge or statistical techniques do not allow us to identify the small boy whose leukemia is a result of bomb testing or of the commercial use of atomic energy does not mean that he does not exist.

Secondly, the "no noticeable damage" principle is based on a simplistic and inaccurate picture of the living world. It is possible to ignore the absolute quantity of radioactive wastes being discharged into our air and water only when it is assumed that, once sufficiently diluted, the wastes have ceased to be a problem. But we have already seen that this is emphatically not the case. What we have been doing, quite simply, is to avoid killing or injuring anyone directly by spreading the damage thin over the whole environment. But that damage will not disappear; it will accumulate, slowly and inevitably, until the level of "no noticeable damage" is passed, not for a single isolated area, but for the earth as a whole.

At present, salt-water fish caught far from land contain some DDT, washed from fields to streams and to the ocean, where it is concentrated by microscopic plants and then by the fish themselves. Nearly every bite of food each of us in this country takes adds another dose of pesticide to our bodies. Rainwater throughout the country contains a bewildering variety of chemicals, ranging from the nitrates of agricultural fertilizer to gasoline additives.

Radioactive wastes are now beginning to repeat this pattern, and in the coming years our food and water will be increasingly burdened with radiation. The first step in this new assault on the environment was taken with atomic-bomb testing, in secrecy and in almost complete ignorance. That first step having been taken, we are continuing with nuclear power plants. In other forms of air and water pollution, we had to reach the point of real disaster before beginning to think of control. This must not be allowed to happen with radioactive wastes; once they are released into the atmosphere, there is no conceivable way of retrieving radioactive gases; once entered on their winding course through the environment, radioactive isotopes are out of reach of man's control. The damage, once done, is irremediable. If we do not begin now to invest the ingenuity and the money which are necessary to prevent the release of radiation through the commercial use of atomic power, we will end by damaging the very fabric of life on this planet.

The Vienna Declaration

The Third Pugwash Conference of Scientists

---

1. Necessity to End Wars

We meet in Kitzbühel and in Vienna at a time when it has become evident that the development of nuclear weapons makes it possible for man to destroy civilization and, indeed, himself; the means of destruction are being made ever more efficient. The scientists attending our meetings have long been concerned

Chapter 59 of *The Atomic Age* edited by Morton Grodzins and Eugene Rabinovitch, © 1963 by Basic Books, Inc., Publishers, New York. Reprinted by permission of the publisher.

with this development, and they are unanimous in the opinion that a full-scale nuclear war would be a worldwide catastrophe of unprecedented magnitude.

In our opinion defense against nuclear attack is very difficult. Unfounded faith in defensive measures may even contribute to an outbreak of war.

Although the nations may agree to eliminate nuclear weapons and other weapons of mass destruction from the arsenals of the world, the knowledge of how to produce such weapons can never be destroyed. They remain for all time a potential threat for mankind. In any future major war, each belligerent state will feel not only free but compelled to undertake immediate production of nuclear weapons; for no state, when at war, can be sure that such steps are not being taken by the enemy. We believe that, in such a situation, a major industrial power would require less than one year to begin accumulating atomic weapons. From then on, the only restraint against their employment in war would be agreements not to use them which were concluded in times of peace. The decisive power of nuclear weapons, however, would make the temptation to use them almost irresistible, particularly to leaders who are facing defeat. It appears, therefore, that atomic weapons are likely to be employed in any future major war, with all their terrible consequences.

It is sometimes suggested that localized wars, with limited objectives, might still be fought without catastrophic consequences. History shows, however, that the risk of local conflicts growing into major wars is too great to be acceptable in the age of weapons of mass destruction. Mankind must therefore set itself the task of eliminating all wars, including local wars.

2. Requirements for Ending the Arms Race

The armaments race is the result of distrust between states; it also contributes to this distrust. Any step that mitigates the arms race, and leads to even small reductions in armaments and armed forces, on an equitable basis and subject to necessary control, is therefore desirable. We welcome all steps in this direction and, in particular, the recent agreement in Geneva between representatives of East and West about the feasibility of detecting test-explosions. As scientists, we take particular pleasure in the fact that this unanimous agreement, the first after a long series of unsuccessful international disarmament negotiations, was made possible by mutual understanding and a common objective approach by scientists from different countries. We note with satisfaction that the governments of the U.S.A., U.S.S.R., and U.K. have approved the statements and the conclusion contained in the report of the technical experts. This is a significant success; we most earnestly hope that this approval will soon be followed by an international agreement leading to the cessation of all nuclear weapon tests and an effective system of control. This would be a first step toward the relaxation of international tension and the end of the arms race.

It is generally agreed that any agreement on disarmament, and in particular nuclear disarmament, requires measures of control to protect every party from possible invasion. Through their technical competence, scientists are well aware that effective control will in some cases be relatively easy, while it is very difficult in others. For example, the conference of experts in Geneva has agreed that the cessation of bomb tests could be monitored by a suitable network of detecting stations. On the other hand, it will be a technical problem of great difficulty to account fully for existing stocks of nuclear weapons and other means of mass destruction. An agreement to cease production of nuclear weapons presents a problem of intermediate technical difficulty between these two extreme examples.

We recognize that the accumulation of large stocks of nuclear weapons has made a completely reliable system of controls for far-reaching nuclear disarmament extremely difficult, perhaps impossible. For this disarmament to become possible, nations may have to depend, in addition to a practical degree of technical verification, on a combination of political agreements, of successful international security arrangements, and of experience of successful cooperation in various areas. Together, these can create the climate of mutual trust, which does not now exist, and an assurance that nations recognize the mutual political advantages of avoiding suspicion.

Recognizing the difficulties of the technological situation, scientists feel an obligation to impress on their peoples and on their governments the need for policies which will encourage international trust and reduce mutual apprehension. Mutual apprehensions cannot be reduced by assertions of good will; their reduction will require political adjustment and the establishment of active cooperation.

3. What War Would Mean

Our conclusions about the possible consequences of war have been supported by reports and papers submitted to our Conference. These documents indicate that if, in a future war, a substantial proportion of the nuclear weapons already manufactured were delivered against urban targets, most centers of civilization in the belligerent countries would be totally destroyed, and most of their populations killed. This would be true whether the bombs used derived most of their power from fusion reactions (so-called "clean" bombs) or principally from fission reactions (so-called "dirty" bombs). In addition to destroying major centers of population and industry, such bombs would also wreck the economy of the country attacked, through the destruction of vital means of distribution and communication.

Major states have already accumulated large stocks of "dirty" nuclear weapons; it appears that they are continuing to do so. From a strictly military point of view, dirty bombs have advantages in some situations; this makes likely their use in a major war.

The local fallout resulting from extensive use of "dirty" bombs would cause the death of a large part of the population in the country attacked. Following their explosion in large numbers (each explosion equivalent to that of millions of tons of ordinary chemical explosive), radioactive fallout would be distributed, not only over the territory to which they were delivered but, in varying intensity, over the rest of the earth's surface. Many millions of deaths would thus be produced, not only in belligerent but also in nonbelligerent countries, by the acute effects of radiation.

There would be, further, substantial long-term radiation damage to human and other organisms everywhere from somatic effects such as leukemia, bone cancer, and shortening of the lifespan; and from genetic damage affecting the hereditary traits transmitted to the progeny.

Knowledge of human genetics is not yet sufficient to allow precise predictions of consequences likely to arise from the considerable increase in the rate of mutation which would ensue from unrestricted nuclear war. However, geneticists believe that they may well be serious for the future of a surviving world population.

It is sometimes suggested that in a future war, the use of nuclear weapons might be restricted to objectives such as military bases, troop concentrations, airfields, and other communication centers; and that attacks on large centers of population could thus be avoided.

Even tactical weapons now have a large radius of action; cities and towns are commonly closely associated with centers of supply and transportation. We, therefore, believe that even a "restricted" war would lead, despite attempted limitation of targets, to widespread devastation of the territory in which it took place, and to the destruction of much of its population. Further, an agreement not to use cities for military purposes, entered into in order to justify their immunity from attack is unlikely to be maintained to the end of a war, particularly by the losing side. The latter would also be strongly tempted to use nuclear bombs against the population centers of the enemy, in the hope of breaking his will to continue the war.

4. Hazards of Bomb Tests

At our first conference it had been agreed that while the biological hazards of bomb tests may be small compared with similar hazards to which mankind is exposed from other sources, hazards from tests exist and should receive close and continued study. Since then, an extensive investigation by the United Nations Scientific Committee on the Effects of Atomic Radiation has been carried out and its authoritative conclusions published. In this case, too, scientists from many different countries have been able to arrive at a unanimous agreement. Their conclusions confirm that the bomb tests produce a definite hazard and that they will claim a significant number of victims in present and following generations. Though the magnitude of the genetic damage appears to be relatively small compared with that produced by natural causes, the incidence of leukemia and bone cancer due to the radioactivity from test explosions may, in the estimate of the U.N. committee, add significantly to the natural incidence of these diseases. This conclusion depends on the assumption (not shared by all authorities in the field) that these effects can be produced even by the smallest amount of radiation. This uncertainty calls for extensive study and, in the meantime, for a prudent acceptance of the most pessimistic assumption. It lends emphasis to the generally agreed conclusion that all unnecessary exposure of mankind to radiation is undesirable and should be avoided.

It goes without saying that the biological damage from a war, in which many nuclear bombs would be used, would be incomparably larger than that from tests; the main immediate problem before mankind is thus the establishment of conditions that would eliminate war.

5. Science and International Cooperation

We believe that, as scientists, we have an important contribution to make toward establishing trust and cooperation among nations. Science is, by long tradition, an international undertaking. Scientists with different national allegiances easily find a common basis of understanding: they use the same concepts and the same methods; they work toward common intellectual goals, despite differences in philosophical, economic, or political views. The rapidly growing importance of science in the affairs of mankind increases the importance of the community of understanding.

The ability of scientists all over the world to understand one another, and to work together, is an excellent instrument for bridging the gap between nations and for uniting them around common aims. We believe that working together in every field where international cooperation proves possible makes an important contribution toward establishing an appreciation of the community of nations. It can contribute to the development of the climate of mutual trust, which is necessary for the resolution of political conflicts between nations, and which is an essential background to effective disarmament. We hope scientists everywhere will recognize their responsibility, to mankind and to their own nations, to contribute thought, time, and energy to the furthering of international cooperation.

Several international scientific undertakings have already had considerable success. We mention only the century-old worldwide cooperation in weather science, the two International Polar Years which preceded (by seventy-five and twenty-five years respectively) the present International Geophysical Year, and the Atoms for Peace Conferences. We earnestly hope that efforts will be made to initiate similar collaboration in other fields of study. Certainly they will have the enthusiastic support of scientists all over the world.

We call for an increase in the unrestricted flow of scientific information among nations, and for a wide exchange of scientists. We believe that nations which build their national security on secrecy of scientific developments sacrifice the interests of peace, and of the progress of science, for temporary advantages.

It is our belief that science can best serve mankind if it is free from interference by any dogma imposed from the outside, and if it exercises its right to question all postulates, including its own.

6. Technology in the Service of Peace

In our time, pure and applied science have become increasingly interdependent. The achievements of fundamental, experimental, and theoretical science are more and more rapidly transformed into new technological developments. This accelerated trend is manifest alike in the creation of weapons of increased destructiveness, and in the development of means for the increased wealth and well-being of mankind. We believe that the tradition of mutual understanding and of international cooperation, which have long existed in fundamental science, can and should be extended to many fields of technology. The International Atomic Energy Agency, for example, aims not merely at cooperation for establishing facts about atomic energy, but also at helping the nations of the world to develop a new source of energy as a basis for the improvement of their material welfare.

We believe that international cooperation in this and other fields, such as economic development and the promotion of health, should be greatly strengthened.

The extremely low level of living in the industrially underdeveloped countries of the world is and will remain a source of international tension. We see an urgent need to forward studies and programs for the effective industrialization of these countries. This would not only improve the level of living of the majority of the population of the world; it would also help reduce the sources of conflict between the highly industrialized powers. Such studies would offer fruitful scope for cooperative efforts between scientists of all nations.

The great increase in the ease and speed of communications, and our increasing understanding of how the forces of nature influence the living conditions of nations in different parts of the world, show us, in a way not previously possible, the extent to which the prosperity of individual nations is connected with, and dependent upon, that of mankind as a whole; and how rapidly it could be increased by common international effort. We believe that through such common effort, the coexistence between nations of different social and economic structure can become not merely peaceful and competitive, but to an increasing degree cooperative, and therefore more stable.

As scientists, we are deeply aware of the great change in the condition of mankind which has been brought about by the modern development and application of science. Given peace, mankind stands at the beginning of a great scientific age. Science can provide mankind with an ever increasing understanding of the forces of nature, and the means of harnessing them. This will bring about a great increase in the well-being, health, and prosperity of all men.

7. The Responsibility of Scientists

We believe it to be a responsibility of scientists in all countries to contribute to the education of the peoples by spreading among them a wide understanding of the dangers and potentialities offered by the unprecedented growth of science. We appeal to our colleagues everywhere to contribute to this effort, both through enlightenment of adult populations, and through education of the coming generations. In particular, education should stress improvement of all forms of human relations and should eliminate any glorification of war and violence.

Scientists are, because of their special knowledge, well equipped for early awareness of the danger and the promise arising from scientific discoveries. Hence, they have a special competence and a special responsibility in relation to the most pressing problems of our times.

In the present conditions of distrust between nations, and of the race for military supremacy which arises from it, all branches of science—physics, chemistry, biology, psychology—have become increasingly involved in military developments. In the eyes of the people of many countries, science has become associated with the development of weapons. Scientists are either admired for their contribution to national security, or damned for having brought mankind into jeopardy by their invention of weapons of mass destruction. The increasing material support which science now enjoys in many countries is mainly due to its importance, direct or indirect, to the military strength of the nation and to its degree of success in the arms race. This diverts science from its true purpose, which is to increase human knowledge, and to promote man's mastery over the forces of nature for the benefit of all.

We deplore the conditions which lead to this situation, and appeal to all peoples and their governments to establish conditions of lasting and stable peace.

Section Six

The Electronic Galaxy

The electronic galaxy is the group of electronic devices that extends human proficiency in the sensing, communicating, and information-processing areas. The products of the electronic revolution—radio, television, radar, and computers—together with techniques of microminiaturization—have changed communication and information. The computer not only provides an ultra-sophisticated research tool allowing for complex systems analysis, but it has made automatic control, assessment, and response possible in fields beyond human access. Television has transformed all areas of communication from education to entertainment. In this sense, McLuhan's "global village" has been realized. Communication and data processing at the speed of light have multiplied human intellectual powers by a factor of billions, much as nuclear power has multiplied chemical power.

The electronic galaxy is a perfect case study of the technological order—the lag of social controls behind the explosion of techniques, the backlash of invasion of privacy and the tendency to subvert human decision making, the full manifestation of Big Science, the exponential growth rates common to all viable areas of electronics, and the inherent questions of human will and determinism, values and choices. The possibility of linking electronic devices to our knowledge of brain physiology suggests new possibilities of Orwellian control. Each day Americans are becoming aware of the rapid evolution toward a "dossier dictatorship." Revelations about military intelligence "bugging" politicians are being matched by daily abuses of privacy by government agencies, institutions, and collection and credit organizations. The possibility of computer sharing threatens the privacy of every American.

We have had confrontations with the "machine" in the past, over the replacement of muscle power. Now, automation has shown the possibility of shortening the work week, reducing the needed size of the labor force, changing human roles, and creating new leisure. These changes are already creating enormous psychological and ethical problems, which can only increase in intensity. Our institutions and belief systems continue to lag behind this communication and information revolution, increasing social stress particularly among our youth. Yet laws defining and guaranteeing the right to privacy and assuring the right of redress for false information have not yet been legislated.

Total surveillance may now be possible with the use of sophisticated sensing systems tied into computer banks. The basic question of who will control this unprecedented power remains unanswered. If the Ellulian concept of the technological order persists, then 1984 is upon us now.

The first article in this section provides a general but neutral picture of the "electronic galaxy," a term coined by Marshall McLuhan, the so-called prophet of the new communications. Ricks' article is a rather pointed critique of McLuhan. The selections by Westin are all concerned with the problem of the invasion of privacy. John C. McDonald's paper deals with the impact of automation on work patterns and meanings.

Introducing the Amazing Electron

Stanley L. Englebardt

Nobody has ever seen one. If you wanted to measure an electron, you'd need a decimal point and a bag full of zeroes. Its diameter in centimeters is only .0000000000001—much too small to be viewed by any microscope—and its weight, or mass, is only 1/1,850 the nucleus of a hydrogen atom, the smallest of all the elements. In fact, it would take about 30 billion billion billion of them just to equal one ounce.

Stanley L. Englebardt, "Introducing the Amazing Electron," in *Electronics* (New York: Pyramid Publications Inc., 1963), pp. 11-20.

Yet these submicroscopic particles of energy—basic constituents of every atom—are the hardest working, most energetic and most wonder-making little particles ever known to man. We've been aware of electrons for only half a century. Yet in this comparatively short time they have been the subject of more effort, more research and more thought than anything else in the long, dramatic history of science. And today they are the very foundation of their namesake technology: electronics.

We use electrons day in and day out. Flick on a light switch and you send untold billions of them into wild oscillations. Like rush hour commuters jamming into a New York City subway at 5 P.M., they rush through heavy copper wires and thin tungsten filaments in a frantic effort to get "home." They move one way and then another, they bump into each other or go ploughing into atoms that stand in their way. They bounce, collide, penetrate and rebound in a mass migration toward the anode, or positive source of electricity.

But this electron stampede is not quite as random as it seems. We take advantage of this energy in many different ways, some of them quite sophisticated. For example, we put a glass-enclosed thin tungsten filament in their path and produce light of varying intensity. We keep time with them on clocks that "count" their back-and-forth movement. We use electrons to burn our toast, boil our eggs and percolate our coffee. We heat, cool and ventilate with them. We use them to run radios, television sets, power tools and scores of other gadgets.

All of this, of course, falls under the familiar title of "electricity." Although we may not be aware of individual electrons pouring through wires and elements, we do understand, respect and utilize electricity every single day of our lives.

But let someone drop the term "electronics" into the conversation and most people freeze up. Somehow "electronics" sounds far more formidable and mysterious than plain old "electricity." We tend to think of huge electronic computers and strange invisible radar beams. And all this seems so complex and remote.

But it needn't be either. Electronics is simply the electron moving through seemingly solid crystal materials or apparently empty glass tubes, rather than through wires. And as it moves we guide and control it to provide electrical energy used in power, transportation, medicine, space, vision, industry, research and the home.

The story of electronics is one of the most exciting in the history of science. Its cast of characters includes such names as Franklin, Einstein, Faraday, Edison, Thomson, Millikan, Bohr and Planck. Its settings run the gamut from outer space to the depths of the oceans. And its high points are the development of the new devices and techniques we hear about, read about and use every day.

Let's take a quick look at some of these new devices. Not long ago 115 passengers boarded a Trans World Airlines Boeing 707 jet at London's airport and settled back for a flight to the United States. The flight itself was uneventful, but the trip was far from routine. This was the first time in commercial airline history that an aircraft made the tricky Atlantic crossing without benefit of a navigator. Instead, a small box packed with electronic gear—much of it solid-state crystals actually grown in laboratory test tubes—did all the guiding.

The electronic device in this case was a new Doppler system, developed by the Bendix Corporation, which sent a series of invisible electronic beams from the plane to earth and back. The Doppler effect, named after the Austrian physicist who discovered it, is a change in radio wavelength caused either by the motion of the source of the signals away from or toward a point of observation, or by the motion of the observation point toward or away from the source. This effect is very similar to the change in the sound of a locomotive whistle, or a crossing bell, as you move nearer to or farther from it in a car.

In the jet's system the changing wavelengths are constantly analyzed by the "box's" electronic components, and the exact position of the craft computed every five seconds. By contrast a human navigator would require at least fifteen minutes to take one reading—and even then there would always be the chance of human error. Thus, passengers and crew get the benefit of 180 times as many readings, with each reading far more accurate than could ever be possible under a manual method.

Projecting such a device a bit further turns up some staggering possibilities. Suppose we could run our automobiles this way, not only using the beams to establish our geographic position but to detect obstacles and regulate the car's direction and speed, as well. This sounds fantastic, yet right now such devices are in existence and within the decade we should be using some of them.

There are a number of ways in which automobiles can be operated electronically. One possibility is a Doppler-like system linked directly to the accelerator and brakes. As beams sweep the road area, the electronic gear would use their changing wavelengths to compute the distance between the car and any obstacles ahead of it. With the device programmed, or instructed, to maintain a certain minimum distance between vehicles, it could adjust the speed of the automobile in line with the nearness of other cars. And if a pedestrian should suddenly dart out in front of the auto, the beam system, with overlap areas capable of detecting such an occurrence before the individual is in the path of the vehicle, would automatically slam on the brakes.

Another automatic system now being tested involves a metal strip buried in the center of a lane and an electronic device in the car which locks onto it. The device is geared directly to the steering wheel, accelerator and brakes, and all impulses travel through the strip rather than through the air. Still another method involves infra-red devices positioned along the shoulders of a road to detect, by heat emission, the relationship of cars to each other and any other obstacles present. Whenever a vehicle strays out of line, the infra-red unit sends out a signal which is picked up by electronic gear in the car and used either to control the vehicle directly or to signal the driver—who may be dozing or distracted—with an audible or visible alarm.

Ten years ago a "hands off" car was in the realm of science fiction. Today it is a laboratory reality. Why? Because of a remarkable electronic component known as a transistor. Transistors, most of them so tiny they must be manufactured with the aid of a microscope, are simply electronic amplifiers. That is, they take extremely small electric currents, such as those received in radio or television electromagnetic wave signals, and magnify them to the point where they are useable.

The British call these electronic amplifiers "valves" and, in many respects, the term is much more descriptive. The common garden hose nozzle is a valve that is somewhat analogous to our transistor. With very little effort we can adjust this valve to convert a steady flow of water into a fine mist or a heavy stream even more powerful than the original flow. Similarly, a slight push of your toe on the valve-like accelerator pedal of an automobile will translate the engine's power into the needs of the car.

In both of these cases—the accelerator and the nozzle—the relatively small effort of our foot or hand is able to control a large power input to the point where it does our bidding.

The same is true of an electronic amplifier. The input in this case is not water or engine power, but a large flow of direct current from a battery, or alternating current from a wall outlet which is converted to direct current by a rectifier. Instead of using our hands or feet, we "adjust" the valve with the comparatively weak electromagnetic signals sent out by a transmitter. And the result, or output, is an exact duplicate of the electromagnetic signal, only magnified to the point where we can use it in many different ways.

It must be stressed that vacuum tubes do the same thing as solid-state components. But there are three major differences between these two methods of amplifying signals that place them worlds apart as far as you and I are concerned: First, transistors are about one hundred times smaller than most tubes. Most are about half the size of the eraser at the end of a pencil, with the crystal itself about the size of the period at the end of this sentence. Thus, through the use of these solid-state devices, radios, transistors, computers, hearing aids, television sets and countless other electronic gadgets can be made very compact.

Secondly, solid-state components provide a degree of reliability and impact strength never before possible. While tubes may burn out or be broken fairly easily, transistors can keep performing indefinitely. It would take almost a direct hammer blow to put one of them out of commission.

Finally, these minute parts give off no heat and require very little electrical power. A tube needs a fairly substantial power input to get its filament hot enough to start emitting electrons. But almost the first electrical impulse entering a transistor is enough to get it going.

What does this all mean in practical terms? It means basketball-sized satellites streaking through space and performing experiments that formerly required a roomful of electronic gear to accomplish the same results. It means military communication equipment compact enough to be carried in the helmets of foot soldiers. It means radios no bigger than a pocket watch, and television sets weighing less than six and-one-half pounds. It means electronic computers once requiring over a thousand square feet of floor space, now contained in a desk-sized unit. It means briefcase-sized air conditioners capable of cooling in the summer and heating in the winter.

It also means life for scores of individuals who, just a scant five years ago, were destined to spend the remainder of their uncertain years in bed. There is a 65-year-old grandmother in Glendale, California, for example, who uses a remote control transistorized gadget about the size of a cigarette case to adjust her heartbeat in line with her physical activity. The woman's heart has a timing defect which prevents it from increasing the blood supply as her body expends energy. Scientists solved this problem by implanting a small electronic device in the woman's chest, with wires leading directly to the main nerves of her heart. Then they gave her a compact power pack which emits a signal to the implanted device whenever there is need for increased pumping. The woman simply adjusts the pack for the beating rate required, and the electronic gear does the rest.

Similarly, there are over eighty people who walk around with a tiny electronic device and battery implanted in their chests constantly giving off tiny electrical impulses which keep their hearts going. These hearts have lost virtually all ability to regulate their own beat. Now this is done through a miniaturized electronic unit and battery which stays in them at all times. The battery, by the way, is designed to operate for five years and gives off a special signal well before it runs down.

This is just a glimpse into the present and near future of solid-state electronics. The list of applications already in use, or on the drawing boards, would almost fill the rest of this book. Right now there are electronic refrigerators and ice-makers built entirely from solid-state components, with not a single moving part in them, operating at far greater efficiency than any other cooling machine ever marketed. There are appliances—power tools, bottle warmers, portable electric typewriters, and electronic clocks—which can operate indefinitely on power provided by a rechargeable battery the size of a sugar cube.

There are also fabrics, with the feel and weight of dacron or cotton, that have tiny electronic thermocouples woven into them so that the wearer can cool or warm himself at the flick of a switch. There are houses under construction with entire walls built from almost invisible electronic components which emit heat or cold according to the dictates of the thermometer. And there are electroluminescent lights that glow forever from a power input that costs no more than a penny a year.

But we might just as well stop here and get into the fabulous story of electronics. Our subject is not a mysterious technology used by an exclusive group of super-intelligent men, but an entirely new way of life that affects every one of us. For some it may mean new employment; for others protection, health, convenience or comfort. There is no doubt, though, that we will all benefit. So let's begin at the beginning and see what it's all about.

Electronic Man

Christopher Ricks

The importance of *Understanding Media* has nothing to do with worth. Marshall McLuhan is now a power in more than one land, and not only as Director of the Centre for Culture and Technology at Toronto. Since a great many people are concerned about the effects of TV, films, advertisements and the press, they will turn more and more to a praised expert. And there is, too, a market for heady prophecies, especially those which skillfully and at the last moment substitute a sermon for a forecast. Like Jacques Barzun, Mr. McLuhan has the suspenseful air of being about to lift the veil. Does Telstar bode? Yes, indeed, and we may expect (excitement mounts), we may expect that

the time factor in every decision of business and finance will acquire new patterns. Among the peoples of the world strange new vortices of power will appear unexpectedly.

'Unexpectedly' is about right, for all the help we actually get from Mr. McLuhan's clutch of crystal balls. The car has altered everything, 'and it will continue do so for a decade more, by which time the electronic successors to the car will be manifest.' Nostradamus redivivus? A reader who crosses Mr. McLuhan's palm with two guineas may feel gulled.

Three themes cohabit, not very fruitfully. First: electronics and 'electric speed' are different in kind from the mechanical (which is linear, typographic, uniform and repeatable). Our present culture partakes of both. The mechanical or typographic culture necessitated sequence, fragmentation and specialisation; but the new electronic culture 'retribalises,' makes the world a village, and is organically instantaneous.

Man can now look back at two or three thousand years of varying degrees of mechanisation with full awareness of the mechanical as an interlude between two great organic periods of culture.

Christopher Ricks, "Electronic Man," in *The New Statesman*, December 11, 1964. Ricks studied at Balliol College, Oxford. He is a fellow and tutor at Worcester College, Oxford, and University lecturer in English literature since 1958. He has written for many journals in the United States and England, and among his books is *Milton's Grand Style* (1963).

The second theme is 'The Extensions of Man':

Whereas all previous technology (save speech, itself) had, in effect, extended some part of our bodies, electricity may be said to have outered the central nervous system itself, including the brain.

Third:

Political scientists have been quite unaware of the effects of media anywhere at any time, simply because nobody has been willing to study the personal and social effects of media apart from their 'content.'

These are important themes, but they are altogether drowned by the style, the manner of arguing, the attitude to evidence and to authorities, and the shouting.

Any medium has an effect *qua* medium, over and above its content. To have said so would have been to have written a sadder and a wiser book (and a shorter one). But Mr. McLuhan's contempt for people who attend to the 'content' leads him to deny that content plays any part at all. 'The medium is the message,' he intones again and again. 'The effects of technology'—and by technology he means all 'extensions of man'—'do not occur at the level of opinions or concepts, but alter sense ratios or patterns of perception steadily and without any resistance.' If he had said 'do not occur *only* at the level of opinions'—but no, for him the sole effect is that of the medium itself. Literacy creates individualism, and 'this fact has nothing to do with the *content* of the alphabetised words.' 'The effects of radio are quite independent of its programming.' TV creates 'total involvement in all-inclusive *nowness*,' and 'this change of attitude has nothing to do with programming in any way.'

All of which means that *Understanding Media* cuts off its extension of man to spite its face. How can Mr. McLuhan possibly use the medium of the *book* (typographic, linear, fragmented) in order to speak in this way about the electronically instantaneous? On his own terms, a book cannot but enforce the typographical attitudes which he insists are cramping Western man. If his arguments are true, how silly to annul them by using a medium which has no option but to annul them.

He wriggles in this unmentioned predicament, and does his best to escape by abandoning all the sequential virtues of a book. He says the same thing on every page, and repeats whole chunks when he feels like it—which is perhaps one kind of instantaneity. He praises the Eastern ('oral') mode of thought: 'The entire message is then traced and retraced, again and again, on the rounds of a concentric spiral with seeming redundancy.' But if this 'oral' tradition could be incorporated in a book, his arguments would all collapse. The attempt may be pluckily preposterous, but the outcome is not just 'seeming' redundancy. The moral position, too, is shaky, and not even the quotation from Pope Pius XII about media quite manages to shore it up. Mr. McLuhan may insist that he is 'withholding all value judgments when studying these media matters,' but in fact his terms are about as neutral as a bigot. Who will be found to speak for literacy (which has 'fragmented' and 'mutilated') when the electronic culture is described in these terms—humble involvement and deep commitment, participation, heightened human awareness and unifying the life of the senses? 'Contemporary awareness had to become integral and inclusive again, after centuries of dissociated sensibilities'—does that withhold value judgments? And is it an act of neutrality to give a chapter to each of 26 media but no chapter to the theatre?

Very well—people were wrong to ignore the nature of a medium. But that doesn't beautify the airy hauteur to which the arguments rise whenever they confront facts, earthy political facts. Possibly radio does inevitably inflame, and TV does cool, but the authorial tone is too epigrammatically Olympian. 'Had TV occurred on a large scale during Hitler's reign he would have vanished quickly. Had TV come first there would have been no Hitler at all.' Vanished? Like a Walt Disney ogre? So confident a magic wand does not like the fact that there are facts. Can we be quite so sure that Nazi TV would have had no choice but to intervene so coolingly and so effectively? Is 'content' (even anti-Semitic content) really a matter of total indifference in comparison with 'the medium proper'? Mr. McLuhan may perhaps be right, but Hitler seems to me a subject where too serene a confidence in one's own theories can easily look unfeeling. After all, there are those of us who would have traded all of Pope Pius's words about mass media for just a word or two about the massacre of the Jews.

Mr. McLuhan's confidence, quite without irony, sees the computer as a type of the Holy Ghost: 'The computer, in short, promises by technology a Pentecostal condition of universal understanding and unity.' So much for greed, crowding, hunger, and all the hard facts which make universal understanding and unity a matter of intractable things as well as of language and media. When Mr. McLuhan invokes his Pentecost, there is no doubt about the mighty rushing wind, but where are the tongues of fire?

It seems that we have been fools, but now at last we will be put right about it all, though our patient teacher can't quite prevent his eyelid from drooping disdainfully. 'It is not the increase of numbers in the world that creates our concern with population,' rather it is 'our electric involvement in one another's lives.' Our 'concern' may well have been pricked by the media, but it is not entirely evolved from them, since there remains the glumly objective fact of the increasing population, a fact which to any man who wants to live as something more than 'a student of media' is in itself a cause of concern. Could it be that Mr. McLuhan averts his eyes from the fact because the Catholic Church wishes it weren't a fact? When the facts would be embarrassing, Mr. McLuhan passes by on the other side. It seems that 'literate man' is a warped creature, 'quite inclined to see others who cannot conform as somewhat pathetic.' And then, without a pause: 'Especially the child, the cripple, the woman, and the coloured person appear in a world of visual and typographic technology as victims of injustice.' But in this world, the world of facts as well as of media, coloured people do not merely *appear* (thanks to tricksy typography) to be victims of injustice, they *are* such. Not every single individual, of course, but quite enough for Mr. McLuhan's enlightened detachment to get tarnished. He long-sufferingly tut-tuts—how naïve of people to be upset by circumstances, instead of realising that it is all just the built-in preconceptions of media.

Media, apparently, and not moral convictions, get things done: 'the real integrator or leveller of white and Negro in the South was the private car and the truck, not the expression of moral points of view.' Notice 'was,' as if it were all a thing of the past, so that now the historian can bask in equanimity. Notice, too, that it isn't said that the truck was in the end the most effective or most important integrator or leveller—no, it was 'the real' one, which leaves 'moral points of view' (a prettily placid piece of phrasing) as merely unreal. As if there weren't enough people willing to be told that justice in the South (a) has been achieved, and (b) is no moral concern of theirs, without our author handing them warrant (don't worry, the truck'll change all that). This may all be unwitting, in which case it is the consequence of Mr. McLuhan's furious rebound. Since everybody else will talk about nothing but 'content,' he will talk about nothing but media—nice, neutral, omnipotent media.

There is a similar stoniness when he discusses 'labour-saving' devices, toasters or washing-machines or vacuum cleaners: 'Instead of saving work, these devices permit everybody to do his own work. What the 19th century had delegated to servants and housemaids we now do for ourselves.' Oh no we don't. When we switch on the automatic washing machine, Mr. McLuhan and I are not in any meaningful sense doing the same *work* as servants used to do. There is something unimaginative about a deftness that is so very interested in 'devices' and so little interested in how 19th-century servants really did work. 'Today, in the electronic age, the richest man is reduced to having much the same entertainment, and even the same food and vehicles as the ordinary man.' Try telling that to the many ordinary men who live in 'the other America,' let alone three-quarters of the globe. Mr. McLuhan may claim the licence of a prophet, but even a prophet will be the more humane if he does not state as today's fact what may perhaps one day come to pass.

Such indifference to fact is not always politically disagreeable, but it is always absurd. Literate societies don't like B.O.? That must be because the odour 'is far too involving for our habits of detachment and specialist attention.' But why shouldn't it just be that we don't like the smell? Ah, but what about 'the strange obsession of the bookman with the press-lords as essentially corrupt?' That must, it seems, be due to the antagonism of the book to the newspaper as a medium. Yet what if it weren't a strange obsession, but a fact, that press-lords are corrupt?

The style is a viscous fog, through which loom stumbling metaphors. And Mr. McLuhan's subject, after all, is the imagination and the emotions. Nothing could be less imaginative than all this talk of 'a complex and depth-structured person,' especially as the depth resembles a sump: 'people begin to sense a draining-away of life values.' What we need is 'the mosaic of the press' which 'manages to effect a complex many-levelled function of group-awareness.' Fortunately 'the tactile mesh of the TV mosaic has begun to permeate the American sensorium'—hence the 'complex togetherness of the corporate posture.' What makes it all so grisly is that this unfelt, unfeeling and nerveless style is forever insisting on how media grip, how they touch, how they create.

The tastes are of a piece with the style. He asserts that ours is 'one of the greatest ages of music, poetry, painting, and architecture alike.' Later he comes to think that this was a bit half-hearted, so he steps it up: 'the arts of this century' have an 'ascendancy over those of other ages comparable to that which we have long recognised as true of modern science.' And the justification for such a claim? Well, there is the 'extraordinary intensity' of Agatha Christie's *Labours of Hercules.* And there are advertisements.

The ads are by far the best part of any magazine or newspaper. More pains and thought, more wit and art go into the making of an ad than into any prose feature of press or magazine.

Anybody who thought that advertisements have as much ugly lying as witty art would simply be exposing himself as one of the 'media victims, unwittingly mutilated by their studies.' 'Ads are ignored or deplored, but seldom studied and enjoyed'—as if it weren't even a possibility that one might study and then deplore. Since he so admires advertisements, it is not surprising that he uses them as evidence. Is Mrs. Khrushchev's plain cotton dress an icon of thrift? Yes— a very ingenious ad' has said so. Are the Greeks more sensuously involved? Yes— a travel guide has said so. *Vogue* proves one fact (and I don't mean about *Vogue*), and *Life* another, as if they were irreproachable works of history.

Mr. McLuhan uses his authorities about as convincingly as his evidence. No doubt there is still a lot to be said for Bergson and Toynbee, but it is not now possible to plonk down their names as if they settled a matter. Mr. McLuhan invokes Lynn White's *Medieval Technology and Social Change* for its argument that at a particular time the stirrup profoundly affected ways of life—but he does not mention that there are unridiculous historians who believe that the arguments are important but the evidence (especially as to dating) far from complete. Similarly, great play is made with that dread 'dissociation of sensibility' which at some unspecified date overtook Western man—as if any scrupulous cultural historian now thought the phrase anything but a faded bright idea. It is not only those who have been twisted by literacy who will find all these arguments short on evidence. Perhaps Mr. McLuhan's history is more accurate than are his literary quotations. The audacity is impressive, as when he take E. E. Cummings as a type of the poet whose work is for the ear and not for the eye: Cummings must be 'read aloud with widely varying stresses and paces,' since 'people who feel that poetry is for the eye and is to be read silently can scarcely get anywhere with Hopkins or Cummings.' I would like to hear Mr. McLuhan rendering Cummings's '.gRrEaPsPhOs).' But even so great a vocal skill would not be a substitute for cogency or clarity of argument. Or for an accurate text of Cummings—Mr. McLuhan does not give us Cummings's spelling, capitalisation, hyphenation, lineation or spacing. The masters of the subtle schools are controversial, polymath. Mr. McLuhan shifts from ham to ham, stirring the water in his bath.

The Functions of Privacy in Society

Alan F. Westin

To its profound distress, the American public has recently learned of a revolution in the techniques by which public and private authorities can conduct scientific surveillance over the individual. In chilled fascination the press, television programs, and popular books have described new means of telephone tapping, electronic eavesdropping, hidden television-eye monitoring, "truth measurement" by polygraph devices, personality testing for personnel selection, and growing dossiers of personal data about millions of citizens. Some of these accounts of new surveillance technology have gone on to speculate uneasily about future developments in the next decade, from data surveillance by computer systems to drug-aided interrogations and the possibility of brain-wave analysis. As examples mount of the uses made of the new technology, worried protests against "Big Brother" have set alarms ringing along the civic-group spectrum from extreme left to radical right. Reflecting this concern, "invasion of privacy" has become a leading topic in law-review articles and social-science journals, as well as the subject of legislative and executive investigations at the state and federal levels and of a growing number of exploratory judicial rulings

Excerpted from *Privacy and Freedom* by Alan F. Westin. Foreword by Oscar M. Ruebhausen. Copyright ©1967 by The Association of the Bar of the City of New York. Reprinted by permission of Atheneum Publishers. Westin is both a lawyer and a political scientist. A member of the District of Columbia Bar, he has taught at Harvard, Yale, and Cornell universities, and is now professor of public law and government at Columbia University. His books include *The Uses of Power, Views of America*, and *Privacy and Freedom.*

throughout the country. As the late 1960's arrived, it was clear that American society had developed a deep concern over the preservation of privacy under the new pressures from surveillance technology.

This condition suggests that the thoughtful reader has little need for further ringing denunciations of "Big Brother in America" or popular volumes devoted to documenting the spread of privacy-invading practices in our society. That job has been accomplished. The real need is to move from public awareness of the problem to a sensitive discussion of what can be done to protect privacy in an age when so many forces of science, technology, environment, and society press against it from all sides.

Such an analysis seems to call for at least four inquiries. First, privacy must be defined rather than simply invoked, and its psychological, sociological, and political dimensions must be described on the basis of leading theoretical and empirical studies. Second, the new techniques of surveillance, their present uses, and their future prospects must be described, forsaking Orwellian imagery for hard facts. Third, the ways in which American society has reacted to the new surveillance techniques must be examined in depth to see what has been happening to our norms of privacy during the past two decades and whether there are trends in interest-group and general public opinion that may help to guide American policy-makers. Finally, there should be a discussion of how American law has dealt with the issue of privacy and surveillance, as the backdrop for an analysis of specific measures that public and private authorities might take to ensure the continuation of privacy in the 1970's as a cornerstone of the American system of liberty. Exploring these four topics does not guarantee wise policy decisions, but it is hard to see how we can come to grips with the dilemmas of privacy and freedom unless these are the problems we study.

Probing the Mind: Psychological Surveillance

Alan F. Westin

Under psychological surveillance are grouped those scientific and technological methods that seek to extract information from an individual which he does not want to reveal or does not know he is revealing or is led to reveal without a mature awareness of its significance for his privacy.

The heart of the privacy issue in psychological surveillance at present lies in polygraph and personality testing, which have been present on the American scene since the early twentieth century, but which were swept into greatly increased use for corporate and government purposes since World War II.

The polygraph—the most widely used of the various devices known popularly as "lie detectors"—was developed in its modern form during the 1920's, as an instrument to aid police in the detection of crime. The theory behind the polygraph is that lying causes distinctive and measurable physiological reactions in a person who knows that he is not telling the truth. The polygraph operator asks questions in a special pattern while testing the subject's heart and pulse rate, relative blood pressure, breathing, and perspiration rate. (Some polygraph machines also test muscle tension, and it is common to photograph and tape-record the entire examination secretly for later study.) Bodily changes are recorded by pens on graph paper, producing "squiggles" resembling those on an electrocardiogram or seismograph. By interpreting these records, a trained polygrapher is supposed to be able to identify untrue responses to critical questions.

Several important technological advances in polygraphing were made during the later 1950's and early 1960's. Federal agencies developed techniques for administering lie-detection tests without the knowledge of the subject. These rely on a seemingly "normal" chair which has equipment built into it to register body heat, changes in limb volume, and nervous movements. Hidden cameras are also used in such covert polygraphing to measure changes in eye-pupil size as an indicator of stress during the interview. There has been some doubt expressed whether maximum stress is generated when the subject is not told that he is being put under "scientific, machine measurement." However, the covert polygraph techniques are considered valuable for situations in which it is not feasible to require a polygraph test or even to let someone know he is under suspicion.

Another new technique is computer interpretation of polygraph tracings. Since the weakest link in polygraphing is admittedly the variations in readings of the test results among polygraph operators, computers have been used to provide more rigorous and "objective" interpretation of stress levels. Such computer readings are particularly useful for collating and comparing new sensors which can be added to the test, such as devices to measure blood volume in fingertip arteries by photoelectric cells, changes in blood color and pulse waves, eye-pupil dilation, body-temperature fluctuation, and even brain wave patterns (through electro-encephalograph helmets). One scientist has developed a means of taking off and measuring nineteen different channels of stress responses on a recording device.

Personality testing is the use of written or oral examination to discover traits of personality for purposes of judging an individual's psychological strength, especially to predict his future performance in some role such as employment. Such tests may be in the form of pencil-and-paper quizzes, in which the subject answers questions about himself, his emotions, preferences, values, and attitudes, or they may be "projective" tests, in which the individual is asked to draw a picture, interpret ink blots, comment on ambiguous pictures, or perform other acts that provide psychological clues to his personality. In general, personality tests differ from tests of intelligence or aptitudes because the personality test does not measure more or less objective factors, such as language skills, logic, or physical dexterity, but seeks to measure emotions, attitudes, propensities, and levels of personal adjustment. In addition, personality tests traditionally include questions asking the subject to reveal his attitudes toward sexual, political, religious, and family matters, since these are considered the significant areas for distinguishing deviations from norms of belief in the population being tested. The issue of privacy obviously raised by both polygraphing and personality testing is whether employers or the government should be allowed to require individuals to have their inner processes probed through machine or test measurements. . . .

Automation and the Changing Meaning of Work

John C. McDonald

Why is it that the thinking a society does about its problems usually turns out to be about 20 years out of date? It is because almost all the thinking is about current problems with little thought or planning directed to the future. By the time that such thinking makes an impact on policy, the problems themselves have often changed.

As long as the tempo of technical and social change was fairly slow, this lag was not too serious. So far it has always been possible to mount crash programs of one kind or another to pick up the pieces and patch society together again. But in the sort of world into which we are now beginning to move, this lack of what the late C. Wright Mills referred to as 'sociological imagination' could prove disastrous.

It is of crucial importance that we formulate the broad fundamental principles of our plan for utilizing the new technology now. It should then be possible to implement this plan in several stages, cushioning the impact of automation, and allowing us to make a successful transition between two different kinds of worlds. Without such a plan, automation may produce a culture shock so severe that it may traumatize us to the point of social paralysis.

At the outset it may be helpful to clarify what I mean by automation. Down through the centuries the human brain has been acting upon the natural environment to change and improve the material lot of mankind. The broad term that we commonly use to encompass this process of discovery, invention, innovation, adaptation and diffusion is technical or technological change.

One of the most rapid periods of technological change we have experienced was the Industrial Revolution in the second half of the 19th century. The result of the harnessing of power and machines has been an unprecedented rate of mechanization. By mechanization, I am referring to the sort of technological change that allows a machine operated by a human being to accomplish the amount of work or production that it would previously have taken many

John C. McDonald, "Automation and the Changing Meaning of Work," Economics and Research Branch, Dept. of Labour, Canada, 1963, pp. 1-9. Reproduced with permission of the Queen's Printer for Canada and Information Canada. McDonald is a social scientist who works for the Economics and Research Branch of the Canadian Department of Labour.

men working with muscle power and hand tools to perform. In economic terms, mechanization increases the capital equipment side of the capital-labour input ratio. In addition to creating an unparalleled quantity and variety of goods, mechanization resulted in fundamental social changes—the substitution of the division of labour and the factory system for the older system of small agricultural holdings and cottage industries, an urban pattern of living to replace rural life, the nuclear family with its high mobility in place of the traditional three-generation family and extended kinship group, and a complex, inter-dependent system of exchanging goods and services to replace the economic self-sufficiency of the traditional household units.

One of the main points that I want to make about our contemporary economic and social situation is that we are still assimilating the impact of a century of rapid mechanization. A great deal of what is popularly referred to as automation is really an advanced form of mechanization. It is my opinion that, rather than being well-launched into the era of automation, we are now only standing on the threshold.

What is automation and what does it hold in store for our economic and social system? Like mechanization, automation is a type of technological change. The fundamental scientific and technical breakthroughs that make automation possible have already occurred. They took place during and immediately following World War II. The three major elements in automation are transfer machinery, closed-loop control, and the electronic computer.

The Breakthrough

Transfer machinery is sometimes called 'Detroit automation' because the most dramatic innovation took place on the engine block lines of the automobile industry. In some ways, this is the least revolutionary development in the field of automation in the sense that it is almost more an advanced form of mechanization than true automation. It is a type of equipment which combined with multipurpose machine tools can create an automated assembly line. Manpower is no longer required to position materials for successive operations or to manipulate and control the machines, but only to intervene to replace worn tools and conduct regular maintenance and repairs.

The second breakthrough—closed-loop control—is often called 'feedback.' The main invention that made feedback control possible was the servo mechanism. These systems of communication and control vary widely in their reliance on electric, electronic, pneumatic and electro-mechanical instrumentation. What they have in common, however, is that they are self-regulating systems which make human intervention unnecessary. The most commonly quoted example is the ordinary household thermostat, but such control systems in industry may be very sophisticated, automatically regulating relationships between temperature, humidity, viscosity, etc., within very fine tolerances. At the moment. these developments have progressed furthest in the continuous-flow industries such as petroleum refining.

Perhaps the most dramatic of the technical breakthroughs is the development of the electronic computer. Conceptually, the computer is a simple mechanism that can only add up discrete electrical impulses. The revolutionary aspects of the computer are first, that the vacuum tube and, more recently, the transistor allow such calculations to be made at electronic speeds and second, the development of information storage or 'memory' allows the computer to be programmed or instructed to perform logical decision-making at the lower performance levels of the human brain. The result is that these machines can accomplish either scientific or engineering computations that would have taken hundreds of man-years work by the most efficient traditional methods or carry out the relatively simple processing on vast quantities of the routine paperwork handled by the ordinary business office.

At the moment, there are many examples of each of these elements of automation operating in Canadian business and industry. However, it is in the years ahead when appropriate combinations of these discrete elements are brought together in integrated systems that we will have moved into the era of true automation—the age of the fully-automatic or push-button factory. This prospect is now possible technically. The speed and extent of its implementation depend on economic and social considerations.

Push-Button Factory

It would seem quite apparent that the first fully-automated production systems will occur in the continuous-flow industries such as petroleum, chemicals, plastics, some types of food processing and so on. For many people, this prospect is viewed with some relief in the sense that it suggests relatively clearly defined limits beyond which automation will not trespass. For example, a large part of the manufacturing industry deals with hard rather than soft materials and does not appear to lend itself to the continuous-flow principle.

However, the really revolutionary thing that distinguishes automation from previous kinds of technological change is not so much the new equipment but, as John Diebold has pointed out, a completely different philosophy of production. Mechanization has primarily been a question of inventing and adapting machinery to perform operations traditionally carried out by human labour. Automation concentrates on the redesign of end-products, the substitution of materials, and the layout of the production process so that the full potential of the new technology may be exploited.

As an illustration of this conceptual distinction between mechanization and automation, consider the case of the fabrication of automobile bodies. Mechanization has meant that machines designed to shape, rivet, grind and polish have greatly decreased the labour input required for a given level of production. Automation may mean that the production of automobile bodies is converted to a continuous-flow industry by substituting plexiglas or vinyl for steel sheet, obviating the human labour requirement virtually completely.

Optimism and Hope

Students of automation looking forward to the years ahead tend to fall into one of two camps. There are the optimists and the pessimists. The optimists argue that automation is really nothing new and that like all technological progress, while causing a certain amount of dislocation in the short run, will eventually result in more jobs, greater productivity and prosperity, and a combination of a higher material standard of living and more leisure for all groups in the society. They suggest that automation will generate whole new industries and a host of new occupations and employment opportunities that we haven't even thought of; that an increasing population will provide adequate consumer demand to assimilate the increased production; and that whatever slack automation may cause in employment in primary production and manufacturing will be taken up by the rapidly expanding service occupations.

To cap off this appealing glimpse into the future promised by automation, the optimists point out that the majority of jobs in our mechanized society are dull, dirty and undignified and that it is precisely these unskilled and semi-skilled jobs that automation will eliminate. The result will be a reintegration of task, an upgrading of skill and corresponding rise in monetary reward, while challenge, interest and satisfaction will redeem work from its present status of a nasty but necessary evil. And finally, if such an automated Utopia is a bit too much to expect, we really have no choice anyway because we must explore the potential of automation in order to increase our industrial productivity and gross national product, raise the over-all rate of our economic growth, and compete successfully in world markets.

Gloom and Doom

The pessimists view our automated society of the future in an altogether different light. They reason that automation by definition means that society's work will be done by machines instead of men. The result will be widespread unemployment and human misery. Unemployment by depressing consumer demand will trigger a downward economic cycle that will make the depression of the 1930's pale by comparison. They argue that automation will relieve the bulk of the labour force from the killing tedium of routine, repetitive work only to cast them into the far more desperate economic and psychological plight of unemployment.

Responsibility and power will become concentrated in the hands of a scientific and engineering elite with a monopoly on the crucial knowledge and know-how and this will sound the death knell of democracy. For the relatively small number of workers required to operate the automated system, the combination of tedium and tension involved in monitoring dials and waiting for breakdowns to occur may prove more intolerable than the assembly line or the continuous moving belt. The deadliness of the job content will only be exceeded by the schedule according to which the work will have to be performed. The huge capital investment in an automated system, combined with the continuous nature of the process, will dictate work on shifts around the clock. With shiftworking will come the peptic ulcers, nervous breakdowns, marital break-ups, and withdrawal from family and community participation which are its natural accompaniments.

Finally, the pessimists argue that in the unlikely event that we are able to find some mechanism other than work for pay by which to distribute purchasing power to the non-working majority, the result of automation will still prove a disaster for a population unprepared for leisure. Leisure time will simply precipitate a relapse into apathy and *anomie*—a sort of beer and television culture approximating the bread and circuses society that characterized the decline and collapse of Roman society.

Friend or Foe

In this controversy, I find myself either an optimistic pessimist or a pessimistic optimist—I am not sure which. The decades ahead could prove the prognosis of either school of thought to have been correct. The important point is that automation, like any other technology, is morally neutral. The effects of automation on our society are going to depend entirely on how we decide to use it.

Our experience with mechanization and limited forms of automation thus far tends, on balance, to support the optimist's position. Summarizing the Department of Labour's research work on the impact of technological change before the Special Committee of the Senate on Manpower and Employment in 1961, the then Director of the Economics and Research Branch indicated that, while the physical volume of production had increased considerably more than total employment in the industries studied, nevertheless each industry had enjoyed an expansion in employment ranging from 7 to 40 per cent during the decade 1949 to 1959. He demonstrated further that the employment effect of technological change appeared to have been a differential one, resulting in proportionally fewer new employment opportunities for blue-collar workers engaged in direct production compared with a growing demand for white-collar workers and various categories of more highly skilled personnel such as professionals, engineers, and technicians of various kinds.

In my own research work on the impact of the introduction of electronic data processing on office employment and occupations, the results so far do not seem particularly frightening. In large offices where the more routine clerical work seems to have been institutionalized as a 20th century form of the dowry, normal labour turnover is usually sufficiently high to cushion any redundancy that may occur without necessitating layoffs. Furthermore, the electronic computer has generated hundreds of brand new occupational opportunities for interesting and highly skilled jobs such as systems designers, programmers, and console operators. Even at the clerical level, at least the short-run impact of EDP seems to be to produce more work for data origination and data control personnel to prepare and check the input and output of the system.

This should not, of course, be interpreted to mean that the process of technological change occurs without causing serious dislocation for individuals and groups. From the point of view of the first-hand melter, whose sixth sense as to just when to pour the molten steel has been superseded by instrumentation, or the middle-aged female clerical supervisor unable to learn computer programming, technological change may be every bit as shattering as the invention of the tractor was for the village blacksmith. Whole occupational groups such as older workers, and unskilled young people dropping out of school and failing to find jobs, are particularly vulnerable to the impact of technological change. Also, each of the people adversely affected may be a family breadwinner or an important contributor to the family income. And their problems, both economic and non-economic, if unrelieved, will sooner or later increase society's level of pathology.

Effect on the Future

I would like to devote the balance of this essay to a frankly speculative discussion of the possibilities and pitfalls that may accompany automation in the longer-run future. No one is sufficiently clairvoyant to predict how extensive the impact of automation will be nor how rapidly or slowly automation will develop in our economy and society. I have deliberately chosen to argue from a rather extreme point of view, partly because I felt that such a controversial point of view may prove more stimulating, and partly because it is my own personal belief that automation will develop much more quickly and widely than is generally believed.

I mentioned that, being morally neutral, the effects of automation will depend entirely on how we decide to direct and utilize it. Unlike the utilitarian economists, I don't believe in the operation of an unseen economic hand directing such a force toward the inevitable attainment of the greatest good for the greatest number. The aspect of automation that disturbs me most is that far short of having a long-range plan to exploit automation to build 'the good society,' we haven't really begun to study and understand the fundamental economic and social implications of automation, or for that matter even to talk about the problems and possibilities at a reasonably informed level. Both as individuals and as a society we seem to be confused about our identity and our destiny. We appear to have no consensus of conviction or commitment about our social goals. The result is that there is no positive social context in which to fit the controversy over automation.

It seems to me that in our secular society we have tried to make economic instrumentalities such as economic growth, industrial productivity, and a high material standard of living serve as our goals. Surely, it is time we returned to our senses and affirmed that as long as a society is going to be made up of human beings, the success or failure of that society must be judged in terms of meaning and satisfaction in the lives of its members. This is not to deprecate the importance of economic growth and a decent material standard of living but simply to put them in their correct perspective as factors contributing to human development and well being.

Our Value System

The upside-downness of our contemporary value system is bound to land us in an even more serious situation if we approach automation suffering from the distorted conception that human beings are to be manipulated and adjusted to the requirements of the technologic and economic system rather than committed to the policy that automation must be controlled and directed to the enrichment of the quality of human living.

The reason that I stress the importance of getting our value orientation back into human scale is that that's just about the only star we are going to have to steer by in the period of transition we are moving into. Automation is not going to simply transform our system of economic production and distribution. It is going to challenge and shake the whole fabric of our society—our social institutions, our individual and group behaviour patterns, and the traditional ways in which the individual relates himself to his fellows and to his society.

My further remarks will be divided between a brief comment about the economic impact of automation and a somewhat fuller treatment of the social and psychological considerations raised by the new technology. I want specifically to acknowledge my lack of qualification to speak as a professional economist. My remarks will be those of the layman looking at the problem from what I hope is a common sense point of view.

In theory, at least, automation has the potential to turn out a hundredfold our present level of goods production with a labour force restricted to a relatively small minority of engineers, maintenance technicians, and other categories of highly skilled personnel. Indeed, the only ultimate limits on the quantity and variety of goods that could be produced would be set not by the supply of labour but by the supply of physical and natural resources. The economic threat of automation in a society in which work for pay is the main mechanism for distributing purchasing power is that of unemployment being allowed to spread into a general and major unemployment situation precipitating a recession or a general economic depression.

The Balances

Many economists argue that there are countervailing tendencies in the system, such as population growth, that will offset the negative employment effect of automation. They postulate an infinite capacity for human wants and consumption to expand and argue that if we can stimulate a sufficiently increased rate of economic growth and improve our competitive position in foreign markets, we can absorb automation as fast as it can be introduced while still maintaining full employment. Those who look forward to automation with confidence and enthusiasm argue that, like traditional technological progress, the long-term effect will be to produce whole new industries, new occupations, and hundreds of thousands of new job opportunities.

It is probably correct to argue that in the short run any increase in economic growth will provide additional employment. But if one accepts the fact that automation means that the traditional capital labour-input ratio is going to shift radically in favour of the capital factor, then every new development in automation means that we are going to double and treble our output with an ever-decreasing proportional expansion in our labour requirements. Projected far enough, this means that in order to maintain full employment with an expanded labour force we will have to increase our output first at twice the rate the labour force is growing then at three times the rate, and there would appear to be no end to this process until the assumption of the infinite proclivity to consume is pushed beyond all reasonable bounds.

Even in an affluent society, given the prospect of population growth and unresolved pockets of poverty, there can be little argument about the desirability of economic growth. But we may be well advised to be somewhat sceptical about pursuing economic growth as a cure for unemployment. In the future, the great expansion in our productive output is likely to be achieved through automation rather than through an expanding or harder working labour force. Undoubtedly, automation will give rise to new products and new industries, but far from offering alternative job opportunities to those displaced from traditional pursuits, these new industries will likely be the most automated of all. In a similar way, automation is likely to curtail the ability of the service industries to soak up unemployment as so many services lend themselves to partial, if not complete, automation. . . .

Future Prospects in Data Collection and Processing

Alan F. Westin

Pending proposals and prospective developments of the next decade promise to raise even broader issues of privacy. For example, several study groups and a presidential task force have been working on proposals for a central federal data bank, to collect records of twenty federal agencies, such as Treasury, Labor, Commerce, Agriculture, and Health, Education and Welfare. These agencies already have 100 million punch cards and 30,000 computer tapes containing information about individuals and businesses. The data center would allow sharing of information within the federal government and access for other groups, such as businesses, research organizations, and state and local agencies. Material classified as confidential would not be given out, but what constitutes confidential material is far from clear and uncontested. Another computer facility under consideration by the federal government is a medical-data bank, holding tapes of the medical case histories of all Americans. Conceding its value for public-health purposes and for treating persons taken ill away from their home physicians, the question has already been raised as to who could press the button and get the medical print-out on an individual—his employer? a Congressional committee? the White House? Such a record would include such items as past mental or nervous problems, social diseases, sexual deviations, and the like, which could gravely compromise individuals if it came into the wrong hands. Another system recommended already by a federal study commission is a national, computerized job bank, with employment files on job seekers to match against job openings as these are reported in.

The likelihood of further computerization of financial transactions has been predicted by spokesmen of IBM, RCA, Bell Telephone, and many others. A typical presentation of what the system would be like in the 1970's was written by Stanley M. Humphrey, vice president of a leading management consultant firm. Daily life would run as follows, he speculated, starting with the housewife's trip to the suburban shopping center. Here, a universal credit card would be presented at each store she visited. By inserting the card in a slot and pushing a button, the clerk would record the transaction without sales slips, credit checks, or presentation of cash or checks. From department store to grocery store, each item would be ordered by the same process. The merchandise would then be automatically routed by an electric cart to the housewife's car which she had previously parked (also billed by credit card).

Humphrey sees few problems in establishing such a system. Low-cost simple recording devices placed in each store would feed essential financial information to a central communication office in the shopping center. From there it would be automatically "transmitted downtown to the Second National Finance Utility of Metropolis" (the larger institutions that would replace banks) where the family's "fund account" would be charged for the purchases. No paper would be exchanged in the entire operation. Weekly statements from the finance utility would go to the stores and to the customers. Data processing accomplishes inter-utility communication as well, eliminating clearing house and transit operations between banks as we know them today.

Similarly, public utility charges—gas, water, telephone services—would all be billed and paid through monthly collections of meter readings at a central data center without human intervention. The consumer would learn of charges and payments only after the entire transaction had been completed. Installment payments of all types could also be handled with easy efficiency.

Recording of income would be just as automatic. Through internal and transit computer operations, the finance utility would credit the family's fund account with monthly salaries, stock investments and other income sources.

Humphrey sees the dial telephone as an integral part of this computerized system. From simple items like travel and hotel reservations to more complicated private financial transactions such as doctor bills and rental payments on individually owned property, the individual would merely have to dial the finance utility's data processer to record the information. For travel, of course, no tickets would be needed. For hotels, only advance registration required. "There will be no midnight wait at the registration desk—use of the credit card automatically ejects an appropriate key." Commuting via train or bus would require only the insertion of the credit card into a slot—no tokens, tickets, or change would be necessary.

In winding up his portrait, Humphrey could not help mentioning at least one unpleasant potential of the system:

Such an integrated communication and processing system as described above on a nationwide basis could have important benefits for state and federal governments. Certainly, the Bureau for Printing and Engraving could be almost entirely eliminated—very little cash would be required. Also, the Internal Revenue Department could dispense with its investigating agents, and income tax revenue would rise drastically. Why? Every financial transaction of any importance for every individual in the country would be recorded as it occurred. Consequently, you as an individual would no longer prepare an income tax return including generous allowances for charitable contributions, local sales taxes, and so on. Instead, your fund account at Second National would be automatically charged as a result of a governmental calculation on an exact, accurate basis (using Second National tapes) of your income tax liability. As I said, an important by-product—frightening, isn't it?

Another disturbing fact in this prospective universal credit system is that the life of an individual would be almost wholly recorded and observable through analysis of the daily "transactions" of "Credit Card No. 172,381,400, Humphrey, Stanley M." Whoever ran the computers could know when the individual entered the highway and where he got off; how many bottles of Scotch or Vermouth he purchased from the liquor store; who paid the rent for the girl in Apartment 4B; who went to the movies between two and four P.M. on a working day at the office; who was at lunch at Luigi's or the Four Seasons on Tuesday, September 15; and the hotel at which Mrs. Smith spent the rainy afternoon last Sunday. Where every dollar came from that a government official banked, and where every dollar went that was spent by each corporation and labor union would also lie in the great treasury house of the computer. There would be few areas in which anyone could move about in the anonymity of personal privacy and few transactions that would not be fully documented for government examination.

Still another technological prospect is the collection, in various functional master memory systems, of basic information about each major aspect of the individual's life, an idea that has strong advocates in the governmental, scientific, and professional communities. The individual's complete educational record from pre-school nursery to post-graduate courses could be in the educational master file, including the results of all intelligence, aptitude, and personality tests taken during his lifetime. The individual's complete employment record could be in another master computer dossier.

This record would include every job held, rate of pay, efficiency ratings, employer evaluations, personality tests, recommendations, outside interests, family relation to work, and so on, and would be available on instant point-out when the individual was being considered for new employment by a private organization or government agency. The master credit file could contain all the information needed to do a thorough financial analysis of the individual: his income, fixed expenditures, pattern of past discretionary spending, savings, investment, predicted expenses based on personal and family history, and predicted promotion levels, and the like. Other central dossiers could deal with health, civic activity, telephone records, and criminal records. Every person could have a personal identification number, and computer scanning of a card-holder's fingerprint or voice-print could control assumption of another's number or identity.

For the average citizen, even one well informed about public affairs and general scientific news, this must often seem to be so speculative and distant that it really belongs in the George Orwell file, with a due date of 1984. Used to thinking about the problems of storing and using written information, the citizen imagines future data centers as giant installations in huge rooms, with tens of thousands of reels of tape being lifted on and off machines by clerks, and time-consuming human operations required for any significant comparisons to be made of information about a given person scattered through the data bank. In this portrait, time, cost, efficiency, and the requirement of cooperation by considerable numbers of data-bank employees are assumed to provide real limitations on data surveillance. Nothing could be more mistaken, either in terms of the general growth predicted for the computer in America or of specific adaptations of computers to data-bank and dossier purposes.

The general trends of the next decade have been carefully outlined in several studies done for the RAND corporation by Paul Armer and W. H. Ware. Between 1955 and 1965, the size of the central processing unit of the computer decreased by a factor of 10, from 1,000 cubic feet to 100 cubic feet. By 1975, fully integrated circuits will reduce this by a factor of 1,000, to one tenth of a cubic foot.

Between 1955 and 1965, the internal speed of computers increased by a factor of 200, from 25,000 additions per second to 5 million per second. By 1975, this will be increased another 200 times, making possible operations at the rate of a billion per second.

In terms of operational costs, the price of doing a million additions declined between 1955 and 1965 from $10 to about 3.5 cents. By 1975, this cost will be reduced by another factor of 300, to one two-hundredth of a cent.

If all this still seems to be limited by the amount of computing power available to perform these operations, this factor too must be eliminated as a source of hope for substantial limitations on data surveillance. In 1955, all the installed computers in the United States, working together, could do 500,000 additions per second. By 1965, this capability had increased by 400, to 200 million additions per second. If we take one of the more pessimistic forecasts of computer growth in the next decade, a mere twenty fold, computing power will increase by 1975 to a capability of 5 billion additions per second. If the same growth rate takes place in 1965-1975 as in 1955-1965, as many computer experts think quite possible, the increase in power would be by 400, for a capability of 250 *billion* additions per second.

What these estimates of computer speed, power, cost, and storage capacities mean for data surveillance may be made even more concrete by describing the world not of 1975 but of 1967. The Precision Instrument Company of Palo Alto, California, has developed and demonstrated the model of a new laser process that burns minute craters along parallel lines of the opaque coating of plastic tape. By this process, 645 *million* bits of digital data can be put onto one square inch of plastic tape. (The present capacity for storage is 5,600 bits per square inch.) The laser used has a speed-recording rate of 12 million bits per second. Accuracy of recording is assured by a "light-pipe" system which takes the light passing through the clear spots in the tape, translates this into electrical impulses by a photomultiplier, and compares these with the input data to verify the recording. The tape is read by passing another laser beam across the tape as it rolls by the reader. The light passes through the holes (without altering them) and is translated into electrical pulses which are then fed to a computer, recorder, or print-out machine.

This laser memory process will permit unprecedented storage capacity and rapid retrieval of data. One small unit, containing one 4,800-foot reel of one-inch plastic tape, will be able to store in digital form about twenty pages of information (250 words of typing to the page) for every person in the United States, including women and children. Specific information from a person's twenty-page dossier on this reel could be retrieved in a maximum search time of four minutes, and the entire dossier could be printed out for dispatch to an inquiring source in a matter of a few more minutes. All of this, let us note again, on just one reel of tape, searched swiftly while on its moving mechanism, without platoons of clerks or shifting of storage reels from place to place to signal the operation. Ten such reels would make possible 200-page dossiers on every American, and a mere 100 reels would begin to offer real possibilities of a progressive life-record dossier of each American from birth to death.

For planning, efficiency, and social control, these government data centers, computerized transaction systems, and central record files of the future could bring enormous benefits to society. But unless safeguards for privacy are placed carefully in the planning and administration of systems that most computer experts feel to be inevitable developments of the next two decades, the growth in data surveillance will be awesome. Meanwhile the present dossiers and computerized information systems continue to increase, without many legal or administrative guidelines as yet to cope with the issues of privacy that they raise.

Section Seven

The Crisis in Values

The ultimate questions raised in this reader are those of human values. This period is one of transition; traditional values, unable to serve survival or fulfillment, are being shattered by the acceleration of social change, and a new code, while generally viewed as necessary, is not yet clearly defined or operational. Moreover, the source of this value crisis seems to be contemporary technology with its necessary dichotomies of power and love, growth and control, quantity and quality, profit and welfare.

The symptoms of the value crisis are everywhere. Stress, alienation, and disorientation take their toll of man's psychosocial balance. New disquietude threatens us every day. The war is not confined to South East Asia or the Middle East. It is in our streets, in our homes, and in ourselves. Affluence and poverty confront each other between citizens and nations. The generation gap transcends all boundaries, cultures, and ideologies, and a world youth revolution challenges authority at every level from home to government.

All the problems of uncontrolled growth that we discussed previously as the quadrilemma are ultimately questions of human values. They all involve a crisis of choice. This is the decade of ultimate choice. Unless we can discover the solutions we will perish. The solutions involve a change in our values and a revolutionary restructuring of our national and international economic and political systems. Fortunately, the explosion in science and technology is now being matched by an explosion of human consciousness and conscience, a revolution of hope. More and more, individuals and groups are speaking out. The material hang-up, with its growth syndrome and power complex, is being questioned in fundamental terms.

The scientist is a central figure in this crisis. He is adopting an operational ethic involving relevance and responsibility and assuming the role of an early warning system. The technologist, too, is beginning to adopt a new professional ethic of assessment and concern. Young engineers are questioning their professional training and practices, demanding a more interdisciplinary approach and, in particular, an ecological concern for their products and processes. Also an operational ethic "When in ignorance, refrain" is being adopted by some of the younger technologists. Scientists and engineers are beginning to think in terms of a technology of cure and a technology of assessment and control. Some have proposed the mobilization of large-scale, even worldwide groups of creative thinkers to work toward the resolution of our crises. The United Nations, after 25 years of frustration and failure, senses a new basis for hope in these great global threats. Accompanying the anticipatory functions of scientists, people everywhere in the world are beginning to stir, holding out the hope that participation in government may assure the retention of human values, of diversity and unity, freedom and responsibility. Only hope, commitment, and involvement have survival value.

All the selections in this section are concerned with the confrontation between technology and human values. It begins with the foreword to *Brave New World*, Aldous Huxley's prophetic book about a world whose people are controlled by eugenics, the organized manipulation of our hereditary material. This possibility is becoming a reality with the rapid discoveries in the new genetics. The emergence of a biological order having the Ellulian character is now a genuine possibility. Commoner's article deals with the basic issue of control of science while Ferry suggests such control may involve changes in the Constitution. The article on Sakharov, the Soviet physicist, indicates that these questions cross all ideological boundaries and reflect a world awareness of crisis. Bundy's article reflects the need to broaden our understanding of the complexities of the environmental threat. Jungk writes about the student revolt and how it has responded to the threat of uncontrolled technology. Finally, Platt's article, "What We Must Do," illustrates the growing consensus among scientists that they must act together in some way to help create a future that eliminates the threats to our existence.

Foreword to *Brave New World*

Aldous Huxley

Chronic remorse, as all the moralists are agreed, is a most undesirable sentiment. If you have behaved badly, repent, make what amends you can and address yourself to the task of behaving better next time. On no account brood over your wrongdoing. Rolling in the muck is not the best way of getting clean.

Art also has its morality, and many of the rules of this morality are the same as, or at least analogous to, the rules of ordinary ethics. Remorse, for example, is as undesirable in relation to our bad art as it is in relation to bad behaviour. The badness should be hunted out, acknowledged, and, if possible, avoided in the future. To pore over the literary shortcomings of twenty years ago, to attempt to patch a faulty work into the perfection it missed at its first execution, to spend one's middle age in trying to mend the artistic sins committed and bequeathed by that different person who was oneself in youth—all this is surely vain and futile. And that is why this new *Brave New World* is the same as the old one. Its defects as a work of art are considerable; but in order to correct them I should have to rewrite the book—and in the process of rewriting, as an older, other person, I should probably get rid not only of some of the faults of the story, but also of such merits as it originally possessed. And so, resisting the temptation to wallow in artistic remorse, I prefer to leave both well and ill alone and to think about something else.

In the meantime, however, it seems worth while at least to mention the most serious defect in the story, which is this. The Savage is offered only two alternatives, an insane life in Utopia, or the life of a primitive in an Indian village, a life more human in some respects, but in others hardly less queer and abnormal. At the time the book was written this idea, that human beings are given free will in order to choose between insanity on the one hand and lunacy on the other, was one that I found amusing and regarded as quite possibly true. For the sake, however, of dramatic effect, the Savage is often permitted to speak more rationally than his upbringing among the practitioners of a religion that is half fertility cult and half *Penitente* ferocity would actually warrant. Even his acquaintance with Shakespeare would not in reality justify such utterances. And at the close, of course, he is made to retreat from sanity; his native *Penitente*-ism reasserts its authority and he ends in maniacal self-torture and despairing suicide. 'And so they died miserably ever after'—much to the reassurance of the amused, Pyrrhonic aesthete who was the author of the fable.

Today I feel no wish to demonstrate that sanity is impossible. On the contrary, though I remain no less sadly certain than in the past that sanity is a rather rare phenomenon, I am convinced that it can be achieved and would like to see more of it. For having said so in several recent books and, above all, for having compiled an anthology of what the sane have said about sanity and all the means whereby it can be achieved, I have been told by an eminent academic critic that I am a sad symptom of the failure of an intellectual class in time of crisis. The implication being, I suppose, that the professor and his colleagues are hilarious symptoms of success. The benefactors of humanity deserve due honour and commemoration. Let us build a Pantheon for professors. It should be located among the ruins of one of the gutted cities of Europe or Japan, and over the entrance to the ossuary I would inscribe, in letters six or seven feet high, the simple words: Sacred to the memory of the World's Educators. *Si Monumentum Requiris Circumspice.*

But to return to the future . . . If I were now to rewrite the book, I would offer the Savage a third alternative. Between the utopian and the primitive horns of his dilemma would lie the possibility of sanity—a possibility already actualized, to some extent, in a community of exiles and refugees from the Brave New World, living within the borders of the Reservation. In this community economics would be decentralist and Henry-Georgian, politics Kropotkinesque and cooperative. Science and technology would be used as though, like the Sabbath, they had been made for man, not (as at present and still more so in the Brave New World) as though man were to be adapted and enslaved to them. Religion would be the conscious and intelligent pursuit of man's Final End, the unitive knowledge of the immanent Tao or Logos, the transcendent Godhead of Brahman. And the prevailing philosophy of life would be a kind of Higher Utilitarianism, in which the Greatest Happiness principle would be secondary to the Final End principle—the first question to be asked and answered in every contingency of life being: 'How will this thought or action contribute to, or interfere with, the achievement, by me and the greatest possible number of other individuals, of man's Final End?'

Brought up among the primitives, the Savage (in this hypothetical new version of the book) would not be transported to Utopia until he had had an opportunity of learning something at first hand about the nature of a society composed of freely cooperating individuals devoted to the pursuit of sanity. Thus altered, *Brave New World* would possess an artistic and (if it is permissible to use so large a word in connexion with a work of fiction) a philosophical completeness, which in its present form it evidently lacks.

But *Brave New World* is a book about the future and, whatever its artistic or philosophical qualities, a book about the future can interest us only if its prophecies look as though they might conceivably come true. From our present vantage point, fifteen years further down the inclined plane of modern history, how plausible do its prognostications seem? What has happened in the painful interval to confirm or invalidate the forecasts of 1931?

One vast and obvious failure of foresight is immediately apparent. *Brave New World* contains no reference to nuclear fission. That it does not is actually rather odd; for the possibilities of atomic energy had been a popular topic of conversation for years before the book was written. My old friend, Robert Nichols, had even written a successful play about the subject, and I recall that I myself had casually mentioned it in a novel published in the late twenties. So it seems, as I say, very odd that the rockets and helicopters of the seventh century of Our Ford should not have been powered by disintegrating nuclei. The oversight may not be excusable; but at least it can be easily explained. The theme of *Brave New World* is not the advancement of science as such; it is the advancement of science as it affects human individuals. The triumphs of physics, chemistry, and engineering are tacitly taken for granted. The only scientific advances to be specifically described are those involving the application to human beings of the results of future research in biology, physiology, and psychology. It is only by means of the sciences of life that the quality of life can be radically changed. The sciences of matter can be applied in such a way that they will destroy life or make the living of it impossibly complex and uncomfortable; but, unless used as instruments by the biologists and psychologists, they can do nothing to modify the natural forms and expressions of life itself. The release of atomic energy marks a great revolution in human history, but not (unless we blow ourselves to bits and so put an end to history) the final and most searching revolution.

This really revolutionary revolution is to be achieved, not in the external world, but in the souls and flesh of human beings. Living as he did in a revolutionary period, the Marquis de Sade very naturally made use of this theory of revolutions in order to rationalize his peculiar brand of insanity. Robespierre had achieved the most superficial kind of revolution, the political. Going a little deeper, Babeuf had attempted the economic revolution. Sade regarded himself as the apostle of the truly revolutionary revolution, beyond mere politics and economics—the revolution of individual men, women, and children, whose bodies were henceforward to become the common sexual property of all and whose minds were to be purged of all the natural decencies, all the laboriously acquired inhibitions of traditional civilization. Between Sadism and the really revolutionary revolution there is, of course, no necessary or inevitable connexion. Sade was a lunatic and the more or less conscious goal of his revolution was universal chaos and destruction. The people who govern the Brave New World may not be sane (in what may be called the absolute sense of that word); but they are not madmen and their aim is not anarchy but social stability. It is in order to achieve stability that they carry out, by scientific means, the ultimate, personal, really revolutionary revolution.

But meanwhile we are in the first phase of what is perhaps the penultimate revolution. Its next phase may be atomic warfare, in which case we do not have to bother with prophecies about the future. But it is conceivable that we may have enough sense, if not to stop fighting altogether, at least to behave as rationally as did our eighteenth-century ancestors. The unimaginable horrors of the Thirty Years War actually taught men a lesson, and for more than a hundred years the politicians and generals of Europe consciously resisted the temptation to use their military resources to the limits of destructiveness or (in the majority of conflicts) to go on fighting until the enemy was totally annihilated. They were aggressors, of course, greedy for profit and glory; but they were also conservatives, determined at all costs to keep their world intact, as a going concern. For the last thirty years there have been no conservatives; there have only been nationalistic radicals of the right and nationalistic radicals of the left. The last conservative statesman was the fifth Marquess of Lansdowne; and when he wrote a letter to *The Times*, suggesting that the First World War should be concluded with a compromise, as most of the wars of the eighteenth century had been, the editor of that once conservative journal refused to print it. The nationalistic radicals had their way, with the consequences that we all know—Bolshevism, Fascism, inflation, depression, Hitler, the Second World War, the ruin of Europe, and all but universal famine.

Assuming, then, that we are capable of learning as much from Hiroshima as our forefathers learned from Magdeburg, we may look forward to a period, not indeed of peace, but of limited and only partially ruinous warfare. During that period it may be assumed that nuclear energy will be harnessed to industrial uses. The result, pretty obviously, will be a series of economic and social changes unprecedented in rapidity and completeness. All the existing patterns of human life will be disrupted and new patterns will have to be improvised to conform with the nonhuman fact of atomic power. Procrustes in modern dress, the nuclear scientist will prepare the bed on which mankind must lie; and if mankind doesn't fit—well, that will be just too bad for mankind. There will have to be some stretchings and a bit of amputation—the same sort of stretchings and amputations as have been going on ever since applied science really got into its stride, only this time they will be a good deal more drastic than the past. These far from painless operations will be directed by highly centralized totalitarian governments. Inevitably so; for the immediate future is likely to resemble the immediate past, and in the immediate past rapid technological changes, taking place in a mass-producing economy and among a population predominantly propertyless, have always tended to produce economic and social confusion. To deal with confusion, power has been centralized and government control increased. It is probable that all the world's governments will be more or less completely totalitarian even before the harnessing of atomic energy; that they will be totalitarian during and after the harnessing seems almost certain. Only a large-scale popular movement toward decentralization and self-help can arrest the present tendency toward statism. At present there is no sign that such a movement will take place.

There is, of course, no reason why the new totalitarianism should resemble the old. Government by clubs and firing squads, by artificial famine, mass imprisonment, and mass deportation, is not merely inhumane (nobody cares much about that nowadays); it is demonstrably inefficient—and in an age of advanced technology, inefficiency is the sin against the Holy Ghost. A really efficient totalitarian state would be one in which the all-powerful executive of political bosses and their army of managers control a population of slaves who do not have to be coerced, because they love their servitude. To make them love it is the task assigned, in present-day totalitarian states, to ministries of propaganda, newspaper editors, and schoolteachers. But their methods are still crude and unscientific. The old Jesuits' boast that, if they were given the schooling of the child, they could answer for the man's religious opinions, was a product of wishful thinking. And the modern pedagogue is probably rather less efficient at conditioning his pupils' reflexes than were the reverend fathers who educated Voltaire. The greatest triumphs of propaganda have been accomplished, not by doing something, but by refraining from doing. Great is the truth, but still greater, from a practical point of view, is silence about truth. By simply not mentioning certain subjects, by lowering what Mr. Churchill calls an 'iron curtain' between the masses and such facts or arguments as the local political bosses regard as undesirable, totalitarian propagandists have influenced opinion much more effectively than they could have done by the most eloquent denunciations, the most compelling of logical rebuttals. But silence is not enough. If persecution, liquidation, and other symptoms of social friction are to be avoided, the positive sides of propaganda must be made as effective as the negative. The most important Manhattan Projects of the future will be vast government-sponsored inquiries into what the politicians and the participating scientists will call 'the problem of happiness'—in other words, the problem of making people love their servitude. Without economic security the love of servitude cannot possibly come into existence; for the sake of brevity, I assume that the all-powerful executive and its managers will succeed in solving the problem of permanent security. But security tends very quickly to be taken for granted. Its achievement is merely a superficial, external revolution. The love of servitude cannot be established except as the result of a deep, personal revolution in human minds and bodies. To bring about that revolution we require, among others, the following discoveries and inventions. First, a greatly improved technique of suggestion—through infant conditioning and, later, with the aid of drugs, such as scopolamine. Second, a fully developed science of human differences, enabling government managers to assign any given individual to his or her proper place in the social and economic hierarchy. (Round pegs in square holes tend to have dangerous thoughts about the social system and to infect others with their discontents.) Third (since reality, however utopian, is something from which people feel the need of taking pretty frequent holidays), a substitute for alcohol and the other narcotics, something at once less harmful and more pleasure-giving than gin or heroin. And fourth (but this would be a long-term project, which would take generations of totalitarian control to bring to a successful conclusion), a foolproof system of eugenics, designed to standardize the human product and so to facilitate the task of the managers. In *Brave New World* this standardization of the human product has been pushed to fantastic, though not perhaps impossible, extremes. Technically and ideologically we are still a long way from bottled babies and Bokanovsky groups of semi-morons. But by A.F.600, who knows what may not be happening? Meanwhile the other characteristic features of that happier and more stable world—the equivalents of soma and hypnopaedia and the scientific caste system—are probably not more than three or four generations away. Nor does the sexual promiscuity of *Brave New World* seem so very distant. There are already certain American cities in which the number of divorces is equal to the number of marriages. In a few years, no doubt, marriage licences will be sold like dog licences, good for a period of twelve months, with no law against changing dogs or keeping more than one animal at a time. As political and economic freedom diminishes, sexual freedom tends compensatingly to increase. And the dictator (unless he needs cannon fodder and families with which to colonize empty or conquered territories) will do well to encourage that freedom. In conjunction with the freedom to daydream under the influence of dope and movies and the radio, it will help to reconcile his subjects to the servitude which is their fate.

All things considered, it looks as though Utopia were far closer to us than anyone, only fifteen years ago, could have imagined. Then, I projected it six hundred years into the future. Today it seems quite possible that the horror may be upon us within a single century. That is, if we refrain from blowing ourselves to smithereens in the interval. Indeed, unless we choose to decentralize and to use applied science, not as the end to which human beings are to be made the means, but as the means to producing a race of free individuals, we have only two alternatives to choose from: either a number of national, militarized totalitarianisms, having as their root the terror of the atomic bomb and as their consequence the destruction of civilization (or, if the warfare is limited, the perpetuation of militarism); or else one supra-national totalitarianism, called into existence by the social chaos resulting from rapid technological progress in general and the atom revolution in particular, and developing, under the need for efficiency and stability, into the welfare-tyranny of Utopia. You pays your money and you takes your choice.

Is Science Getting Out of Hand?

Barry Commoner

The age of innocent faith in science and technology may be over. We were given a spectacular signal of this change on a night in November 1965. On that night all electric power in an 80,000-square-mile area of the northeastern United States and Canada failed. The breakdown was a total surprise. For hours engineers and power officials were unable to turn the lights on again; for days no one could explain why they went out; even now no one can promise that it won't happen again.

The failure knocked out a huge network which was supposed to shift electric power from areas with excess generating capacity to those facing a heavy drain. But on that night the power grid worked against its intended purpose. Instead of counteracting a local power failure, it spread the trouble out of control until the whole system was engulfed and dozens of cities were dark.

The trouble began with the failure of a relay which controlled the flow of electricity from the Sir Adam Beck No. 2 power plant in Queenston, Ontario, into one of its feeder lines. The remaining lines, unable to carry the extra load, shut down their own safety switches. With these normal exits blocked the plant's full power flowed back along the lines that tied the Queenston generators into the U.S.–Canadian grid. This sudden surge of power, traveling across New England, quickly tripped safety switches in a series of local power plants, shutting them down. As a result the New England region, which until then had been feeding excess electricity into the Consolidated Edison system in New York, drained power away from that city; under this strain the New York generators were quickly overloaded and their safety switches shut off. The blackout was then complete. The system had been betrayed by the very links that were intended to save local power plants from failure.

Barry Commoner, "Is Science Getting Out of Hand?" in *Science and Survival* (New York: The Viking Press Inc., 1967), pp. 3-8. Reprinted by permission of the author. Commoner is professor of plant physiology and chairman of the department of Botany at Washington University. For six years he was chairman of the Committee on Science in the Promotion of Human Welfare of the American Association for the Advancement of Science, and he is now a member of the board of directors of the Association. At present he is the director of Washington University's Center for the Biology of Natural Systems.

In one of the magazine reports of the great blackout, there is a photograph that tells the story with beautiful simplicity. It shows a scene in Consolidated Edison's Energy Control Center. Stretched purposefully across the photograph is an operational diagram of the New York power system; an intricate but neat network of connections, meters, and indicators symbolizing the calculated competence of this powerful machine. In the foreground, dwarfed by the diagrammatic system and in curious contrast to its firm and positive lines, is a group of very puzzled engineers.

This same contrast between man and machine is expressed in the accompanying text:

The Northeast grid was magnificently interconnected and integrated. But only machines spoke over it, one to the other. They asked each other mechanical questions and gave each other mechanical responses. No human responsibility had immediate control over this entire system. Thus, no human being can answer the still-unanswered question: Why?

But this electronic thinking did not protect the people of the city.

It was required that New York come to the brink of chaos to refresh an old truth: People—men of frailty, judgment and human decisions—must control machines. Not vice versa.

One man, however, if he had lived to see it, would not have been surprised by the great blackout—Norbert Wiener, the mathematician who did so much to develop cybernetics, the science which guides the design of complex electrical grids and their computerized controls. Cybernetics has produced electronic brains and all the other marvelous machines that now operate everything from election reports to steel plants; that have made the robot no longer a cartoon but a reality; that made the U.S.-Canadian power grid feasible.

Just six years before the blackout Dr. Wiener reviewed a decade of remarkable progress in the science which he helped to create. He reported at that time on the development of a new kind of automatic machine, a computer that had been programmed to play checkers. Engineers built into the electronic circuits a correct understanding of the rules of checkers and also a way of judging what moves were most likely to beat the computer's opponents. The computer made a record of its opponent's moves in the current and previous games. Then, at great speed, it calculated its opponent's most likely moves in any given situation and, having figured those out, adjusted its own game, move by move, to give itself the best chance of winning. The engineers designed a machine that not only knew how to play checkers but could learn from experience and actually improve its own game.

Dr. Wiener described the first results of the checkers tournaments between the computer and its programmers. The machine started out playing an accurate but uninspired game which was easy to beat. But after about ten or twenty hours of practice the machine got the hang of it, and from then on the human player usually lost and the machine won.

Dr. Wiener emphasized this point: Here was a machine designed by a man who built into it everything that it could do. Yet, because it could calculate complicated probabilities faster than the man could, the machine learned to play checkers against the man better than he could against the machine. Dr. Wiener concluded that it had become technically possible to build automatic machines that "most definitely escape from the complete effective control of the man who has made them."

The U.S.-Canadian power grid is just such a machine. By following the rules built into its design, the machine acted—before the engineers had time to understand and countermand it—in a way that went against their real wishes.

One month after the great blackout, there occurred in Salt Lake City, Utah, a little-noticed event that can take its place beside the power failure as a monument to the blunders which have begun to mar the accomplishments of modern science and technology. There, nine children from Washington County, Utah, entered a hospital for tests to determine whether abnormal nodules in their thyroid glands were an indication of possible thyroid disease: nontoxic goiter, inflammation, benign or malignant tumors. Fifteen years earlier these children had been exposed to radioactive iodine produced by fallout from the nearby Nevada atomic test site.

It will be some time before any one can tell whether the incidence of thyroid nodules in this group of children is statistically significant, and if so, whether the nodules are really due to fallout. But regardless of the outcome, the mere fact that health authorities felt compelled to look for an effect of fallout on the health of these children is itself a surprise.

The chain of events which brought the children into the hospital began in the 1950s when the AEC started a long series of nuclear explosions at its Nevada test site in the conviction that ". . . these explosives created no immediate or long-range hazard to human health outside the proving ground." But among the radioactive particles of the fallout clouds that occasionally escaped into the surrounding territory was the isotope iodine-131. As these clouds passed over the Utah pastures, iodine-131 was deposited on the grass; being widely spread, it caused no alarming readings on outdoor radiation meters. But dairy cows grazed these fields. As a result, iodine-131, generated in the mushroom cloud, drifted to Utah farms, was foraged by cows, passed to children in milk, and was gathered in high concentration in the children's thyroid glands. Here in a period of a few weeks the iodine-131 released its radiation. If sufficiently intense, such radiation passing through the thyroid cells may set off subtle changes which, though quiescent and hidden for years, eventually give rise to disease.

Like the Northeast blackout, this too is a chain reaction. Where the blackout reaction chain took minutes, the iodine-131 chain took days and in a sense years. But in both cases the process was over and the damage done before we understood what had happened.

Modern science, and the huge technological enterprises which it produces, represent the full flowering of man's understanding of nature. Scientific knowledge is our best guide to controlling natural forces. In this it has been magnificently successful; it is this success which has given us the marvels of modern electricity, and the tremendous power of nuclear bombs.

The power blackout and the Utah thyroid problem have cast a shadow—small, but deeply troubling—over the brilliance of these scientific successes. Is it possible that we do not know the full consequences of the new power grids and the new bombs? Are we really in control of the vast new powers that science has given us, or is there a danger that science is getting out of hand?

Charting the Complexities

McGeorge Bundy

While it is indisputable that we must act now to save our environment from pollution and to limit the psychological stress and physical degradation inherent in population density, we also have an overwhelming need to learn more clearly how the myriad acts of man affect the stability of all of nature's systems.

As a National Academy of Sciences study group pointed out in a recent appraisal of "the crisis," we cannot effectively manage the environment without knowing what it is, what it was, and what it can be. On a national scale, we do not at present measure environmental quality comprehensively or regularly. We do not know how and to what extent it is changing and has already changed. Much of the information now gathered under the aegis of such environmentally orientated agencies as the Environmental Science Services Administration, the Geological Survey, the Bureau of Commercial Fisheries, the National Air

McGeorge Bundy, "Charting the Complexities," *Saturday Review,* April 4, 1970. Copyright 1970 Saturday Review, Inc. Reprinted by permission of the publisher and author. Bundy is president of the Ford Foundation. He served Presidents Kennedy and Johnson as special assistant for national security affairs. Before that he was dean of the Faculty of Arts and Sciences at Harvard University. He was the co-author, with Henry L. Stimson, President Roosevelt's Secretary of War, of "On Active Service in Peace and War" and author of "The Strength of Government." This article is based on remarks by Mr. Bundy addressed to the 1970 meeting of the advisory panel of the Committee on Science and Astronautics, U.S. House of Representatives.

Pollution Control Administration, and the Federal Water Pollution Control Administration is obtained for special purposes. Not surprisingly, no agency is either assigned to or assumes responsibility for conducting an overall, ecological evaluation of the quality of the environment, nor is any common interchangeable or comparative sampling method now being used, although the quality of the air, for example, quite clearly affects the quality of water.

If the first requirement is to provide a systematic, comprehensive system of ecological observation and data collection, there is also pressing need for broad-gauged analysis of information to identify simple correlations between independently observed and measured phenomena, and for the testing of intellectually ambitious models of ecological reality to improve our powers of prediction, to spur our defensive and preventive view of our environment and its interrelating subsystems, and to address issues of strategic management and preservation. Information technology fortunately makes it possible for the first time to do these things.

Indeed, some scholars (often with Ford Foundation support) are now approaching environmental analysis from two sides: the economic and the ecological. Each approach strives to understand the complex interrelationships of the parts of man-made or natural systems, and the causes of equilibrium or instability. Each approach explores and seeks to identify relationships of dependency between independently observed phenomena.

When considering a stream, for example, analysts attempt to define the relationship between the discharge of specific amounts of organic materials at specific locations and the stream's need of oxygen at the same locations. Out of a series of such equations comes a mathematical model that, at its best, may represent a primitive skeleton of a complex system. Its formalized, quantitative relationships lend themselves to mathematical manipulation as verbal descriptions of reality cannot. With the goal, for example, of achieving a given standard of water purity in the stream, a good model should enable us to discern the range in cost of several alternative "clean-up" strategies, each of which combines elements of industrial plant relocation and modified production methods.

Ecologists and economists have already demonstrated that model-building and analysis can yield more penetrating insights than might come exclusively from the logic of lay observation or common sense, and those approaches can also have practical application.

Economists at Resources for the Future (RFF) recently challenged a U. S. Army Corps of Engineers plan to build a number of dams on the upper Potomac and its tributaries. The Corps proposed, in part, to construct these dams to hold water that could subsequently be released in dry seasons to dilute wastes in the lower river and thereby sustain throughout the year a steady standard of water quality. The RFF constructed a mathematical model of the hydrology of the river basin and explored the costs of a number of alternative methods of assuring the given water standards, as well as higher and lower ones. They found that all alternatives (combining various treatment methods) were substantially cheaper than the proposed dams, and some would cost only one-tenth as much.

Such a model offers promising evidence that the analysis of complexity can enhance the rationality of decision-making. Even if one knows that a reservoir is a more expensive way of keeping the Potomac clean than advanced waste treatment would be, one may still prefer to keep the river clean in this more expensive fashion. Models make deliberation possible and, indeed, in some sense enforce it, which is not the least of their social value.

The Ford Foundation's experience with its five-year-old program in resources and environment suggests to us the high priority that should be attached to the study and appraisal of environment on the broadest scale. We have recently intensified discussions with scholars and public officials on this matter. While we have no formal recommendations as to ways and means at this date, we are encouraged to believe that there is a vital, complementary role that philanthropic institutions can play in conjunction with Congress, the Executive branch of the federal government, other educational and research institutions, and indeed, the family of nations acting in concert to facilitate the broadened intellectual attack these problems require.

The environmental dangers we face, the systems to be understood, and the remedies to be fashioned will frequently be international in character, an aspect properly recognized by the recent, relatively under-reported decision of Secretary of State William Rogers to create in the Secretary's office an Office of Environmental Affairs, headed by Christian Herter, Jr. I personally am convinced that energy for both rigorous study and prompt action must derive from national governments, and must not be remanded to or anticipated from supranational agencies or voluntary assemblies of motivated individuals who share the same concerns or intellectual training across political boundaries. At the same time, I also see important possibilities for international cooperation and collaboration in these urgent environmental tasks.

There is not only the manifest fact of our national interdependencies relative to the environment, there is also no obvious ideological basis for disagreement over causes or relative responsibility. Nor is there political gain to be realized from a posture of isolation. Indeed, there is reason to believe that even potential adversaries will welcome and be responsive to an initiative for communication and intellectual consultation on these complex scientific and technical questions. And there is certainly reason to hope that a fruitful intellectual consideration of our common stake in preserving the environment would facilitate discussion of even harder issues of common concern.

In addition to the political possibility for cooperation, there is the undeniable fact that we confront problems of awesome complexity. The intellectual talent that must be encouraged to address these problems is not only exceedingly scarce but also geographically and politically dispersed. Every experience that I have had in exploring issues of common concern with the intellectual and scientific leaders of other societies and states has confirmed what I have always felt to be true—that the best ideas or perceptions are likely to emerge from circles of intellectual competence deliberately made as inclusive as possible.

Thus, as we launch this decade of attention to the environment, there is much to be said for activation and steady cultivation, wherever possible, of a workable process of international intellectual consultation and collaboration with nationals of countries that may be potential adversaries as well as traditional friends. This process will not happen automatically. It needs to be made someone's business, necessarily requires a new order of collaboration among the State Department, the science agencies, and the nongovernmental National Academy of Sciences, and ought to have Congressional encouragement as well as Executive direction. One can conceive of three different levels of fruitful international exchange.

First, we should make every effort to ensure that national systems for monitoring, collecting, and storing environmental data are compatible. I believe that early, serious effort across political boundaries to achieve intellectual consensus concerning the key phenomena to be observed and the quality indices to be established will obviate dangers of poor or nonexistent linkages between mechanical national arrangements for collection, storage, retrieval, and exchange.

Second, assuming that each nation will independently pursue research and experimentation in remedial actions, information on work in progress as well as on results and understandings, however tentative, must flow freely across political boundaries. There simply is too little time, brain power, and public money for nations to operate either in a chauvinistic or unconsciously introverted fashion; or for countries to run up blind alleys trodden earlier by others or remain ignorant of promising approaches under scrutiny elsewhere. The responsibility for ensuring the necessary exchange of information in these matters rests with each nation and its interested intellectual community. The priority for public policy here is the provision of resources for an expanded flow of personnel and information materials from points of national origin, rather than the creation of new, allegedly coordinative international agencies.

Third, when the necessary intellectual mobilization begins to yield operational applications, there will surely be an opportunity for shared international effort. The developed countries will have their traditional obligations vis-à-vis the emerging countries, and new patterns of international law and management seem likely to be required with respect to our priceless, collective, oceanic, inner- and outer-space assets.

The prospects for a successful defense of our natural environment, within our own political sphere as well as in cooperation with others, cannot be ensured simply by a commitment to a deeper and broader intellectual inquiry, as fundamental as I believe that to be. It will also depend upon at least two other important factors: the health of our system of higher education and the health of our political process. I share the anxiety that many feel today over the adequacy and well-being of each of these vital systems.

No modern society is going to succeed if it fails to connect its muscular actions to a discriminating intellect. The demand for guidance and understanding by that intellect has never been greater, not only with respect to the environment but also to the voracious demands of modern society for more powerful intellectual insight concerning the learning process, the aging process, the reproductive process, urbanization, and all the forces compelling human adaptation and institutional change in the technological era.

The national debate—in part, clearly, a political debate requiring initiation by responsible government leaders—to define and affirm the goals of our system of higher education for both individuals and society, and the terms of national public support and accountability, although barely begun, is becoming increasingly urgent. In this necessary discussion, the Congress and the public have a right to expect the academic community to come forward in its turn with the professional, curricular, and organizational innovations and protections that an era of engagement with issues of individual welfare and social policy will require.

The nation's political process will also be sharply tested by any serious approach to environmental preservation and restoration. There will be no obvious, consensual, and painless technical panacea available to us. We will not be able to avoid a widened definition of the processes of industrial production that embraces the full costs of safely disposing of or recycling waste materials. There will be sharp political conflict over the assignment of these additional cost burdens. There will be a clearer understanding of the price to the current generation of environmental damage unconscionably shunned in earlier eras.

We will be enormously dependent on the ability of men of scholarship and knowledge to communicate dangers and to explain the range of promising strategies and operational urgencies in terms that are understandable to the general public and to those with political responsibility for action. We will also need a political process that is both open and coherent. On the legislative side, it must afford the opportunity for the representation of views by individuals with a human interest as well as by organized groups with a more tangible economic interest. It must consider the unvoiced but nonetheless real stake of future generations as well as that of participants in the next general election. And in execution of the generally approved programmatic course, our political process should be strong enough to avoid bureaucratic splitting of the difference of underlying disagreement, or encouraging several Executive agencies to operate independently and inconsistently, thus undoing with today's directive or action on this side of town what was painfully resolved in someone else's office yesterday.

In the end, effective translation of the desire of man to preserve his environment will depend on the skill of the public man. Societies can become paralyzed over a plethora of facts and the absence of obvious conclusions. Or they may freeze when the indisputable facts and necessities offend received values and conventional wisdom. Neither form of paralysis is likely when the linkages between the arena where policy is forged and the relevant circle of informed and disinterested citizens and scholars are firm and easy.

Must We Rewrite the Constitution to Control Technology?

Wilbur H. Ferry

I shall argue here the proposition that the regulation of technology is the most important intellectual and political task on the American agenda.

I do not say that technology *will* be regulated, only that it *should* be.

My thesis is unpopular. It rests on the growing evidence that technology is subtracting as much or more from the sum of human welfare as it is adding. We are substituting a technological environment for a natural environment. It is therefore desirable to ask whether we understand the conditions of the new as well as we do those of the old, and whether we are prepared to do what may be necessary to see that this new environment is made suitable to men.

Until now, industrial man has only marginally and with reluctance under-taken to direct his ingenuity to his own welfare. It is a possibility merely—not a probability—that he will become wise enough to commit himself fully to that goal. For today the infatuation with science and technology is bottomless.

Here is where all the trouble begins—in the American confidence that technology is ultimately the medicine for all ills. This infatuation may, indeed, be so profound as to undercut everything of an optimistic tone that follows. Technology is the American theology, promising salvation by material works.

I shall argue that technology is merely a collection of means, some of them praiseworthy, others contemptible and inhumane. There is a growing list of things we *can* do that we *must not* do. My view is that toxic and tonic potentialities are mingled in technology and that our most challenging task is to sort them out.

A few cautionary words are in order.

First, I am aware of the distinctions between science and technology but intend to disregard them because the boundary between science and technology is as dim and confused as that between China and India. Besides, it is impossible to speak of public regulation of technology while according the mother-lode, science, a privileged sanctuary. At the same time, it must be granted that the

Wilbur H. Ferry, "Must We Rewrite the Constitution to Control Technology?" *Saturday Review*, March 2, 1968. Copyright 1968 Saturday Review, Inc. Wilbur H. Ferry is a vice president of the Fund for the Republic, Inc., and a staff associate of its Center for the Study of Democratic Institutions, at Santa Barbara, California.

scientists have been more conscientious than the technologists in appraising their contributions and often warning the community of the consequences of scientific discovery.

Next, I shall use everyday examples. Some will therefore consider my examples superficial. But it appears to me to be better to illustrate the case by situations about which there is considerable general knowledge. I shall rely on well known contemporary instances of technological development chiefly to show the contrast between their popular aspects, including popular ideas about control, and those less well known side effects that in the long run threaten to cancel out promised benefits.

The first point to be made is that technology can no longer be taken for granted. It must be thought about, not merely produced, celebrated, and accepted in all its manifestations as an irresponsible and essentially benign human phenomenon. The treason of the clerks can be observed in many forms, but there is no area in which intellectuals have been more remiss than in their failure to comprehend technology and assign it its proper place in humane society. With many honorable exceptions—I give special recognition to Lewis Mumford, who for forty years has been warning against the castration of spirit by technique—the attitude of the physical scientists may be summarized in advice once proffered to me, "Quit worrying about the new scientific-technical world and get with it!" And the disposition of the social scientists, when they notice technology at all, is to suggest ways of adjusting human beings to its requirements. Kenneth Keniston says in *The Uncommitted*: "We have developed complex institutions to assure (technology's) persistence and acceleration (and we) seldom seek to limit its effects."

We are here near the core of the issue. Technology is not just another historical development, taking its place with political parties, religious establishments, mass communications, household economy, and other chapters of the human story. Unlike the growth of those institutions, its growth has been quick and recent, attaining in many cases exponential velocities. Federal expenditure for research and development in 1940 was $74,000,000—less than 1 per cent of total government spending. In 1966 it was $16 billion—15 per cent of federal spending. This is not history in the old sense, but instant history. Technology has a career of its own, so far not much subject to the political guidance and restraints imposed on other enormously powerful institutions.

This is why technology must be classed as a mystery and why the lack of interest of the intellectuals must be condemned. A mystery is something not understood. Intellectuals are in charge of demystification. Public veneration is the lot of most mysteries, and technology is no exception. We can scarcely blame statesmen for bumbling and fumbling with this phenomenon, for no one has properly explained it to them. We can scarcely rebuke the public for its uncritical adoration, for it knows only what it is told, and most of the information comes now from the high priests and acolytes of technology's temples. They are enraptured by the pursuit of what they most often call truth, but what in fact is often obscene curiosity, as when much of a nation's technological quest is for larger and more vicious ways of killing—the situation today.

There is an analogy between the rise of modern economics and that of the new technology that one would have thought intellectuals would be especially eager to examine. Technological development today is in the enshrined position in political-economic theory that was accorded to economic development in the nineteenth and early twentieth centuries. Unguided and self-directed technology is the free market all over again. The arguments justifying *laissez faire* were little different from those justifying unrestrained technology. The arguments in both cases are either highly suspect or invalid. The free market dwindles in real importance, though the myth remains durable enough. But we know now that the economic machine needs to be managed if it is not to falter and behave eccentrically and needlessly injure people. That we have not yet conquered the political art of economic management only shows how arduous and thought-demanding a process it is, and why we should get after the equivalent task in technology at once.

Quite a lot of imaginative writing has been done about the world to come, whether that world develops from the technological tendencies already evident or is reconstructed after a nuclear war. This future-casting used to be known as Utopian writing. Utopias today are out of fashion, at least among novelists and poets, who are always the best guides to the future. With only two exceptions, the novels I have read tell of countries that no one here would care to live in for five minutes.

The conditions imagined are everywhere the same. High technology rules. Efficiency is the universal watchword. Everything works. All decisions are made rationally, with the rationality of the machines. Humans, poor folk, are the objects of the exercise, never the subjects. They are watched and manipulated, directed, and fitted in. The stubborn few in whom ancient juices of feeling and justice flow are exiled to Mars or to the moon. Those who know *how* are the ones who run things; a dictator who knows *all* reigns over all; and this dictator is not infrequently a machine, or—more properly—a system of procedures. I need go no further, for almost everyone is familiar with Orwell's *1984.*

I proceed to examples of the benign and malignant capacities of technology. I am aware that many will find unacceptable my treatment of technology as a semi-autonomous force. These critics say that *tonic* and *toxic* are words to apply to human beings, to ignorant or wise statesmen, to thoughtless or conscientious engineers, to greedy or well-intentioned entrepreneurs. To holders of this viewpoint, there is no intrinsic flaw or benefit or value in technology itself. But I hope to demonstrate that technology has an ineluctable persistence of its own, beyond the reach of all familiar arguments based on the power structure.

My first example is privacy, today a goner, killed by technology. We are still in the early days of electronic eavesdropping, itself an offshoot of communications research, and at first celebrated as a shortcut to crime control. But now no office, schoolhouse, or bedroom is any longer safe from intrusions. A good many people, including Senators, casino operators, felons, and executives on holiday with their secretaries have been made conscious of possible bugs in their cocktail olives and automobiles as well as in their telephones. A good many others were aroused when it was disclosed some time ago that the FBI possesses the fingerprints of tens of millions of citizens. What are we to think of the proposal for a National Data Center, which will have the capacity and perhaps the responsibility to collect every last bit of information concerning every citizen? Not only tax records, but police records, school grades, property and bank accounts, medical history, credit ratings, even responses to the Kinsey sexual behavior questionnaire.

To its credit, Congress has already taken a cautious look. A subcommittee of the House Committee on Government Operations took several hundred pages of testimony in the summer of 1966 on "The Computer and Invasion of Privacy." Referring to the programs designed to "help America" under the efficient guidance of the Data Center, Subcommittee Chairman Cornelius Gallagher said: "Such programs should not be at the cost of individual privacy. What we are looking for is a sense of balance. We do not want to deprive ourselves of the rewards of science; we simply want to make sure that human dignity and civil liberties remain intact . . . . Thought should be given to these questions now, before we awaken some morning in the future and find that . . . liberty as we know it has vanished."

Chairman Gallagher then said he did not doubt that some way of reconciling the claims of efficiency and privacy would be found. To me, however, this is by no means a foregone conclusion. It ought to be against public policy to take any chance whatever with the little privacy remaining to Americans.

We have been reading a lot recently about the greatest intrusion on privacy yet dreamed up, in terms of numbers of people affected. I refer to the supersonic transport plane, a multibillion-dollar folly to which the nation is now apparently committed irrevocably. In a few years' time, the sonic boom of the SST will daily and nightly waken sleepers; worsen the condition of the sick; frighten tens of millions; induce neuroses; and cause property damage beyond estimate.

At least three European countries are considering putting the traveling thunderclap of the sonic boom on the forbidden list by passing legislation which would prevent SSTs from flying over their territories. The position of these countries on this issue is people first, machines second.

The idea has been wafted about by the Federal Aviation Authority of the United States—which has been more than ordinarily slippery on the issue of the SST—that we will spend the billions required for SST but forbid its use overland in this country. I don't believe it for a moment. Overland flight is where the big profits are to be made. If, as seems to be the case, SSTs will be built here, there can be no doubt that tens of millions of Americans will be subjected to sonic bombardment.

The doctrine of the United States is that whatever can be done must be done; otherwise, the United States will fall behind in the technological race. That is the thesis. Therefore, if the SST can be built, it must be built. This technological imperative is bolstered by dozens of irrelevant arguments in support of SST. It is said that other nations will gather the glory and profit and jobs resulting from SST manufacture. American manufacture of SST will help the balance of payments. These arguments are as popular as they are off the mark. Against them are many equally valid.

It has not occurred to many that the argument should be about the superiority of SST, all things considered, as a means of getting from here to there. It should be about the benefits to the thousands and the disbenefits to the millions. The pursuit of super-speed is being conducted by experts who might better be working to make present aviation super-safe. The socially necessary tasks to which these nimble minds might be turned are uncountable if we should take seriously the proposition that people must come first, machines second.

The deep irony is that we, the taxpayers, are paying for this unprecedented attack on ourselves. The unalterable fact is that the privacy and right to quiet of millions of Americans will shortly be sacrificed to an undertaking that thereby becomes fundamentally senseless. Their welfare goes down before the desires of a few hundred or thousand people who may ultimately be able to get from Los Angeles to New York in half the present time.

When SST proponents are asked to justify the assault on the bodies and minds of human beings, the customary answer is, "They'll get used to it." Some technologists, however, are more direct. Speaking of the sonic boom, Engineer Charles T. Leonard gives this prescription: "A greatly more tolerant populace than is presently assumed to be the case . . . may well become mandatory if the SST is to realize its full potential."

It may turn out this way: We may be compelled to become tolerant of every and all techniques—but at what human expense we may not appreciate for generations. Silicosis among miners was not discovered until long after they had become used to dust-laden mineshafts. Neurophysiologists warn that the growing din of modern life is already making us deaf, and ravaging sensibilities and nervous systems. This is part of the price already being exacted by technology; and with SST we are choosing, as a nation, to raise the price enormously.

"Choosing" is perhaps the wrong word, although authority for SST has been tentatively granted by Congress. And a silly Senate has recently authorized a further $143 million in development funds—at the exact time it was reducing expenditures on programs for people. But it is not a true choice, for reasons already given. Congress, lacking the understanding of the evils of technology because of the slackness of the intellectuals, merely has been swept along in the technological madness.

That public servants can act with good sense and foresight when informed about the impact of technology is illustrated by the City Council of Santa Barbara. Responding to incessant boombarding of that quiet city, the council recently passed an anti-boom ordinance.

In only one case, that of atomic energy, has this country had enough imagination about results to put a stiff bridle on technology. The Atomic Energy Commission came into being partly because of the lethal potentialities of the new force and partly because of a few leaders—mainly scientists—who were able to convince Congress that this cosmic threat should never be a military monopoly.

The ineffectuality of efforts toward smog control in the last twenty years is instructive. In the first few years, not enough was known to do anything about it. Air pollution was considered an unavoidable evil of modern life, as the ear pollution of the SST is now said to be by its proponents. For the last ten years the air pollution problem has been clearly identified, yet there is as much smog as ever, or more. Federal, state, county, and city governments all are working on the control of air pollution, so it is idle to say that public attention is lacking. We gain little yardage by declaiming against the automobile and petroleum interests, though assuredly their products are the main source of the garbage-laden air. Technology is the villain.

The fact that so much of the smog control effort is going into scrubbing the atmosphere obscures the real scope of the problem. For instance, Frank Stead, in *Cry California*, says that the way to deal with it is "to serve legal notice that after 1980 no gasoline-powered motor vehicles will be permitted to operate in California." So far, so good. The non-emission-producing automobile would be a clear gain for urban areas, and not only for California. At the moment, the automobile industry is making piteous sounds about giving up the gasoline engine, explaining week after week how costly and difficult it is going to be to produce a substitute.

Now, it is hard to think that a new kind of automobile is an insuperable technical challenge to a nation that can dock ships in space. Designing a fume-free car would seem a far more worthy objective for government research than placing a man on the moon or re-creating the deadly plague, another of our bloodiest technical preoccupations. Yet the absurdly small sums allocated for federal research in new motor car design show how serious we are about alternatives.

We must not, incidentally, be misled by the optimistic publicity now being emitted by auto and petroleum industry centers. The dean of smog-studiers, Professor A. J. Haagen-Smit of Caltech, says, "I have yet to see a smog control plan that gives me any confidence we will some day have reasonably clean air."

Mr. Stead says little about the larger question, that of the entire transportation technology. He has hold of a very sharp technical thorn, but it is only one of a large cluster. Suppose, for instance, a way were found to dissipate the atmospheric peculiarities that lead to air pollution. Replacing internal combustion by electricity may lower the incidence of emphysema and eye trouble. By itself, however, it will do nothing about the equally troubling questions of urban congestion and dedication of more and more land, rural and urban, to asphalt. Not a little of the furor in Watts arose from lack of inexpensive transportation to jobs and recreation. One will say, "What about rapid transit?" The answer is, yes, of course, but still that is not the resolution, as the situations of those cities with well-developed transit systems attest. Buses, subways, and commuter trains may only compound the misery, as any visitor to New York will be able to testify.

What is needed is a firm grasp on the technology itself, and an equally clear conviction of the primacy of men, women, and children in all the calculations. This is a resounding prescription, and I regret to admit that I am more clear about ultimate steps than I am about how to do what needs to be done in the near future.

I am convinced only that political institutions and theory developed in other times for other conditions offer little hope. We now have, by courtesy of the 89th U. S. Congress, a Department of Transportation whose task is, in the words of President Johnson, "to untangle, to coordinate, and to build the national transportation system that America is deserving of." Under what authority, and by what means?

The mind wanders to the lengths of asking what would happen if the new department might one day soon feel itself compelled to limit by fiat the manufacture of cars and trucks; to coerce car owners by tax or otherwise to use public transportation; to close state and city borders to visitors approaching by car; to tear up rather than to build freeways, garages, bridges, and tunnels.

I turn to my final example of technological invasion. American business executives a half dozen years ago wakened to the existence of a multibillion-dollar market—education. It was hard to ignore. Today's real growth industry is education. The $4 billion we spent on it at the end of World War II has grown to $50 billion plus—an annual rate of increase of more than 12 per cent. New corporate marriages have been hastily arranged. Large hardware companies wed large software companies. The object is profits, not education, although the public relations experts have got together on a prothalamion designed to convey the notion that these new matrimonial arrangements aim basically at the welfare of the educational enterprise, from the grade to the graduate schools. As always, the central claim is efficiency. Mass education, it is said, requires mass production methods. The result is already discernible, and may be called technication. The central image of technication is the student at the console of a computer.

Our educational purposes have never been very clear. Technication may compel removal of the ambiguities and establishment of straightforward aims. But who will undertake this task? How shall we assure that the result is the betterment of children and not the convenience of machines? Are we really all that crazy about efficiency, or what we are told is efficiency? Already, tests are being devised that can be applied and graded by machines, thereby getting the cart squarely in front of the horse. I am not pressing the panic button but the one next to it. I am not denying that certain advantages to education are offered by the new technology. I'm repeating that tonic and toxic technology are here mixed in unknown proportions.

The forces of technication are already infiltrating our grade schools, encountering little resistance. Once again we are in the area of narrow choices. How shall we distinguish between what helps and what hurts? I know that education has suffered from lack of research for years, and that much of what is projected may well modernize anachronistic practices. We have no standards as to what shall be admitted, what rejected. The temptations to rely unquestioningly on technology are very great. The possibilities that are said to be inherent in the new gadgetry are dazzling. We are told that the high costs of technication will bar widespread use for a long while. This is what was said of television in the early days.

The perils are manifest. One of them lies in adopting the totally wrong notion that an educational system can be thought of in terms like those of a factory for producing steel plate or buttons. Another peril is to that indefinable relation between teacher and taught: Dare we think of it as a mere holdover from another world, as subject to the junkpile as the horse-drawn fire engine has been? A third peril is that the ends of education, already a near-forgotten topic, will be gobbled up by the means.

Webster College President Jacqueline Grennan speaks for education, not technication, when she asks for the development "not of one voice of democracy but of the voices of democracy." The great need, she says, "is to enable an individual to find his own voice, to speak with it, to stand by it. . . . Learning is not essentially expository but essentially exploratory."

Technication means standardization. The history of factories shows the benefits and limits of standardization. Factories are fine for producing things, but their record with people is terrible. We cannot expect to hear the voices of democracy emerging from education factories; we can hear only the chorus. Technication, as Robert M. Hutchins observes, will "dehumanize a process the aim of which is humanization."

The effect on the taught is crucial. The rebellion at Berkeley centered on the indifference of multiversity's mechanism to the personal needs of the students. When the protesters pinned IBM cards to their jackets—an act duplicated on campuses throughout the land—they were declaring against impersonality and standardization; and it cannot be said too often that impersonality and standardization are the very hallmarks of technology.

I have offered not-very-penetrating illustrations of the way technology is raising conspicuous questions about the social and personal welfare of Americans. Behind all these matters, as I remarked at the outset, are dangerous convictions that science and technology provide the panacea for all ailments. It is curious that this conviction should be so widespread, for life today for most people appears to be more puzzling and unsatisfactory and beset with unresolved difficulties than ever before. For most people—but not, I suppose, for the scientists and technologists, the priesthood of the modern theology that is more and more ruling the land, and from whose ingenious devices and fateful decisions we must find a way to make effective appeal.

One must nevertheless be grateful to those few members of the sanhedrin who keep pointing out the dangers as the nation turns doubtful corners. Dr. Murray Gell-Mann of the California Institute of Technology says that "society must give new direction to technology, diverting it from applications that yield higher productive efficiency and into areas that yield greater human satisfaction. . . . Carl Kaysen of the Institute for Advanced

Studies at Princeton emphasizes that government institutions are no longer equal to the job of guiding the uses of technology.

Scientists and technologists are the indubitable agents of a new order. I wish to include the social scientists, for whose contributions to the technological puzzle I could find no space in this paper. Whether the political and social purpose of the nation ought to be set by these agents is the question. The answer to the question is no. We need to assign to their proper place the services of scientists and technologists. The sovereignty of the people must be reestablished. Rules must be written and regulations imposed. The writing must be done by statesmen and philosophers consciously intent on the general welfare, with the engineers and researchers summoned from their caves to help in the doing when they are needed.

How specifically to cope? How to regulate? Answers are beginning to filter through. Not many years ago it was considered regressive and ludditish even to suggest the need for control of technology. Now a general agreement is emerging that something must be done. But on what scale, and by whom?

E. J. Mishan, the British economist, calls for "amenity rights" to be vested in every person. He says, "Men [should] be invested by law with property rights in privacy, quiet, and clear air—simple things, but for many indispensable to the enjoyment of life." The burden would be on those offending against these amenities to drop or mend their practices, or pay damages to victims. Mishan's argument is scholarly and attractive, though scarcely spacious enough for the problems of a federal industrial state of the size of the United States. It does not seem likely that we can maintain our amenities by threat of tort suits against the manifold and mysterious agents, public and private, that are the "enemy."

The most comprehensive and thoughtful approach to the problem of regulation is that of U. S. Congressman Emilio Q. Daddario, chairman of the House Subcommittee of Science, Research, and Development. Representative Daddario starts with the necessity for "technological assessment," which he characterizes as urgent. It will amount to a persisting study of cause-effect relationships, alternatives, remedies. Representative Daddario does not speak of tonic and toxic, but of desirable, undesirable, and uncertain effects.

The subcommittee's study is only beginning, but it is based on some of the convictions that animated the writing of this article. Thus, the introduction to the first Congressional volume on technological assessment speaks of the dawning awareness of "the difficulties and dangers which applied science may carry in its genes" and of "the search for effective means to counter them."

It would be unfair to summarize the scope and method of this promising document in a sentence or two. I must leave it to those interested to look further into a first-rate beginning. It is too early to guess whether Congressman Daddario's group will come out where I do on this matter, but it seems unlikely. The subcommittee will probably come out for certain statutory additions to the present political organization as the proper way to turn back or harness technique's invading forces. There is ample precedent.

We can regard the panoply of administrative agencies and the corpus of administrative law as early efforts in this direction. They have not been very effective in directing technical development to the common good, although I do not wish to minimize the accomplishments of these agencies in other ways. Perhaps they have so far prevented technology from getting wholly out of hand. But it is very clear from examples like the communications satellites that our statutory means for containing technology are insufficient.

America is not so much an affluent as a technical society; this is the essence of the dilemma. The basic way to get at it, in my judgment, would be through a revision of the Constitution of the United States. If technology is indeed the main conundrum of American life, as the achieving of a more perfect union was the principal conundrum 175 years ago, it follows that the role and control of technology would have to be the chief preoccupation of the new founding fathers.

Up to now the attitude has been to keep hands off technological development until its effects are plainly menacing. Public authority usually has stepped in only after damage almost beyond repair has been done: in the form of ruined lakes, gummed-up rivers, spoilt cities and countrysides, armless and legless babies, psychic and physical damage to human beings beyond estimate. The measures that seem to me urgently needed to deal with the swiftly expanding repertoire of toxic technology go much further than I believe would be regarded as Constitutional.

What is required is not merely extensive police power to inhibit the technically disastrous, but legislative and administrative authority to *direct* technology in positive ways: the power to encourage as well as forbid, to slow down as well as speed up, to plan and initiate as well as to oversee developments that are now mainly determined by private forces for private advantage.

Others argue that I go too far in calling for wholesale revision of our basic charter. They may be right. Some of these critics believe that Constitutional amendment will do, and that what is needed is, in effect, reconsideration of the Bill of Rights, to see that it is stretched to cover the novel situations produced by technology. This is a persuasive approach, and I would be content as a starter to see how far Constitutional amendments might take us in protecting privacy and individual rights against the intrusions of technique.

But I also think that such an effort would soon disclose that technology is too vast, too pervasive to be dealt with in this way. The question is not only that of American rights, but of international relations as well, as Comsat illustrates. Technology is already tilting the fundamental relationships of government, and we are only in the early stages. A new and heavy factor has entered the old system of checks and balances. Thus, my perception of the situation is that the Constitution has become outdated by technical advance and deals awkwardly and insufficiently with technology's results.

Other critics tell me that we are sliding into anarchy, and that we must suffer through a historical period in which we will just "get over" our technological preoccupations. But I do not face the prospect of anarchy very readily.

So that my suggestion of fundamental Constitutional revision is not dismissed as merely a wild gasp of exasperation, I draw attention to the institutions dominating today's American scene which were not even dimly foreseen by the Founding Fathers. I refer to immense corporations and trade unions; media of communication that span continent and globe; political parties; a central government of stupendous size and worldshattering capabilities; and a very unJeffersonian kind of man at the center of it all.

It seems to me, in face of these novelties, that it is not necessarily madness to have a close look at our basic instrument in order to determine its ability to cope with these utterly new conditions, and especially with the overbearing novelty of technique. Technology touches the person and the common life more intimately and often than does any government, federal or local; yet it is against the aggrandizement of government that we are constantly warned. Technology's scope and penetration places in the hands of its administrators gigantic capabilities for arbitrary power. It was this kind of power the Founding Fathers sought to diffuse and attenuate.

Constitutional direction of technology would mean planning on a scale and scope that is hard now to imagine. Planning means taking account, insofar as possible, of the possibilities of technique for welfare. It means working toward an integrated system, a brand-new idea in this nation.

I recognize all the dangers in these suggestions. But leaving technology to its own devices or to the selfish attentions of particular groups is a far more hazardous course. For it must not be forgotten that the enormous proliferation of technology is today being planned by private hands that lack the legitimacy to affect the commonwealth in such profound measure.

The wholesale banning of certain techniques becomes absolutely necessary when technical development can no longer help but only harm the human condition. Scientists Jerome Wiesner and Herbert York exemplify this dictum in its most excruciating aspect when they say:

Both sides in the arms race are ... confronted by the dilemma of steadily increasing military power and steadily decreasing national security. It is our considered professional judgment that this *dilemma has no technical solution. ... If the great powers continue to look for solutions in the area of science and technology only, the result will be to worsen the situation.*

Though many lives are being wrecked, though the irrationality and human uselessness of much new technology is steadily becoming more evident, we are not yet over the edge. I close with Robert L. Heilbroner's estimate of the time available:

... the coming generation will be the last generation to seize control over technology before technology has irreversibly seized control over it. A generation is not much time, but it is some *time. ...*

Sakharov: Soviet Physicist Appeals for
Bold Initiatives

Louise Campbell

In a 10,000-word essay, circulated and discussed in Soviet scientific-intellectual circles, a nuclear physicist who helped develop the Soviet H-bomb has urged "peaceful coexistence and intellectual freedom" while the two main world powers use the "scientific method . . . deep analysis of facts . . . unfearing open discussion and conclusions" to deal with the "great possibilities and dangers linked with the scientific-technical revolution."

In his belief that the method of science can avert thermonuclear war, famine in the poor countries, and environmental pollution in the advanced ones, Academician Andrei Dmitrievich Sakharov joins many other eminent scientists in both the United States and the U. S. S. R. who have been seeking this objective outside official channels. But Sakharov goes farther than any other influential spokesman in either country in advancing an explicit and detailed proposal for rapprochement and cooperation between the two countries and in taking a bold look at the "mass myths that put entire peoples and continents under the power of cruel and treacherous demagogues." The statement is without precedent from a man of his rank in Soviet life.

The gist of Sakharov's essay was first reported by the New York *Time's* Moscow correspondent, Raymond Anderson, on 12 July. Anderson later was able to send a complete copy to the *Times*, which translated and printed the essay in full, using three pages in the 22 July edition.

While reflecting a deep commitment to Marxism and socialism in the classic sense, Sakharov says that "both capitalism and socialism are capable of long-term development, borrowing positive elements from each other and actually coming closer to each other in a number of essential aspects." To accelerate what he calls an "inevitable convergence," Sakharov urges the two world powers to disarm and join together to avert world catastrophe by applying one-fifth of their national incomes to development of the poorer half of the world. To this end, both nations must abandon "extremist ideologies that reject

Louise Campbell, "Sakharov: Soviet Physicist Appeals for Bold Initiatives, "*Science*, 9 August 1968, Volume 161, pp. 556-558. Copyright 1968 by the American Association for the Advancement of Science. Reprinted by permission of the publisher. Mrs. Campbell is a former staff member of AAAS.

all possibility of rapprochement, discussion and compromise." Both must make "significant changes in their foreign and domestic policies."

The United States, Sakharov says, must accept a "serious decline in the United States rate of economic growth" in order to support "worldwide efforts to change the level of living of billions of people," and must be "willing to do this ... for the sake of preserving civilization and mankind on our planet." White citizens of the United States must accept "minimum sacrifices to eliminate the unequal economic and cultural position of the country's black citizens."

Sakharov concentrates much of his discussion on changes in Soviet society that he believes necessary to consolidate the achievements of socialism. The chief of these is development toward "intellectual freedom ... essential for human society" and the "key to a progressive restructuring of the system of government in the interests of mankind."

At a time of grave official Soviet concern over liberalizing trends in Czechoslovakia, Sakharov's eloquent plea for intellectual freedom may reflect a rising attitude among Soviet professionals. Sakharov says that the Czechoslovaks understand the essential nature of intellectual freedom. "We should support their bold initiative, which is so valuable for the future of socialism and all mankind. That support should be political and, in the early stages, include increased economic aid."

Some Western observers suggest that facing the Kremlin is the blunt fact that the massive and still unevenly developed Soviet society cannot cope with change at the Czech pace. Nevertheless, one of the foremost Soviet experts in the U.S. said that the "fact that a top Soviet scientist can write along these lines, addressing fundamental issues in fearless terms, reflects great credit to the U.S.S.R. and is evidence of the basic strength of Soviet society."

Top U.S. scientists, some of whom have participated in the Pugwash conferences in which American and Russian scientists have met for discussion since 1961, reflected the same view. Paul Doty, Harvard physical chemist, member of the National Academy of Sciences, and a former member of the President's Science Advisory Committee, said: "It adds prestige to Soviet society that such idealism and objectivity are being brought to bear on major problems." Referring to Sakharov's detailed discussion of the "10 to 15 million deaths" and other results of 24 years of Stalinism, Doty, who has made many trips to the U.S.S.R. since 1960 on both official and nonofficial missions, said: "The extent to which Sakharov discusses Stalinism reflects the extent to which the damage of these years is still a problem in Soviet society. Just as generations were needed in the U.S. to deal with the residual damage of our Civil War, so prolonged efforts will be needed to deal with the consequences of the Stalinist period in Soviet society. The Sakharov text may signal a healthy departure from the main way of dealing with the Stalinist experience in the U.S.S.R.—that is, not talking about it."

Jerome Wiesner, M.I.T. physicist, head of the President's Science Advisory Committee in the Kennedy administration, and member of the National

Academy of Sciences, who visits the U.S.S.R. once a year with the hope of finding common ground with Soviet scientists for action along the lines suggested by Sakharov, said: "Sakharov's essay is a statement that I would be proud to have written. It is addressed to our government as well as to that of the U.S.S.R.—in fact, to all governments of the world."

"Sakharov's statement is tremendously interesting," said Polykarp Kusch, the Columbia physicist who won the Nobel prize for measurement of the electron dipole moment, work that laid the foundation for quantum electrodynamics. "That a man of this scientific stature has circulated such a statement without going through the machinery of the political apparatus is new evidence of how much the views of the scientific community are being respected. It suggests a new Russian style; it is inconceivable to me that this could have happened a few years ago."

Gerard Piel, publisher of the *Scientific American*, another frequent visitor to the U.S.S.R. and participant in the Pugwash conferences, said: "The Sakharov article is another expression of the honesty and sense of personal responsibility that scientists of this rank have. It is part of a sequence of events suggesting that scientists of stature have indeed gotten closer to the center in this kind of decision making on both sides of the Iron Curtain."

Said Edward Teller, Lawrence Radiation Laboratory physicist, chief developer of the H-bomb in the United States, and member of the National Academy: "I like what Sakharov says about freedom. I can't agree with the emphasis he places on socialism as the best form of economic structure. In many places he sounds a little naive but if I were to go into detail on politics I would sound naive."

A major part of Sakharov's essay is discussion of "three technical aspects of thermonuclear weapons that have made thermonuclear war a peril to the very existence of humanity." This discussion, which parallels many published statements by U.S. physicists who shared in the development of fission and fusion weapons, describes the "enormous destructive power of a thermonuclear explosion, the relative cheapness of rocket-thermonuclear weapons and the practical impossibility of an effective defense against a massive rocket-nuclear attack."

In support of this last point, Sakharov mentions an article written by Nobel laureate Hans Bethe and Richard L. Garwin, director of applied research at IBM's Thomas J. Watson Research Center, and published in the March 1968 *Scientific American*. The article, "Anti-Ballistic-Missile Systems," argues that fairly cheap penetration methods can make such intercontinental nuclear weapons ineffective.

"I was directing my remarks as much at the Russians as at the U.S.," Bethe said. "Whether the article influenced the Russian government, I think I will never know."

Bethe, who won the Nobel prize for contributions to the theory of nuclear reactions, has also worked for 10 years on the problem of antiballistic missiles for the Abco Missiles System, Wilmington, Massachusetts. Some observers believe that the effect of the Bethe-Garwin article on scientists in both countries had a role in the U.S.–Soviet agreement to discuss offensive and defensive missile systems, announced by President Johnson on 1 July.

The Bethe-Garwin view is supported by Herbert York, chairman of the department of physics of the University of California, former head of Lawrence Radiation Laboratory, and top scientist in the Defense Department during both the Eisenhower and Kennedy administrations. York told *Science*, "I think I know enough about military technology to know there isn't any safety in an anti-missile system. This problem doesn't have a technological fix; solutions must be sought along political lines."

Only meager facts about Sakharov are available here; of the many eminent physicists reached by *Science* who travel regularly to the Soviet Union, only Wiesner remembers meeting him, quite briefly at a reception at the Soviet Academy. At 47, Sakharov has spent all his life under Communism and more than half of it under the Stalinist system. A U.S. source describes him as having presented the most brilliant thesis ever offered in physics at Moscow University, work done early in World War II under the late I. V. Kurchatov, father of the Soviet H-bomb. He won the Order of Lenin and the Stalin prize in 1948.

In 1950 Sakharov, with Igor E. Tamm, who won the Nobel prize for elucidation of the theory of the Cerenkov effect, proposed a model for controlled nuclear fusion reactions that helped set the direction of most of the current research in this field. The model outlined how a magnetic field could be used to confine a plasma of bare nuclei and electrons, brought to the kindling temperature for nuclear fusion of above 100 million degrees Kelvin. Similar proposals were made by scientists in other countries and to date magnetic-confinement seems the most effective way to meet the principal problem in controlled nuclear fusion: how to prevent the charged particles of the plasma from striking the walls of a solid-state container.

In a 1958 paper in the Soviet *Journal of Atomic Energy* Sakharov estimated the amount of genetic damage resulting from "nuclear tests already performed" and said that "continued testing ... cannot be reconciled with humanity or international law."

In a recent paper, Sakharov describes several systems he has designed for using explosives to raise a magnetic field to megagauss intensity. C. W. Fowler of the Lawrence Radiation Laboratory at Los Alamos, New Mexico, published a similar method in 1960. Other teams in this country and in Italy are trying to apply the method to plasma confinement. Sakharov believes the explosive method for reaching megagauss magnetic fields may ultimately be applied to particle accelerators, producing acceleration up to 100 Bev (the Weston accelerator now being built reaches 200 Bev).

Sakharov's nonappearance abroad may be due as much to his extraordinary scientific value (he was, for example, elected to the Soviet Academy of Sciences at age 32, without having gone through the route of "corresponding member," a rank at which his senior colleague, Tamm, stayed for 20 years) as to his political maverickism, although there is plenty of that. He vigorously opposed the genetic theories publicized by Lysenko. With other Soviet physicists, he petitioned Party chief Leonid I. Brezhnev to oppose a rumored restoration of Stalin's status. Later he joined in a petition opposing a new law making unauthorized demonstrations a crime.

Sakharov's quality as a scientist gives him a privileged position shared by few others, even in the elite intellectual community, and makes his plain speaking possible. Many governments, including our own, have found it not possible to limit the wide-ranging mind of the theoretical physicist.

Do these top minds speak also for the majority of scientists in the two countries? Says Doty, who knows both: "Some share the world view but perhaps the majority still put their interest and actions into short-range or tactical problems."

Altering the Direction of Technology

Robert Jungk

One of the most significant and—at least for many older observers—surprising aspects of the recent student upheavals was the strong criticism levelled at the technological aspects of modern society. On the walls of Paris you could read:

> DEATH TO THE TECHNOCRATS or
> NO TO THE CONSUMER SOCIETY or
> HE WHO PRODUCES MORE LIVES LESS or
> DOWN WITH THE TECHNOLOGY OF EXTERMINATION.

As these slogans suggest, the students' disenchantment with technology is something quite different from the anti-technological ideologies of romantic or

Robert Jungk, "Altering the Direction of Technology." Reprinted by permission of the author. Jungk works with the Institut für Zukunftsfragen (Institute of Questions about the Future), Berlin.

outright reactionary forces of the recent past, which, by attacking "the machine" were really aiming at the scientific and rational foundations of the industrial revolution. This difference was made quite clear by Herbert Marcuse, whose ideas have sparked student leaders in Paris, Berlin, London and Rome. He has not tried to revive the "Luddite" movement, as some commentators have suggested, but has urged his readers to alter the direction of technical progress—that is, to develop a new technology, for the established technology has become an instrument "of destructive politics."

How would such a "new technology" look? What would be its aims, its shape, its functions? On this point, neither Marcuse nor any of the other penetrating analysts of modern technological developments, such as Lewis Mumford or Günther Anders, offer us more than generalities. "The Good Life," "The Good Society," "Permanent Peace," "Pacified Existence"—these are all general concepts which until now have not been given any specific content. Nor have these goals been translated into social action by suggesting possible strategies to achieve them.

How Decisions Are Made

This gap between goals and strategies will soon have to be bridged because, today, decisions are no longer made in parliaments or other democratic assemblies. Plans are formulated in such new institutions as "Think Factories," "Prognostic Cells," and "Research and Development Departments." Groups of experts form interdisciplinary teams which can draw upon large information banks and other sources of data and try (in the words of Dennis Gabor) to "invent the future." Their analyses and proposals are then handed over to the political or industrial power elites, who base their decisions upon them.

Such brain trusts—to use an earlier and more familiar term—now exist in the back rooms of almost all national and international executive branches in the political and industrial spheres. They were first developed by military staffs who had to design weapons and strategies for the future, and they never really lost that special birth-mark when first large corporations and then governments copied their quite successful methods.

These developments behind the scenes are largely unknown to the citizens, to the "common men" of the world, who still believe that they take part, or may take part, in the decision-making processes. In fact, we are usually asked to approve decisions which have already been made or, at best, are allowed to disapprove of them. We must realize who makes the technological decisions today and begin to grasp that technology can no longer be seen as a neutral force but must be seen as one which is dependent on political and economic power groups whose concepts of "things to come" largely *preempt* the future and shape the world of tomorrow before the young, who will have to live in that world, can have any say in these decisions.

We are saddled with today's largely inhuman and anti-human technology because it was invented, designed and developed largely for non-human or even anti-human ends. Tomorrow's technology, which is already on the drawing boards, will not be much better because it too was created mainly with economic, political and military power in mind. That is the reason why we will have ever more perfect weapons in a world of imperfect housing and growing traffic snarls, why our industrial apparatus will continue to produce millions of neat, shiny consumer articles to be used in an environment which every year gets dirtier and more unhealthy because of the pollution of industrial waste.

Such deterioration and misuse of technology has to be fought at its origins. We will continue to accept or to strike out against a world of more rockets and bombs, of more goods designed for early obsolescence, unless we finally create *our own* "future creating" institutions dedicated to the invention and design of more desirable, more human, more democratic futures. I hope that the student movement, to a greater extent than any other force in our time, may become responsible for such future creating workshops whose task it will be to "alter the direction of technical progress." But the necessary transformation of society in an age of scientific and industrial revolution cannot be achieved by fighting rearguard actions which are lost in advance. The student movement must exercise more and more influence upon the processes of anticipation and planning.

In order to do this, we will have to mobilize a force which has been greatly neglected: imagination, and especially social imagination, making it work within *and* beyond a framework of ever-flowing information and permanent analysis.

The Geometrical Progress of Technology

Looking back into the history of technology—if we relate its development to the scope of its effects—we can see three quite distinct stages. This can be most clearly illustrated by weapons technology, which has from the beginning played a pioneering role in this field. The first stage is characterized by weapons made to be aimed at one person, such as the bow and arrow or later the gun and bullet. The second stage creates weapons which can kill several people at once. It starts with the cannon ball and ends with what are now called conventional bombs which are dropped from planes. The third phase began when the first two atom bombs were exploded over Hiroshima and Nagasaki at the end of World War II. The target was no longer a relatively small group of people; it was a whole city with hundreds of thousands of inhabitants. And speaking of anticipation, the next stage will make it possible to choose a large area, whole provinces, even whole countries, as the possible victims of a single obliterating attack.

Such a geometrical increase is, in effect, typical of almost all aspects of technological development. From the invention of individual "protheses," it grows to the creation of apparatus, which changes the lives first of dozens, then hundreds, then thousands and millions of people. And as the different machines tend to tie into each other, the planet becomes more and more entangled in an ever more tightly woven complex of interdependent machinery.

The consequences of technology began to concern society from the moment when technology began to transcend its limited individual impact and to shape and change the destiny of large collectivities and finally even the fate of mankind as a whole. The fact that numerically small intellectual and technical *élites*, serving the private interest of even smaller power groups, have been free to direct this growing force without strong and decisive control by the millions (or their representatives) who have to bear and suffer its immense impact, accounts for the authoritarian features and centralized nature of modern technology. Machines were a welcome substitute for slaves in an age which had done away with that kind of servitude. But by accepting the more subtle aspects of the relationship between industry and the workers *serving* it, we have really become technology's servants rather than its masters.

If authoritarian power—perfectly symbolized by the button you have only to press in order to unleash all kinds of powerful mechanisms—is one distinctive feature of technology, the efficiency, which in turn depends on economic rentability, is another. An efficient machine would not waste any time or material but would, at least in principle, do what it was built to do in the most economical way possible.

Alternative Futures

The amazing thing is that this kind of technology has increasingly been thought of as the only one possible. A hypothetical machine built upon the principle of division of power was quite inconceivable even in societies whose political system was constructed, at least in theory, on precisely such lines. A deliberately wasteful or slow engine—what nonsense! A piece of apparatus constructed for aesthetic rather than utilitarian purposes—have you ever heard of such a silly idea? Yet do not such expressions of derision and outrage merely illustrate the narrowness of our vision? After all, man has the power to shape things according to his wishes and even his whims. Why should he not be able to think of machines which produce nothing tangible and immediately useful? Why should he not tinker with nuts and bolts and wires and circuits in order to create a piece of art? In fact, such seemingly crazy projects have already been undertaken in our age. The immense particle accelerators, the biggest of all existing machines, with circumferences of hundreds of meters up to several kilometers, produce, at a cost of millions of dollars per year, not a single useful consumable article. They are scientific instruments dedicated to the search for truth. And artists like Schoeffer, Tinguely or Rauschenberg have built strange machines which produce only surprises, aesthetic impressions, and emotional shocks.

A desirable future technology will probably be directed more and more to non-profitable (at least not immediately and privately profitable) goals such as:

—*a technology to control the effects of technology, which would filter smoke and other effluents, deaden noise, or make it possible to hide under the ground a*

*large part of the machinery now impinging upon the beauty of landscapes and
cityscapes;*

*—a less conspicuous technology of deliberately smaller measurements closer
to the human scale;*

—a safer and healthier technology (for production, transportation, and so on);

*—a technology able to put out smaller and more varied products in order to
break the monotony of modern goods;*

—a technology dedicated to easier and more individualized communication;

—a more flexible and varied building technology;

—a vastly improved food technology;

—a universally accessible information technology;

*—a technology which might make decentralized government possible without
the loss of all the advantages of centralization;*

—a technology for controlling disarmament.

This list could be much longer, and in fact it will soon become much longer,
when future creating workshops dedicated to the invention and design of futures
made *for* man and not against him get to work.

A Model Project

A prototype of such a future creating workshop was the study on the
"Glideway System," run a couple of years ago by Assistant Dean William Seifert
of the Massachussetts Institute of Technology and his students. The workshop
started its work because it wanted to answer the challenge of an anticipated
crisis. An interdisciplinary team analyzed the nature of the challenge; it
developed models to cope with the challenge; and it finally presented the best
model to a wider public.

The challenge was the situation of transportation in the so-called northwest
corridor of the United States during the second half of the seventies. In this
densely urbanized area, which will soon have a population of fifty million,
stretching from Boston via New York to Washington, the conditions of
transportation are rapidly moving towards the crisis point, when the flow of
private cars and the movement on airlanes and over airports will result in ever
greater traffic jams. To prevent such a foreseeable collapse of the transportation
network, a new, fast, and convenient public transportation system had been
proposed as early as 1962, and again in the presidential message in January,
1965. But little action had followed these warnings given by experts and
seconded by the highest executive office in the country.

By carrying out a detailed project study of an original mass transportation
system—the "Glideway System"—the students, assisted by eminent experts in
the various relevant fields, acted as a stopgap for government and industry. The
work produced was later hailed as a model of imaginative and inspiring effort,
rich in data and worthy of being taken up by a society which at the present time
wastes its considerable scientific and technical skills on senseless wars and

expensive prestige projects such as the risky and unnecessary operation aimed at being the first nation to reach the moon.

In building their "Castle in the Air" (or, to be more accurate, their "Castle on Printing Paper"), the students learned a number of extremely important things: First, they had to do a thorough "interdisciplinary system study," developing a sensitivity to the complexity of modern technology when applied to larger societal goals. Secondly, they had to think about needs for at least a decade ahead rather than in the usual narrower time scheme, causing them to realize that the anticipation, design, and planning of future projects had to start as soon as possible—right now! This must have opened their eyes to the restrictions put upon vitally important tasks by an economic system which feels that private profits are more important than public functions. The fact that two years after the completion of the study no real move has been made to solve a problem which will become a major headache a few years from now is for them and many others concrete evidence of the "future blindness" and wrong order of priorities prevailing in the USA.

The Possibilities for Student Creativity

If student groups all over the world would answer the social challenges of their present, and even more of their future, by cooperating on similar projects, inventing desirable alternative futures to the present situation, they would be able to put quite clearly before public opinion not only what is being neglected at present in their countries and the world as a whole but would also be able to indicate the exciting possibilities which lie ahead. It is no longer sufficient to say, "If we did not spend our money on arms, we could spend it on schools and hospitals." It is necessary to spell out such demands in greater detail, in exact plans, in concrete anticipations, which will fire the imagination of the people.

But this is only the first step. The next one would be to involve representatives of different classes and professions in such future creating workshops, because only if the citizen can again be drawn into the process of creating future public projects and laws will he regain his interest in politics. Democratic participation has to start as early as possible if we hope to avoid the establishment of new oligarchies in the form of committees run by experts.

I foresee that these future creating workshops will increasingly move from the development of concrete projects for better and more human tomorrows to debates about ultimate goals and meanings. Because of the success of technology—the fact that man can invent and build almost anything he puts his mind and his means to—technology is now less interesting than before; so the really difficult problems are no longer the technical, but the social and philosophical ones. As we begin to exert human and social control over our anarchic and runaway technology, we will again ask ourselves: Where do we go now? What is the meaning of our existence? Here I feel that Christians of the modern type, who know about social and political dynamics as well as about science and technology, will be able to add an important dimension to the never-ending debate about the reasons and aims of human existence. Christian students should not feel inferior because, beyond the most important and urgent questions of hunger and strife, they also dare to cast their thoughts to the non-material problems of man, to the problems of his destiny as a spiritual being. The advice of Christians will be greatly needed by the society of tomorrow, whose problems have already begun to take form and substance today.

What We Must Do

John Platt

There is only one crisis in the world. It is the crisis of transformation. The trouble is that it is now coming upon us as a storm of crisis problems from every direction. But if we look quantitatively at the course of our changes in this century, we can see immediately why the problems are building up so rapidly at this time, and we will see that it has now become urgent for us to mobilize all our intelligence to solve these problems if we are to keep from killing ourselves in the next few years.

The essence of the matter is that the human race is on a steeply rising "S-Curve" of change. We are undergoing a great historical transition to new levels of technological power all over the world. We all know about these changes, but we do not often stop to realize how large they are in orders of magnitude, or how rapid and enormous compared to all previous changes in history. In the last century, we have increased our speeds of communication by a factor of 10^7; our speeds of travel by 10^2; our speeds of data handling by 10^6; our energy resources by 10^3; our power of weapons by 10^6; our ability to control diseases by something like 10^2; and our rate of population growth to 10^3 times what it was a few thousand years ago.

John Platt, "What We Must Do," *Science*, 28 November 1969, Vol. 166, pp. 1115-1121. Copyright 1969 by the American Association for the Advancement of Science. Reprinted by permission of the author and publisher. The author is a research biophysicist and associate director of the Mental Health Research Institute at the University of Michigan, Ann Arbor 48104.

Could anyone suppose that human relations around the world would not be affected to their very roots by such changes? Within the last 25 years, the Western world has moved into an age of jet planes, missiles and satellites, nuclear power and nuclear terror. We have acquired computers and automation, a service and leisure economy, superhighways, superagriculture, supermedicine, mass higher education, universal TV, oral contraceptives, environmental pollution, and urban crises. The rest of the world is also moving rapidly and may catch up with all these powers and problems within a very short time. It is hardly surprising that young people under 30, who have grown up familiar with these things from childhood, have developed very different expectations and concerns from the older generation that grew up in another world.

What many people do not realize is that many of these technological changes are now approaching certain natural limits. The "S-curve" is beginning to level off. We may never have faster communications or more TV or larger weapons or a higher level of danger than we have now. This means that if we could learn how to manage these new powers and problems in the next few years without killing ourselves by our obsolete structures and behavior, we might be able to create new and more effective social structures that would last for many generations. We might be able to move into that new world of abundance and diversity and well-being for all mankind which technology has now made possible.

The trouble is that we may not survive these next few years. The human race today is like a rocket on a launching pad. We have been building up to this moment of takeoff for a long time, and if we can get safely through the takeoff period, we may fly on a new and exciting course for a long time to come. But at this moment, as the powerful new engines are fired, their thrust and roar shakes and stresses every part of the ship and may cause the whole thing to blow up before we can steer it on its way. Our problem today is to harness and direct these tremendous new forces through this dangerous transition period to the new world instead of to destruction. But unless we can do this, the rapidly increasing strains and crises of the next decade may kill us all. They will make the last 20 years look like a peaceful interlude.

The Next 10 Years

Several types of crisis may reach the point of explosion in the next 10 years: nuclear escalation, famine, participatory crises, racial crises, and what have been called the crises of administrative legitimacy. It is worth singling out two or three of these to see how imminent and dangerous they are, so that we can fully realize how very little time we have for preventing or controlling them.

Take the problem of nuclear war, for example. A few years ago, Leo Szilard estimated the "half-life" of the human race with respect to nuclear escalation as being between 10 and 20 years. His reasoning then is still valid now. As long as we continue to have no adequate stabilizing peace-keeping structures for the world, we continue to live under the daily threat not only of local wars but of nuclear escalation with overkill and megatonnage enough to destroy all life on earth. Every year or two there is a confrontation between nuclear powers—Korea, Laos, Berlin, Suez, Quemoy, Cuba, Vietnam, and the rest. MacArthur wanted to use nuclear weapons in Korea; and in the Cuban missile crisis, John Kennedy is said to have estimated the probability of a nuclear exchange as about 25 percent.

The danger is not so much that of the unexpected, such as a radar error or even a new nuclear dictator, as it is that our present systems will work exactly as planned!—from border testing, strategic gambles, threat and counterthreat, all the way up to that "second-strike capability" that is already aimed, armed, and triggered to wipe out hundreds of millions of people in a 3-hour duel!

What is the probability of this in the average incident? 10 percent? 5 percent? There is no average incident. But it is easy to see that five or ten more such confrontations in this game of "nuclear roulette" might indeed give us only a 50-50 chance of living until 1980 or 1990. This is a shorter life expectancy than people have ever had in the world before. All our medical increases in length of life are meaningless, as long as our nuclear lifetime is so short.

Many agricultural experts also think that within this next decade the great famines will begin, with deaths that may reach 100 million people in densely populated countries like India and China. Some contradict this, claiming that the remarkable new grains and new agricultural methods introduced in the last 3 years in Southeast Asia may now be able to keep the food supply ahead of population growth. But others think that the reeducation of farmers and consumers to use the new grains cannot proceed fast enough to make a difference.

But if famine does come, it is clear that it will be catastrophic. Besides the direct human suffering, it will further increase our international instabilities, with food riots, troops called out, governments falling, and international interventions that will change the whole political map of the world. It could make Vietnam look like a popgun.

In addition, the next decade is likely to see continued crises of legitimacy of all our overloaded administrations, from universities and unions to cities and national governments. Everywhere there is protest and refusal to accept the solutions handed down by some central elite. The student revolutions circle the globe. Suburbs protest as well as ghettoes, Right as well as Left. There are many new sources of collision and protest, but it is clear that the general problem is in large part structural rather than political. Our traditional methods of election and management no longer give administrations the skill and capacity they need to handle their complex new burdens and decisions. They become swollen, unresponsive—and repudiated. Every day now some distinguished administrator is pressured out of office by protesting constituents.

In spite of the violence of some of these confrontations, this may seem like a trivial problem compared to war or famine—until we realize the dangerous effects of these instabilities on the stability of the whole system. In a nuclear crisis or in any of our other crises today, administrators or negotiators may often work out some basis of agreement between conflicting groups or nations, only to find themselves rejected by their people on one or both sides, who are then left with no mechanism except to escalate their battles further.

The Crisis of Crises

What finally makes all of our crises still more dangerous is that they are now coming on top of each other. Most administrations are able to endure or even enjoy an occasional crisis, with everyone working late together and getting a new sense of importance and unity. What they are not prepared to deal with are multiple crises, a crisis of crises all at one time. This is what happened in New York City in 1968 when the Ocean Hill-Brownsville teacher and race strike was combined with a police strike, on top of a garbage strike, on top of a longshoremen's strike, all within a few days of each other.

When something like this happens, the staffs get jumpy with smoke and coffee and alcohol, the mediators become exhausted, and the administrators find themselves running two crises behind. Every problem may escalate because those involved no longer have time to think straight. What would have happened in the Cuban missile crisis if the East Coast power blackout had occurred by accident that same day? Or if the "hot line" between Washington and Moscow had gone dead? There might have been hours of misinterpretation, and some fatally different decisions.

I think this multiplication of domestic and international crises today will shorten that short half-life. In the continued absence of better ways of heading off these multiple crises, our half-life may no longer be 10 or 20 years, but more like 5 to 10 years, or less. We may have even less than a 50-50 chance of living until 1980.

This statement may seem uncertain and excessively dramatic. But is there any scientist who would make a much more optimistic estimate after considering all the different sources of danger and how they are increasing? The shortness of the time is due to the exponential and multiplying character of our problems and not to what particular numbers or guesses we put in. Anyone who feels more hopeful about getting past the nightmares of the 1970's has only to look beyond them to the monsters of pollution and population rising up in the 1980's and 1990's. Whether we have 10 years or more like 20 or 30, unless we systematically find new large-scale solutions, we are in the gravest danger of destroying our society, our world, and ourselves in any of a number of different ways well before the end of this century. Many futurologists who have predicted what the world will be like in the year 2000 have neglected to tell us that.

Nevertheless the real reason for trying to make rational estimates of these deadlines is not because of their shock value but because they give us at least a rough idea of how much time we may have for finding and mounting some large-scale solutions. The time is short but, as we shall see, it is not too short to give us a chance that something can be done, if we begin immediately.

From this point, there is no place to go but up. Human predictions are always conditional. The future always depends on what we do and can be made worse or better by stupid or intelligent action. To change our earlier analogy, today we are like men coming out of a coal mine who suddenly begin to hear the rock rumbling, but who have also begun to see a little square of light at the end of the tunnel. Against this background, I am an optimist—in that I want to insist that there is a square of light and that it is worth trying to get to. I think what we must do is to start running as fast as possible toward that light, working to increase the probability of our survival through the next decade by some measurable amount.

For the light at the end of the tunnel is very bright indeed. If we can only devise new mechanisms to help us survive this round of terrible crises, we have a chance of moving into a new world of incredible potentialities for all mankind. But if we cannot get through this next decade, we may never reach it.

Task Forces for Social Research and Development

What can we do? I think that nothing less than the application of the full intelligence of our society is likely to be adequate. These problems will require the humane and constructive efforts of everyone involved. But I think they will also require something very similar to the mobilization of scientists for solving crisis problems in wartime. I believe we are going to need large numbers of scientists forming something like research teams or task forces for social research and development. We need full-time interdisciplinary teams combining men of different specialties, natural scientists, social scientists, doctors, engineers, teachers, lawyers, and many other trained and inventive minds, who can put together our stores of knowledge and powerful new ideas into improved technical methods, organizational designs, or "social inventions" that have a chance of being adopted soon enough and widely enough to be effective. Even a great mobilization of scientists may not be enough. There is no guarantee that these problems can be solved, or solved in time, no matter what we do. But for problems of this scale and urgency, this kind of focusing of our brains and knowledge may be the only chance we have.

Scientists, of course, are not the only ones who can make contributions. Millions of citizens, business and labor leaders, city and government officials, and workers in existing agencies, are already doing all they can to solve these problems. No scientific innovation will be effective without extensive advice and help from all these groups.

But it is the new science and technology that have made our problems so immense and intractable. Technology did not create human conflicts and inequities, but it has made them unendurable. And where science and technology have expanded the problems in this way, it may be only more scientific understanding and better technology that can carry us past them. The cure for the pollution of the rivers by detergents is the use of nonpolluting detergents. The cure for bad management designs is better management designs.

Also, in many of these areas, there are few people outside the research community who have the basic knowledge necessary for radically new solutions. In our great biological problems, it is the new ideas from cell biology and ecology that may be crucial. In our social-organizational problems, it may be the new theories of organization and management and behavior theory and game theory that offer the only hope. Scientific research and development groups of some kind may be the only effective mechanism by which many of these new ideas can be converted into practical invention and action.

The time scale on which such task forces would have to operate is very different from what is usual in science. In the past, most scientists have tended to work on something like a 30-year time scale, hoping that their careful studies would fit into some great intellectual synthesis that might be years away. Of course when they become politically concerned, they begin to work on something more like a 3-month time scale, collecting signatures or trying to persuade the government to start or stop some program.

But 30 years is too long, and 3 months is too short, to cope with the major crises that might destroy us in the next 10 years. Our urgent problems now are more like wartime problems, where we need to work as rapidly as is consistent with large-scale effectiveness. We need to think rather in terms of a 3-year time scale—or more broadly, a 1- to 5-year time scale. In World War II, the ten thousand scientists who were mobilized for war research knew they did not have 30 years, or even 10 years, to come up with answers. But they did have time for the new research, design, and construction that brought sonar and radar and atomic energy to operational effectiveness within 1 to 4 years. Today we need the same large-scale mobilization for innovation and action and the same sense of constructive urgency.

Priorities: A Crisis Intensity Chart

In any such enterprise, it is most important to be clear about which problems are the real priority problems. To get this straight, it is valuable to try to separate the different problem areas according to some measures of their magnitude and urgency. A possible classification of this kind is shown in Tables 1 and 2. In these tables, I have tried to rank a number of present or potential problems or crises, vertically, according to an estimate of their order of intensity or "seriousness," and horizontally, by a rough estimate of their time to reach climactic importance. Table 1 is such a classification for the United States for the next 1 to 5 years, the next 5 to 20 years, and the next 20 to 50 years. Table 2 is a similar classification for world problems and crises.

The successive rows indicate something like order-of-magnitude differences in the intensity of the crises, as estimated by a rough product of the size of population that might be hurt or affected, multiplied by some estimated average effect in the disruption of their lives. Thus the first row corresponds to total or near-total annihilation; the second row, to great destruction or change affecting

Table 1. Classification of problems and crises by
estimated time and intensity (United States).

Grade	Estimated crisis intensity (number affected × degree of effect)		Estimated time to crisis*		
			1 to 5 years	5 to 20 years	20 to 50 years
1		Total annihilation	Nuclear or RCBW escalation	Nuclear or RCBW escalation	★(Solved or dead)
2	10^8	Great destruction or change (physical, biological, or political)	(Too soon)	Participatory democracy Ecological balance	Political theory and economic structure Population planning Patterns of living Education Communications Integrative philosophy
3	10^7	Widespread almost unbearable tension	Administrative management Slums Participatory democracy Racial conflict	Pollution Poverty Law and justice	?
4	10^6	Large-scale distress	Transportation Neighborhood ugliness Crime	Communications gap	?
5	10^5	Tension producing responsive change	Cancer and heart Smoking and drugs Artificial organs Accidents Sonic boom Water supply Marine resources Privacy on computers	Educational inadequacy	?
6		Other problems— important, but adequately researched	Military R&D New educational methods Mental illness Fusion power	Military R&D	
7		Exaggerated dangers and hopes	Mind control Heart transplants Definition of death	Sperm banks Freezing bodies Unemployment from automation	Eugenics
8		Noncrisis problems being "overstudied"	Man in space Most basic science		

*If no major effort is made at anticipatory solution.

Table 2. Classification of problems and crises by estimated time and intensity (World).

Grade	Estimated crisis intensity (number affected × degree of effect)		Estimated time to crisis*		
			1 to 5 years	5 to 20 years	20 to 50 years
1	10^{10}	Total annihilation	Nuclear or RCBW escalation	Nuclear or RCBW escalation	★(Solved or dead)
2	10^9	Great destruction or change (physical, biological, or political)	(Too soon)	Famines Ecological balance Development failures Local wars Rich-poor gap	Economic structure and political theory Population and ecological balance Patterns of living Universal education Communications integration Management of world Integrative philosophy
3	10^8	Widespread almost unbearable tension	Administrative management Need for participation Group and racial conflict Poverty-rising expectations Environmental degradation	Poverty Pollution Racial wars Political rigidity Strong dictatorships	?
4	10^7	Large-scale distress	Transportation Diseases Loss of old cultures	Housing Education Independence of big powers Communications gap	?
5	10^6	Tension producing responsive change	Regional organization Water supplies	?	?
6		Other problems— important, but adequately researched	Technical development design Intelligent monetary design		
7		Exaggerated dangers and hopes			Eugenics
8		Noncrisis problems being "over-studied"	Man in space Most basic science		Melting of ice caps

*If no major effort is made at anticipatory solution.

everybody; the third row, to a lower tension affecting a smaller part of the population or a smaller part of everyone's life, and so on.

Informed men might easily disagree about one row up or down in intensity, or one column left or right in time scales, but these order-of-magnitude differences are already so great that it would be surprising to find much larger disagreements. Clearly, an important initial step in any serious problem study would be to refine such estimates.

In both tables, the one crisis that must be ranked at the top in total danger and imminence is, of course, the danger of large-scale or total annihilation by nuclear escalation or by radiological-chemical-biological-warfare (RCBW). This kind of crisis will continue through both the 1- to 5-year time period and the 5- to 20-year period as Crisis Number 1, unless and until we get a safer peace-keeping arrangement. But in the 20- to 50-year column, following the reasoning already given, I think we must simply put a big "✠" at this level, on the grounds that the peace-keeping stabilization problem will either be solved by that time or we will probably be dead.

At the second level, the 1- to 5-year period may not be a period of great destruction (except nuclear) in either the United States or the world. But the problems at this level are building up, and within the 5- to 20-year period, many scientists fear the destruction of our whole biological and ecological balance in the United States by mismanagement or pollution. Others fear political catastrophe within this period, as a result of participatory confrontations or backlash or even dictatorship, if our divisive social and structural problems are not solved before that time.

On a world scale in this period, famine and ecological catastrophe head the list of destructive problems. We will come back later to the items in the 20- to 50-year column.

The third level of crisis problems in the United States includes those that are already upon us: administrative management of communities and cities, slums, participatory democracy, and racial conflict. In the 5- to 20-year period, the problems of pollution and poverty or major failures of law and justice could escalate to this level of tension if they are not solved. The last column is left blank because secondary events and second-order effects will interfere seriously with any attempt to make longer-range predictions at these lower levels.

The items in the lower part of the tables are not intended to be exhaustive. Some are common headline problems which are included simply to show how they might rank quantitatively in this kind of comparison. Anyone concerned with any of them will find it a useful exercise to estimate for himself their order of seriousness, in terms of the number of people they actually affect and the average distress they cause. Transportation problems and neighborhood ugliness, for example, are listed as grade 4 problems in the United States because they depress the lives of tens of millions for 1 or 2 hours every day. Violent crime may affect a corresponding number every year or two. These evils are not negligible, and they are worth the efforts of enormous numbers of people to cure them and to keep them cured—but on the other hand, they will not destroy our society.

The grade 5 crises are those where the hue and cry has been raised and where responsive changes of some kind are already under way. Cancer goes here, along with problems like auto safety and adequate water supply. This is not to say that we have solved the problem of cancer, but rather that good people are working on it and are making as much progress as we could expect from anyone. (At this level of social intensity, it should be kept in mind that there are also positive opportunities for research, such as the automation of clinical biochemistry or the invention of new channels of personal communication, which might affect the 20-year future as greatly as the new drugs and solid state devices of 20 years ago have begun to affect the present.)

Where the Scientists Are

Below grade 5, three less quantitative categories are listed, where the scientists begin to outnumber the problems. Grade 6 consists of problems that many people believe to be important but that are adequately researched at the present time. Military R&D belongs in this category. Our huge military establishment creates many social problems, both of national priority and international stability, but even in its own terms, war research, which engrosses hundreds of thousands of scientists and engineers, is being taken care of generously. Likewise, fusion power is being studied at the $100-million level, though even if we had it tomorrow, it would scarcely change our rates of application of nuclear energy in generating more electric power for the world.

Grade 7 contains the exaggerated problems which are being talked about or worked on out of all proportion to their true importance, such as heart transplants, which can never affect more than a few thousands of people out of the billions in the world. It is sad to note that the symposia on "social implications of science" at many national scientific meetings are often on the problems of grade 7.

In the last category, grade 8, are two subjects which I am sorry to say I must call "overstudied," at least with respect to the real crisis problems today. The Man in Space flights to the moon and back are the most beautiful technical achievements of man, but they are not urgent except for national display, and they absorb tens of thousands of our most ingenious technical brains.

And in the "overstudied" list I have begun to think we must now put most of our basic science. This is a hard conclusion, because all of science is so important in the long run and because it is still so small compared, say, to advertising or the tobacco industry. But basic scientific thinking is a scarce resource. In a national emergency, we would suddenly find that a host of our scientific problems could be postponed for several years in favor of more urgent research. Should not our total human emergency make the same claims? Long-range science is useless unless we survive to use it. Tens of thousands of our best trained minds may now be needed for something more important than "science as usual."

The arrows at level 2 in the tables are intended to indicate that problems may escalate to a higher level of crisis in the next time period if they are not solved. The arrows toward level 2 in the last columns of both tables show the escalation of all our problems upward to some general reconstruction in the 20- to 50-year time period, if we survive. Probably no human institution will continue unchanged for another 50 years, because they will all be changed by the crises if they are not changed in advance to prevent them. There will surely be widespread rearrangements in all our ways of life everywhere, from our patterns of society to our whole philosophy of man. Will they be more humane, or less? Will the world come to resemble a diverse and open humanist democracy? Or Orwell's *1984*? Or a postnuclear desert with its scientists hanged? It is our acts of commitment and leadership in the next few months and years that will decide.

Mobilizing Scientists

It is a unique experience for us to have peacetime problems, or technical problems which are not industrial problems, on such a scale. We do not know quite where to start, and there is no mechanism yet for generating ideas systematically or paying teams to turn them into successful solutions.

But the comparison with wartime research and development may not be inappropriate. Perhaps the antisubmarine warfare work or the atomic energy project of the 1940's provide the closest parallels to what we must do in terms of the novelty, scale, and urgency of the problems, the initiative needed, and the kind of large success that has to be achieved. In the antisubmarine campaign, Blackett assembled a few scientists and other ingenious minds in his "back room," and within a few months they had worked out the "operations analysis" that made an order-of-magnitude difference in the success of the campaign. In the atomic energy work, scientists started off with extracurricular research, formed a central committee to channel their secret communications, and then studied the possible solutions for some time before they went to the government for large-scale support for the great development laboratories and production plants.

Fortunately, work on our crisis problems today would not require secrecy. Our great problems today are all beginning to be world problems, and scientists from many countries would have important insights to contribute.

Probably the first step in crisis studies now should be the organization of intense technical discussion and education groups in every laboratory. Promising lines of interest could then lead to the setting up of part-time or full-time studies and teams and coordinating committees. Administrators and boards of directors might find active crisis research important to their own organizations in many cases. Several foundations and federal agencies already have in-house research and make outside grants in many of these crisis areas, and they would be important initial sources of support.

But the step that will probably be required in a short time is the creation of whole new centers, perhaps comparable to Los Alamos or the RAND Corporation, where interdisciplinary groups can be assembled to work full-time on solutions to these crisis problems. Many different kinds of centers will eventually be necessary, including research centers, development centers, training centers, and even production centers for new sociotechnical inventions. The problems of our time—the $100-billion food problem or the $100-billion arms control problem—are no smaller than World War II in scale and importance, and it would be absurd to think that a few academic research teams or a few agency laboratories could do the job.

Social Inventions

The thing that discourages many scientists—even social scientists—from thinking in these research-and-development terms is their failure to realize that there are such things as social inventions and that they can have large-scale effects in a surprisingly short time. A recent study with Karl Deutsch has examined some 40 of the great achievements in social science in this century, to see where they were made and by whom and how long they took to become effective. They include developments such as the following:

Keynesian economics
Opinion polls and statistical sampling
Input-output economics
Operations analysis
Information theory and feedback theory
Theory of games and economic behavior
Operant conditioning and programmed learning
Planned programming and budgeting (PPB)
Non-zero-sum game theory

Many of these have made remarkable differences within just a few years in our ability to handle social problems or management problems. The opinion poll became a national necessity within a single election period. The theory of games, published in 1946, had become an important component of American strategic thinking by RAND and the Defense Department by 1953, in spite of the limitation of the theory at that time to zero-sum games, with their dangerous bluffing and "brinksmanship." Today, within less than a decade, the PPB management technique is sweeping through every large organization.

This list is particularly interesting because it shows how much can be done outside official government agencies when inventive men put their brains together. Most of the achievements were the work of teams of two or more men, almost all of them located in intellectual centers such as Princeton or the two Cambridges.

The list might be extended by adding commercial social inventions with rapid and widespread effects, like credit cards. And sociotechnical inventions, like computers and automation or like oral contraceptives, which were in widespread use within 10 years after they were developed. In addition, there are political innovations like the New Deal, which made great changes in our economic life within 4 years, and the pay-as-you-go income tax, which transformed federal taxing power within 2 years.

On the international scene, the Peace Corps, the "hot line," the Test-Ban Treaty, the Antarctic Treaty, and the Nonproliferation Treaty were all implemented within 2 to 10 years after their initial proposal. These are only small contributions, a tiny patchwork part of the basic international stabilization system that is needed, but they show that the time to adopt new structural designs may be surprisingly short. Our clichés about "social lag" are very misleading. Over half of the major social innovations since 1940 were adopted or had widespread social effects within less than 12 years—a time as short as, or shorter than, the average time for adoption of technological innovations.

Areas for Task Forces

Is it possible to create more of these social inventions systematically to deal with our present crisis problems? I think it is. It may be worth listing a few specific areas where new task forces might start.

1. *Peace-keeping mechanisms and feedback stabilization.* Our various nuclear treaties are a beginning. But how about a technical group that sits down and thinks about the whole range of possible and impossible stabilization and peace-keeping mechanisms? Stabilization feedback-design might be a complex modern counterpart of the "checks and balances" used in designing the constitutional structure of the United States 200 years ago. With our new knowledge today about feedbacks, group behavior, and game theory, it ought to be possible to design more complex and even more successful structures.

Some peace-keeping mechanisms that might be hard to adopt today could still be worked out and tested and publicized, awaiting a more favorable moment. Sometimes the very existence of new possibilities can change the atmosphere. Sometimes, in a crisis, men may finally be willing to try out new ways and may find some previously prepared plan of enormous help.

2. *Biotechnology.* Humanity must feed and care for the children who are already in the world, even while we try to level off the further population explosion that makes this so difficult. Some novel proposals, such as food from coal, or genetic copying of champion animals, or still simpler contraceptive methods, could possibly have large-scale effects on human welfare within 10 to 15 years. New chemical, statistical, and management methods for measuring and maintaining the ecological balance could be of very great importance.

3. *Game theory.* As we have seen, zero-sum game theory has not been too academic to be used for national strategy and policy analysis. Unfortunately, in

zero-sum games, what I win, you lose, and what you win, I lose. This may be the way poker works, but it is not the way the world works. We are collectively in a non-zero-sum game in which we will all lose together in nuclear holocaust or race conflict or economic nationalism, or all win together in survival and prosperity. Some of the many variations of non-zero-sum game theory, applied to group conflict and cooperation, might show us profitable new approaches to replace our sterile and dangerous confrontation strategies.

4. *Psychological and social theories.* Many teams are needed to explore in detail and in practice how the powerful new ideas of behavior theory and the new ideas of responsive living might be used to improve family life or community and management structures. New ideas of information handling and management theory need to be turned into practical recipes for reducing the daily frustrations of small businesses, schools, hospitals, churches, and town meetings. New economic inventions are needed, such as urban development corporations. A deeper systems analysis is urgently needed to see if there is not some practical way to separate full employment from inflation. Inflation pinches the poor, increases labor-management disputes, and multiplies all our domestic conflicts and our sense of despair.

5. *Social indicators.* We need new social indicators, like the cost-of-living index, for measuring a thousand social goods and evils. Good indicators can have great "multiplier effects" in helping to maximize our welfare and minimize our ills. Engineers and physical scientists working with social scientists might come up with ingenious new methods of measuring many of these important but elusive parameters.

6. *Channels of effectiveness.* Detailed case studies of the reasons for success or failure of various social inventions could also have a large multiplier effect. Handbooks showing what channels or methods are now most effective for different small-scale and large-scale social problems would be of immense value.

The list could go on and on. In fact, each study group will have its own pet projects. Why not? Society is at least as complex as, say, an automobile with its several thousand parts. It will probably require as many research-and-development teams as the auto industry in order to explore all the inventions it needs to solve its problems. But it is clear that there are many areas of great potential crying out for brilliant minds and brilliant teams to get to work on them.

Future Satisfactions and Present Solutions

This is an enormous program. But there is nothing impossible about mounting and financing it, if we, as concerned men, go into it with commitment and leadership. Yes, there will be a need for money and power to overcome organizational difficulties and vested interests. But it is worth remembering that the only real source of power in the world is the gap between what is and what might be. Why else do men work and save and plan? If there is some future increase in human satisfaction that we can point to and realistically anticipate, men will be willing to pay something for it and invest in it in the hope of that return. In economics, they pay with money; in politics, with their votes and time and sometimes with their jail sentences and their lives.

Social change, peaceful or turbulent, is powered by "what might be." This means that for peaceful change, to get over some impossible barrier of unresponsiveness or complexity or group conflict, what is needed is an inventive man or group—a "social entrepreneur"—who can connect the pieces and show how to turn the advantage of "what might be" into some present advantage for every participating party. To get toll roads, when highways were hopeless, a legislative-corporation mechanism was invented that turned the future need into present profits for construction workers and bondholders and continuing profitability for the state and all the drivers.

This principle of broad-payoff anticipatory design has guided many successful social plans. Regular task forces using systems analysis to find payoffs over the barriers might give us such successful solutions much more often. The new world that could lie ahead, with its blocks and malfunctions removed, would be fantastically wealthy. It seems almost certain that there must be many systematic ways for intelligence to convert that large payoff into the profitable solution of our present problems.

The only possible conclusion is a call to action. Who will commit himself to this kind of search for more ingenious and fundamental solutions? Who will begin to assemble the research teams and the funds? Who will begin to create those full-time interdisciplinary centers that will be necessary for testing detailed designs and turning them into effective applications?

The task is clear. The task is huge. The time is horribly short. In the past, we have had science for intellectual pleasure, and science for the control of nature. We have had science for war. But today, the whole human experiment may hang on the question of how fast we now press the development of science for survival.